The Negotiator

James March's army training, which included service with the SAS, equipped him well for his extraordinary career. Writing under a pseudonym to avoid the revenge of the terrorists he has fooled and to protect the lives of the innocent, James March takes the reader behind the scenes to reveal the amazing secrets of *The Negotiator*.

The Negotiator

James March

Pan Books
London, Sydney and Auckland

First published in Great Britain 1988 by
Weidenfeld & Nicolson

This edition published 1990 by Pan Books Ltd,
Cavaye Place, London SW10 9PG

1 3 5 7 9 10 8 6 4 2

© James March 1988

ISBN 0 330 31165 4

Printed and bound in Great Britain by
Richard Clay Ltd, Bungay, Suffolk

INTRODUCTION

kidnap *v.t.* Steal (child); carry off (person etc.) by illegal force or fraud esp. to obtain ransom. . . .

ransom *n., & v.t., 1.n* (Liberation of prisoner in consideration of) sum of money or value paid for release . . . demand concessions from by threat of . . . damaging action. . . .

The Concise Oxford Dictionary, 6th edition (1976)

THIS book is about the realities of kidnap. It is about the trauma, horror and savage rape of human emotions which go hand in glove with what is arguably the most disgusting of modern crimes. It has developed from those twelfth century days, when a 'king's ransom' was paid to the Archduke of Austria and the Holy Roman Emperor for the release of King Richard the Lionheart, into a hard, uncompromising business.

Many aspects of the business (I choose the word deliberately) are hidden from the public. The media will raise an outcry at the kidnap of a prominent political, industrial or commercial figure. There will be banner headlines at first, followed by front page paragraphs. But soon, within days perhaps, the news dwindles to an occasional mention on the lesser pages. The next headlines will centre on the death, mutilation or safe release of the victim.

The transitional period between kidnap and release receives little publicity. Into this shadowy world have stepped a number of men – men who make a living by advising families how to conduct their affairs during a kidnap. What is the reality of this grey world? Who are the consultants, the negotiators who are occasionally mentioned? How do they operate? By what right do they set themselves up to advise in these life-and-death situations? Good investigative journalists have posed those very questions and met with walls of silence or have been directed down blind alleys, resulting in eventual frustration or loss of interest as the case in question has become less newsworthy.

I have spent many years in the business, and business it certainly is, having been involved in advising on over sixty cases of kidnap. I have seen the shattered and tragic families; I have worked with the police of a number of countries and I have closely observed public and political attitudes. This book is intended to lift the curtain and show the realities of a little-known business amphitheatre.

In setting out to give this insight into the world of The Negotiator I have been constrained in only two areas. Some of the identities of the clients and victims have been obscured. This is necessary for reasons which will be seen. And in some instances I have deliberately drawn a veil over the detail of key tactics used by The Negotiator – this book is not intended to make the kidnappers more efficient!

James March

CHAPTER

1

Author's note
At the time of Doctor Bayardo Alvarez Ruiz's kidnap, Guatemala was in the middle of a debilitating and inept war between an uncompromising army and a number of unco-ordinated guerrilla movements. It is a country where almost all the wealth is in the hands of a very few, infant mortality is high, the illiteracy rate is about eighty per cent and living conditions for all but the wealthy are primitive.

The military leader, elected in 1978, was due to step aside and give the country the chance to elect a new head of state. He himself was intending to stand for re-election; in the event of his failure, it was widely predicted that he would re-take power by force of arms. Potentially the most threatening rival was Donaldo Alvarez Ruiz, brother of the kidnapped Bayardo, and Prime Minister. Against this backdrop of political violence and intrigue, in a country where complaining can be fatal, I found myself involved in the negotiations to effect Bayardo's release.

SHOCK drained the blood from under his olive skin, giving him a peculiar yellow hue. He broke into a sweat and looked at me almost pleadingly. The Prime Minister was sitting well forward, on the edge of the enormous Chesterfield chair. His hands shook as he looked again at the grubby piece of paper.

'Señor March,' haltingly, 'they are dead. Shot. Executed within hours of being taken.' He shook his head slowly and slumped back into the damp leather. 'What do we do? What can we do? It is hopeless.'

I like to think my own fears didn't show; my mind was racing. If the prisoners had been executed then what chance was there for the Prime Minister's brother? He was as good as dead. I spoke, quite sharply, to Ruiz.

'Your Excellency, nothing is hopeless. True, the situation is far from perfect but remember what I said in the beginning; we must look for the strengths in our hand, not dwell on weaknesses. The kidnappers could call within the next few minutes. If they do, stick to your story – you are still searching the prison records to locate the men. I want some time now to go through the whole situation. You have affairs of state to look after. Can I suggest we meet again in a couple of hours to decide on the next move?'

Once again I was surprised at the effect a calm response could have on an anxious relative in these situations. The Prime Minister went with me into the adjoining office which had been given over for my work. He wasn't relaxed when he left but some of his colour had returned and the profuse sweating had stopped.

After he'd gone it was my turn to start worrying!

On 6 March 1981, in Guatemala City, Doctor Bayardo Alvarez Ruiz had been kidnapped in the grounds of the hospital where he worked. The snatch had been violent. There was shooting, physical abuse and a lot of shouting of political slogans. Bayardo had been punched, hustled into a car and driven off at high speed. Eye witnesses were eager to testify that it was the work of 'revolutionaries'. That was ten days ago. In Guatemala a kidnap isn't unusual. It's almost a weekly event. But this case was different. Doctor Bayardo Alvarez Ruiz was the brother of Donaldo Alvarez Ruiz and Donaldo was the Prime Minister of Guatemala and Commandant of the National Police Force. In any other country, at any other time, I'd have run a mile rather than get mixed up in a case of this sort. In Guatemala City in early 1981, I had no choice.

When the statutory coffee appeared at my elbow, I took out the files and began at the beginning.

The first contact had been through Arturo, who looked after my interests in Guatemala. The call had been brief, confined to necessary details; Arturo was not given to opinions and certainly not over the leaky telephone system in Guatemala.

'James? There is a job. A local doctor has gone. The brother wants to employ you. He wants to see you, today. What time can I collect you?' I was surprised at the request. Arturo knew what I was doing.

'I'm already on a case. You know that. Tell the man I can't do it. I can get Carson in to advise but that'll take three or four days. You know the score, I won't walk out on a job.' Arturo came back immediately.

2

'I'm coming to see you right away. You can't turn this one down.'

Arturo's news was hardly welcome. The doctor was the brother of the Prime Minister who was also Commandant of the National Police Force. He'd known exactly how to contact me. That in itself was no great surprise; transient foreigners are watched closely in Latin America. The international hotel telephone operators are regularly quizzed by the police and it was my sixth case in the city.

The disturbing factor was that Arturo was certainly right – I wasn't going to be able to say no. In Guatemala the Prime Minister was only slightly less powerful than God (God being the Head of the Army); as he was also the Police Chief it put him almost on a par! A man can spend an awful lot of time in prison out there at the whim of a petty official, let alone one of this stature. I had to meet the Minister. If I didn't go willingly, I would be collected in a manner which would be uncomfortable to say the least. If I went of my own free will I would retain a measure of dignity and a pretence of freedom of choice. The slightest edge is important, so I instructed Arturo to make the arrangements.

While Arturo was busy, I put a call through to Maria in Bogotá. In our own code I passed on the names and scant details. She'd get whatever information she could to me on the personalities but, even more important, she'd know where I was going. If I disappeared from view at least she'd have a start point on which to try to bring some official pressure to bear. It was a small thing; I'd have liked more cards up my sleeve but that was the only precaution open.

A man I took to be Pierro, the Minister's aide-de-camp, arrived at the hotel in an armoured limousine. Short, urbane and well dressed, his greetings in fluent but heavily accented English were perfunctory. We were on our way within minutes.

The car armouring was expensive. There was a greenish tinge to the window glass and a tell-tale roll as we cornered but apart from that, there was no sign that we were sitting in a bullet-proof cocoon. On the vacant seat beside the chauffeur lay an uncharacteristically clean UZI sub-machine gun. It was cocked with the safety catch off and in full view. It silently spoke volumes. I don't know Guatemala City well, but certainly enough to realise that the route we took to the palace was circuitous. The building was enormous. It would have dwarfed Buckingham Palace, but the flaking paintwork and faded gardens lent it an indefinable air – almost an apology for its grand presence in a city where the haves and havenots are so starkly contrasted. Inside the image changed abruptly. It was sumptuous. This was wealth at its most obscene. The panelled walls along the interminable corridors shone with a patina created by many years of vigorous (and certainly enforced) polishing. We went through a series of ante-rooms filled with people clutching what seemed to be petitions. They were all talking at once, trying to impress the importance of their individual causes onto the deaf ears of male secretaries seated at desks and controlling access to the next and presumably higher office. I think we passed through five or six such rooms, each secured by chrome-helmeted police guards.

As we sailed past, those people must have wondered what powers we had that enabled us to open doors which they may have spent months or even years bribing or cajoling their way through. At every corner and side door after the final office there were armed guards. They were all policemen, alert, smart and in total contrast to their scruffy, illiterate comrades on the street outside. There was an air of quiet menace in those long passage-ways. I was in the presence of a corps d'élite. My every move and gesture was noted and the small hairs at the nape of my neck began to prickle in a way which was reminiscent of the streets of Belfast.

I couldn't help but notice the paintings and the other works of art in proliferation on the walls and in softly illuminated niches, but there was no question of my being allowed to pause and enjoy them. Pierro kept up a fast pace until we eventually reached the Minister's office. Despite the air conditioning, I was sweating lightly; conscious of the odours, I cursed myself for not insisting on the time to take a bath before being collected.

One of the quietly authoritative sentries outside the door ran his hands quickly and expertly over me; I noticed that he removed the pistol from Pierro's armpit before he tapped the footswitch to allow us entry, his gun covering us both until the door closed behind us. Through a small isolation chamber fitted with closed circuit television, we made our way into the inner sanctum. From his huge armchair behind the great leather inlaid desk, the Prime Minister sat and just looked at me. His face was calm. Deeply etched humour wrinkles took away some of the severity, but not the inherent strength. The power was there in those dark brown Latin eyes and he appeared perfectly relaxed. I know I looked unconcerned – I've had enough practice – but inside I was far from feeling at ease.

Ruiz's formal greeting was in halting but correct English. He obviously knew the language well but didn't speak it regularly. He motioned me into a low seat. There were a few moments of general chat and my impatience to get on with the business must have transmitted itself to him. Despite my misgivings, all the old thrills

4

were coming back – the first moments of a case briefing – the time when all is anticipation. He stood up again and walked round to the side of his desk and looked down at me. I wanted to stand but he had carefully positioned himself so that to do so I would have had to push against him.

'Señor March, I love my brother dearly. I want him back unharmed and you will help me. I am not personally wealthy but whatever your fee is, it will be paid. Now, what do we do?'

His statement came as no surprise to me, but I was taken aback by the force of feeling he displayed. He was not to be fooled with.

'Your Excellency, I want no fees from you. It's not a matter of whether I will help you. More to the point is, can I help you.' I carried on, not allowing him to interrupt: 'From what I've already heard this is a political case. It happened ten days ago. I understand from Arturo that a number of prisoners have been named as the ransom. Is this correct?'

'Yes, Señor, that is the case. But there are other things you should know. All in good time. First, why do you say no fees?' I answered carefully.

'As you must know, I'm already handling a case in the city. I'm being paid for that. If I am able to help you it will be on the basis that my first duty is to the other family.'

'Señor March, you keep saying "if". There is no "if". You will help me.' His tone was final.

'Your Excellency, the case I'm involved in is that of a young Guatemalan girl. She is one of your own people. I will not willingly leave that case. You must understand that I've given my word to the family.' I'd gone too far. Ruiz seemed set to explode. Damn it, I had to take that line. I couldn't walk out on the Ortega family. We stared at each other for a long time. I know I still appeared calm but inside I was thinking about the penalties for overstepping the mark. I could feel the prison walls closing in on me; I could smell the cells. Ruiz spoke, quietly and forcibly.

'Enough. You will help. I accept your need to maintain contact with the Ortega family. I will ensure that you have a personal telephone with which to conduct your business. It will be monitored but none of my policemen will interfere with the kidnap. You will stay here in the offices. Ortega will be informed of the reasons. Arturo will have a pass to come and go as you need him for the Ortega business. He will start by bringing your suitcases to the palace. Is this clear? Now, tell me, how shall we proceed?'

To push the matter any further would have been idotic at this stage so I went into the 'opening act'.

'First I want to tell you how to handle the situation if the kidnappers should call in the next few hours. You must tell them that the security of the prisoners they have named is not in your hands. Indeed, it's an area where you have very limited powers. You are doing your best to trace them but it will take time. Do not be diverted from that position. Later on we may change our minds but for the moment that is the stance. Is that clear?' He nodded, stunned at the immediacy and force of my reply.

'Now. It's important that you realise this is a specialist business – yes, business. It's a path I have travelled many times but it's your first venture along it. It's a path full of pitfalls and dangers. First I want to tell you something about myself and how I work.'

I spent twenty minutes giving him the brief. I then cleared my mind of everything except the Ruiz problem. I needed some basic information fast.

'Your Excellency, I need to know three things right away. Have you had any proof that your brother is still alive? Are the prisoners named as the ransom accessible and do the guerrillas know this? I also need whatever information you can give me about the kidnappers; ideologies, locations, past actions, in fact all you know about them. I have good records but you may have something which will supplement my knowledge.'

Ruiz appeared satisfied. He sat down again behind the desk and after indicating that I could remove my jacket, he sent for coffee. Elbows on his desk, fingers interlaced under his chin, he stared at me coolly until the coffee was poured. He then spoke, calmly and logically.

He began at the point when he first became aware that Bayardo had been kidnapped. He received a letter indicating that the exchange would be carried out after three named prisoners had been handed into asylum at the Mexican Embassy and the fact had been broadcast over the city radio and television. Responsibility had been claimed by the Guatemalan Workers Party, the PGT. He'd been sent a signed note which was definitely in his brother's handwriting, although he accepted that the date could be false.

Yes, the named men had been taken prisoner but he had not yet had news of their whereabouts. The Chief of the Army, in whose hands the prisoners were, was a strong and powerful political rival and Ruiz had to use devious means to get any information from the army system. He'd ignored the kidnappers' first letter, simply

6

pretended that he'd never received it. In response to the second letter he'd replied that he was having difficulty locating the prisoners. This he thought would be perfectly believable.

I made a mental note to come back to Ruiz about the rivalry between him and the Chief of the Army. This was going to be central to the whole case. I was secretly pleased at the way he had answered the gang. It was the action of an intelligent man. He continued to tell me about the guerrillas. The revolutionary movement as a whole was growing, gathering momentum as the elections drew nearer (he himself was to stand as a Presidential candidate as was Hernandez, the Chief of the Army). The movement was fragmented; there were many splinter groups.

The splits were caused by a variety of factors; the geographical spread of the population in a country where communications could be difficult; the different interpretations of Marxist doctrines; locally strong leaders and local priorities all served to separate. While this was a good thing from the government's point of view, it tended to make identification difficult at times. The 'father' group, the Ejercito Guerrillas de los Pobres (EGP), was inspired, it seemed, by the ideals of Che Guevara. The leadership committee generally showed more restraint than other groups; at least it made a show of trying the diplomatic route through occasional negotiation with the government.

Until a year ago, Ruiz told me, activity had been confined to the distribution of subversive literature. But more recently, some groups (the PGT among them) had been carrying out bombings of so-called government targets, often with the loss of innocent civilian lives. They were not a popular group. Only a day or so previously, the EGP had placed an open letter in the national newspaper denouncing the actions of the PGT in kidnapping Bayardo.

Ruiz painted a bleak picture. Rather he had confirmed it. He hadn't told me much that I didn't already know after six visits to the country and a lot of homework in between times. A gang with a history of bloody bombings wouldn't hesitate to kill. They seemed not to be experienced kidnappers and amateurs can be dangerously unpredictable; pressure has to be applied slowly and carefully in order not to panic or provoke them into hasty action with fatal results.

Ruiz was looking at me expectantly. I don't know what he was expecting, but I let him wait while I mentally reviewed what I'd learned. Not a lot, but one point had stuck in my mind. The 'father' group, the EGP. They'd already denounced the PGT. Could I use this somehow? There had to be a more tangible reason for the enmity. I asked Ruiz.

'Sir, tell me more about your brother. What sort of man is he? Does he have political ambitions?' Ruiz snorted derisively. The victim's profile would normally have been covered in my initial questionnaire, but due to the manner of our meeting and the initial need to get Ruiz quickly pacified, I preferred to do it this way.

'Politician? Bayardo? Most certainly not. My brother is a rarity in this country. He is a doctor with a passionate feeling for the people. In his profession he could be a very wealthy man indeed, yet he is not. He lives in a rented house in a poor quarter. Señor, the deprived majority of this city love him. He turns no-one away from his door no matter what the time of day or night. I know that he even treats the families of both active and jailed revolutionaries! Putting his own life at risk. Treats them free! Politician? Hah!' Another snort of derision

I checked my notebook and asked Ruiz to tell me more about the rivalry between himself and the Chief of the Army. This was a very sensitive subject; if he were to upset the army he could well be executed in the next coup. Although he clearly didn't understand the reason for the question, he explained the difference between their political leanings (when he described himself as a humane man, I smiled inwardly – however, I suppose that's a relative term in Central America) and the clear division between their responsibilities with the police and the army. The army was much more involved in the rural areas where the bulk of the counter-guerrilla operations were carried out and therefore they were much more vulnerable to attack from the left wing elements of the media who accused them regularly of committing atrocities. (He didn't add that many of these accusers had disappeared.)

'To be fair, Señor, they are much more exposed to the guerrillas than my police force, though I like to think that my treatment of prisoners would be a good deal more lenient. The poor of this country have a lot of legitimate grievances.' The habit of electioneering or a glimpse of a humane man? I didn't know. It was important to the vague plan which was beginning to form in my mind. He'd been remarkably open. It confirmed my previous experience that due to force of circumstances as much as anything else, the police were more popular than the army.

Ruiz's knowledge of kidnap situations was scant and I added to my early brief by explaining the general tactics to him. I pointed out the sort of threats he could expect from the gang and tried to prepare him for the pressures to come. Whichever course I chose to advise him on would be dangerous. He had to understand that. If it all went wrong, I wanted him to know that I'd applied my best efforts to the problem. Efforts based on an experience which I wanted him to fully appreciate.

I asked Ruiz what the state of play was on the communications with the gang; I wanted full details on a chronological basis.

'I received instructions this morning to collect a letter from the men's toilet in a local restaurant. It is full of communist invective. It contains a threat to execute Bayardo if I do not broadcast tonight saying that the prisoners have been found and that they will be released tomorrow. I am hoping that I shall hear soon that they have been located.' Ruiz was beginning to look anxious. I had to get him into some form of action to show him that there were logical things we could do.

'What time is the broadcast?'

It was scheduled for eight p.m. which gave me a few hours thinking time. As a necessary precaution, even though it was unlikely that the gang would use the telephone to contact him before the broadcast, I gave Ruiz some notes to use as a prompt if they did call. The notes would ensure that he stayed with the same story – that he was still having trouble in locating the prisoners; I tended to agree with him that the story was believable in this country of sudden death and unexplained disappearances.

I asked to spend some time by myself thinking things out. I'd been at the desk for less than half an hour when Ruiz came in, sat down on the edge of the great Chesterfield and gave me the news.

'Señor, they are dead. Shot. Executed within hours of being taken. I cannot prove this but I am certain this is the case.'

Well, that was that. Now we knew. A political kidnap. A violent bunch of guerrillas, a totally unco-operative army and, worst of all, a ransom which was absolutely impossible in whole or part! I asked Ruiz a few questions to give myself some thinking time. As far as the tactics were concerned there was no need for immediate change. I told him to stick to the script we'd already prepared and sat down to review what I knew. I decided to assume that the prisoners were dead.

Examination of the letters from the gang in the file which Ruiz left me served only to suggest strongly their amateur status in the kidnap game. The dangers and uncertainties are much greater with an amateur gang. If pressure is applied in the wrong way they can act like startled rabbits.

It was day fourteen of the case and already there had been eight letters from the gang. These had not been placed without risk. A professional gang as often as not will leave a period of silence after the snatch. This is a deliberate ploy to add to the feelings of uncertainty in a worried family. The expectation is that the sudden relief of receiving a demand will be sufficient to make them pay up instantly. This silence can also be used as a threat at any time during a case; it's one of the greatest challenges to the negotiator – how to get the communications restarted.

The letters were full of revolutionary diatribe and communist slogans; they didn't give me much to work on. There was a measure of tenuous comfort in that the deadlines had already been overrun and the threats had apparently not been carried out. This could have given me confidence if I'd allowed myself to conclude that Bayardo would have been killed by now if they'd intended that to happen. With a professional gang this would have been worthy of consideration. Not with amateurs; they're too unpredictable.

I reckoned it was a fair bet that they suspected that their comrades were dead, but I couldn't bank on it. I had to get some form of positive negotiation under way. How could I do this with no ransom figure as a starting point? I couldn't advise Ruiz to come out with the truth and say that the prisoners had died at the hands of the army. If a statement like that appeared in the press Ruiz would be dead or missing within a few hours, despite his status. He knew it and I knew it, though it was never openly stated.

This was the underlying theme to the whole case as far as I could see at that point. Anything and everything we said could be used by the kidnappers to their own ends. We couldn't afford to have any statement spoken or printed which suggested in any way that we were prepared to deal with the gang.

If we could get across to the kidnappers that Ruiz had only very limited control over certain aspects of security and was dependent on other organisations for the information, it was possible that the gang would understand that their friends were probably dead and that it was the army who was responsible and not the Prime Minister. This could lead them to giving us other names, and while we may not be able to produce them it would at least give us a starting point into a negotiation.

It would be tricky. How could Ruiz be seen to attempt to free prisoners? How could the government, let alone a Presidential candidate, be seen to treat with guerrillas? Supposing that this could be hidden from the public, it certainly wouldn't remain a secret from the Chief of the Army for very long – which would lead to Ruiz doing a disappearing act or worse.

One thought I had was worth at least checking out. I called Ruiz on the intercom and asked if the police were holding any prisoners who could be offered to the kidnappers. He came in immediately. He was grave as he spoke.

'Señor March, we do hold prisoners who I am quite sure would be of interest to the guerrillas, but it is a useless thought. I believe this country to be on the verge of yet another coup. I also believe that the leader of that coup will be none other than the Chief of the Army. I and my police force are the only thing standing in the way at the moment. All Hernandez needs is an excuse. If I were to offer prisoners to the guerrillas he would have that excuse. I can tell you, Señor, that he has penetrated my police force and there is no way in which I could hide the fact that I had released prisoners.' He paused and took a deep, rasping breath.

'To be fair to you, I should tell you that you are in the gravest danger,' he continued. 'If Hernandez finds out even that we are in communication with the kidnappers he could make his move and pervert the story of our actions to suit his own ends after he had seized power. The fact that you are a foreigner would afford you no protection whatsoever.' For God's sake; this was cheering news!

'Do you have anyone you can trust?'

'Yes. I believe so, anyway. Pierro I would trust with my life – I have done so many times. He has his own methods of taking instructions from the palace. I do not question them but I do trust him.' Pierro actually blushed, not that this was any comfort. Ruiz gave a slight bow and they both left the office.

I had to buy time. I had to get a negotiable deal before the gang. I tried to put out of my mind the alarming news which Ruiz had just given me. I couldn't. It wasn't just the prison walls closing in on me now, it was also the tightening of the noose or the short, sharp pain of bullets in the chest from a jeering firing squad. There was nothing I could do; I carried on thinking my way through the problem. After an hour, the best I could come up with was the possibility that medical supplies and treatment would be of interest to the guerrillas. They took heavy casualties regularly in their battles with the security forces and the need would be there. There was a slim chance that Ruiz could claim that he was trying to trap the guerrillas if he was interrogated about the offer. It remained to be seen whether it would be attractive enough to suit our purpose. Our purpose? This was survival – the survival of one James March!

In these cases, it isn't a matter of gaining thinking time; I like to achieve impetus – get the gang reacting to my moves as quickly as possible, robbing them of their own planning time. In that way I'm getting information from them the whole time whether it's a telephone call, a tape or a letter. Every message by whatever means gives me the opportunity to learn a little more about them. Coincidental to this is the effect on the family. The more that's going on, the less time they have to ponder the fate of the victim and the less likely they are to get despondent and succumb to the stress of repeated threats. I decided to act and contacted Pierro to ask if I could see the Minister again.

I explained my reasoning to Ruiz and he appeared happy to have a positive plan at last. That evening the message to the guerrillas told them that so far it had proved impossible to locate their comrades and questioned whether they had actually been arrested in the first place. It also asked them quite openly to change their demand to one requesting the medical supplies and treatment which they were known to need.

The next morning, Pierro was instructed to collect a letter from the toilets in the Fu Lu Sho, a Chinese restaurant in the city. The letter was couched in the now familiar vitriolic terms. It demanded copies of the coroner's reports on one of the dead men, set a new deadline for that evening and ignored the request for a change of demand. I was pleased with the letter and Ruiz demanded to know why.

'Your Excellency, the gang have accepted the death of at least one of the prisoners without us actually having to state the fact. It's possible that they knew before they kidnapped Bayardo. They've set us a new deadline which at least implies that your brother is still alive.'

'But they have made no mention of the medicine and treatment. Why is this do you think?'

'I should imagine our request would be mistrusted. But don't worry, they'll be thinking about it. It will produce internal pressures from the wounded and sick in their camp. Now it's obviously impossible to publish coroner's reports. Even if they did exist there's no way we could hide them in press reports. We could deposit them somewhere I suppose for the gang to collect. No. The dangers to you are too great.'

'Señor,' there was scorn in his voice, 'You are right. There would be coroner's reports but they could be misleading. They will have been buried in prison or deposited elsewhere to be discovered as victims of street crime.' I felt the noose tightening again. I knew the country's reputation but this was the first time I'd had such close exposure to the total indifference to life and death. I resolved to look seriously at my own escape lines the moment I had the chance. Ruiz was continuing.

'Have you no other plan?'

'Yes. I have a scheme which may work. It's also very dangerous. You obviously have influence with the press in a general way but do you have any good, trusted contacts?' A positive answer was very important to me. The idea with the medical supplies had led me along another train of thought. I wanted his full acceptance of the plan; I wasn't happy with his ever-changing moods.

'Of course. I have influence everywhere in the city. I am the Prime Minister.' Even though the truculence was still there, I smiled at the thought of the British Prime Minister making a similar statement.

'In the press, I have some trusted friends who will help if the cause is good.' This was excellent. I decided at this stage that as we couldn't free prisoners or pay a ransom in any form, we had to have a Robin Hood type of strategy. Was there a way by which we could persuade the gang that they could achieve considerable kudos by releasing Bayardo, and the reverse of this if they killed him?

In the event of a telephone contact, I suggested that Ruiz took the same stance as before with the gang. The broadcast, I told him, should reflect again the offer of medical supplies. I gave him some articles I'd drafted to be published in the evening newspaper which went out some hours before the broadcast. I temporarily resisted his questions about the strategy but emphasised that if his hand was evident in the business of the publications, it would be very dangerous indeed for his brother. He merely smiled.

'Just as dangerous for you and me, Señor.'

It was now case day fifteen.

That evening the newspapers carried an article in the form of a letter from some of Doctor Bayardo's friends. They asked where he was and pleaded for his safe return. The broadcasts from Ruiz explained the impossibility of obtaining coroner's reports and again asked the gang to change their demand. There was no call from the kidnappers that night.

Over the next two days there was media coverage of a special Mass held at the hospital for Bayardo and a heart-rending plea from his wife, Miriam. The latter was complete with touching photographs of her holding a tearful child.

During that three-day period the gang stayed quiet. There was no reaction at all to the last broadcast. I had warned Ruiz about silence as a tactic, but despite this he grew more and more morose and took to staring at me in a way which did little for my own morale. He took me to the window on one occasion and pointed out the army jeeps which were now permanently stationed outside the palace gates. I asked him whether this was the result of a possible leak in our dealings with the press, but he merely shrugged his shoulders.

My telephone was monitored by his own admission and I had no chance to contact either Maria or Arturo to try to put my own escape plan together. Win or lose, I was here for the duration. It didn't help my concentration at all. I was hoping that the silence was not in fact a deliberate tactic but a sign of the gang's confusion; instinct told me I was right but it didn't help to have Ruiz hovering like a starving vulture and eyeing me up as a tasty piece of carrion.

Case day eighteen, 24 March, brought two calls from the guerrillas giving pick-up instructions.

The letter which Pierro collected pleased me enormously. It was a handwritten note from Bayardo. Ruiz wasn't impressed.

'Why do you look so happy?' he growled. I didn't like his mood at all.

'Excellency, for the first time the gang is reacting to our moves. We didn't ask for proof that Bayardo is alive but they've sent it anyway. They're concerned about the news coverage and are no doubt hoping that we'll publish the fact.'

I saw a glimmer of understanding and went on, explaining how I wanted to escalate the newspaper reports. 'While we are doing this, it's imperative that we continue to negotiate with the gang in the established way or they'll smell a rat and link you to the newspapers.' Ruiz appeared to see the sense of this and actually began to look as though he were enjoying the challenge.

The next day, my fourth arranged article appeared in *Prenso Libre*:

> For Doctor Bayardo Alvarez R.
> Dear Bayardo: We understand your temporary absence ...
> it is surely because you are doing a good deed to someone,
> as you are accustomed to do. Cheer up ... your friends await
> you ... your right to live in peace and quiet is supported by
> God, your patients and us....

Well, they hadn't got my message quite correct but it was probably even more effective with a little Spanish emotion thrown in. A further appeal from Miriam and her child got the front page treatment. The publication elicited a call from the kidnappers the next evening. The letter subsequently picked up was almost a repeat of the previous one. The same insistence on coroner's reports, a further extension of the dealine and yet another note from Bayardo.

I had consciously to resist the temptation to relax. These men were dangerous. At the moment they were confused, they were unsure of themselves. I had to apply more pressure and hope like hell that Ruiz's interference with the media would remain undetected. I stressed this to him as emphatically as I could.

The next five days saw us bombarding the newspaper readers and privileged television watchers of Guatemala City with articles and reports shouting for the release of Bayardo. One inspired touch was a petition signed by literally hundreds of school children begging for the return of their 'Good Doctor Bayardo'. Articles telling how he treated the families of those imprisoned members of the guerrilla group which had abducted him were published alongside pictures of prayer sessions in the poor quarter attended by large crowds.

Ruiz's influence with the press was beyond dispute. I'd only to mention the style of the next article and he swept into action. Indeed, action suited him. It stopped him thinking. Every day I dreaded the news that the Chief of the Army had caught onto the press manipulation. Every hour I expected to hear the sounds of gunfire as the ever present army patrols burst into the palace. I was impotent to influence events outside the advice I was giving Ruiz. As best I could, I switched off to all except the case in hand.

All this time I was pinning my hopes on being able to make the gang appreciate how big a mistake they'd made in kidnapping a man of Bayardo's stature. (I guess even Bayardo would have been surprised at his apparent standing!)

As revolutionaries, the gang were dependent for success on the support of the people. Yet they had seized a man of such immense popularity that they were seriously eroding that support. That was the picture I was trying to paint. They should, by my calculations, be realising this by now. If they tied this to the letter in which the EGP had denounced them in public, they would be in a quandary.

Although confusion is dangerous in amateurs, I was hoping that the one thing which would stand out clearly to them was that if they killed Bayardo they would be in serious trouble. If the moment ever came when they recognised that Ruiz was behind the publicity strategy then I was sure that Bayardo was a dead man! They'd feel that they'd been tricked and anger would overtake reason. If this happened I didn't give much for my own continued well-being either.

Throughout this time the gang continued to send proof that Bayardo lived. And then, without warning, they changed their demands. They didn't ask for medical supplies as we had urged, but they now produced the names of ten more prisoners and gave instructions for their release under the same terms as in the original letter. They were to be given safe conduct into the Mexican Embassy with proof of this being broadcast on the television by an accredited member of that embassy. They insisted in this letter on a meeting with Ruiz and gave a twenty-four-hour deadline, assuring us that this time Bayardo would be instantly killed if the correct reply was not on that evening's broadcast.

Both demands were, of course, impossible. For Ruiz to meet with the gang was inviting his own capture or death, and that in turn would lead to the certain death of his brother as the only witness to the gang's identity. I had to be careful. Things were moving to a critical stage. Was this an act of desperation or were they just playing for time in order to think out a workable solution? I had no way of knowing what effect my press campaign was having. We had to show the gang that we were trying to do what they wanted but compliance with their demands was out of our hands. I drafted two replies for Ruiz.

The first message we sent was to state that it was not possible for Ruiz to make a meeting at such short notice without a departure from his public schedule creating suspicion, but that he would re-arrange his programme and try to make himself available shortly. This went out on that evening's broadcast.

The next message I wrote out for him, after being subjected to Pierro's translation, turned out as:

> The Agro-Commercial Company communicates the following information to the Board of Directors. Concerning the new proposals for laying off ten persons who were thought to be in our employment: the situation is this – there is no information on the second, third and fourth names. Their location is as unknown to us as it is to you. Regarding the final group of six people, these have not been employed in our small company in Mazatenango, a fact which it is easy for you to confirm as many persons arrive and leave daily and therefore the presence of the six would have been communicated externally, very simply.
>
> Regarding the first person on your list, his situation is known but very complicated as he is very much required by

another company in which my influence is limited. However, to resolve the present discussions, I am pressing daily in an attempt to change his status with the intention of placing him in the company you have proposed. Please appreciate the difficulty of my position as the President of my company has received many strong deputations opposing the man's release from our company on the grounds that he is of major importance to us.[1]

This was phrased in such a way that the kidnappers could not reprint it to show that we were negotiating with them.

I explained to Ruiz that I wanted to hold this message. It was only to be used if we were forced into a reply before he had put the next part of my plan into action. I then spent a long time briefing him very carefully as to exactly what I wanted. He understood perfectly but it was my turn to be anxious when I asked the question: 'Can you do it? It must be the day after tomorrow at the latest.' There must have been a shade of doubt in my voice but he took no offence. He laughed.

'Certainly I can do it, James. It will happen tomorrow morning. Get up early.' The 'James' wasn't lost on me but it didn't give me any cause for relaxation. Ruiz and Pierro began making telephone calls. It was 28 March, twenty-two days since Bayardo had been taken. I didn't sleep easily that night. I'd asked a lot of Ruiz and he'd appeared too confident. It was absolutely crucial that he got it right. Twice that night I got out of the makeshift bed and peered down into the gloomy streets below. Did I imagine it or were the soldiers looking directly up at my window?

On 29 March, the citizens of Guatemala City awoke to an amazing sight. Hundreds of women of all ages were marching noisily through the streets carrying placards and banners proclaiming themselves to be the *Mothers of Guatemala*; they were protesting at the evil kidnapping of Doctor Bayardo Alvarez Ruiz. He was their Doctor. Their Doctor who gave them medicine without charge. The man to whom they could take their children at any time of the day or night and know that they would never be turned away. Their Doctor, who nursed the families of the very men who had kidnapped him. In interviews with the reporters and cameramen who flooded the scene, they expressed all these views loudly and vehemently.

If anyone knew where the 'Good Doctor' was being held, they should tell the women and they, the *Mothers of Guatemala* would

[1] Company notices such as these are very common in the Guatemalan daily newspapers. They can run to two or three pages of 'boxes' covering corporate announcements.

force his release. They would hunt out and hound down the kidnappers who had taken this good friend of the poor from the community.

To the observer who knew Guatemala City, there would have been an unusual feature to this demonstration. There was not a policeman in sight! This sort of event was usually guaranteed to bring out the riot squads with a vengeance and I began to fear that Ruiz had overdone it. The demonstration lasted most of the morning and got extensive press, radio and television coverage.

That night and the following morning, the second message I had prepared was published. I explained to Ruiz that the intention was to show the gang that they were in for a long wait even though the Minister was telling them that there was a vague possibility that one of the prisoners might eventually be released.

There was no appeal in the newspapers on that thirtieth day of March but all the media carried further stories of the awesome rage of the *Mothers of Guatemala*.

There was nothing to do but wait for the gang to react. I prepared an emergency script for Ruiz to use if necessary and spent the day poring over the file looking for anything which I may have missed. Together Ruiz and I began to plan an even bigger demonstration by the Mothers. It seemed that it could be organised as often as I wanted. I pointed out to him that if we did decide to use it again, there must be a realistic police presence and a few arrests if we were to avoid suspicion of complicity.

I explained again to him that I wanted the gang to feel totally insecure wherever they were hiding. If they thought that every woman and child in the city was against them and actively searching for them, it must surely worry them. Apart from this direct threat, what about the EGP? They would also be absorbing the same news and getting more and more angry with the splinter group. This latter fact would not escape the kidnappers.

We didn't have long to wait for the next communication from the gang. It was delivered directly to the doctor's wife. In the small hours of the morning of 31 March, outside the doctor's house, a bundle was pushed from a car which then drove off at high speed. Bayardo Alvarez Ruiz was free; apart from a few bruises collected when he hit the pavement, he was unharmed.

I was delighted. Bayardo had been released far more quickly than I had dared hope. He'd been in captivity for only twenty-five days. He was unhurt and no ransom of any kind had been paid. A classic solution to any case but one which evades most negotiators. We'd started with nothing and won everything. Miraculously, the army patrols left as quickly as they'd arrived. Obviously Hernandez, realising that he was not going to find an excuse to start his coup, had withdrawn to await another day.

The farewells with Ruiz were warm but brief. I crossed the city to my hotel and made contact first with a much relieved Maria and then with the Ortega family. Their case was over within a few days and I was able to fly out to Bogotá with considerable relief.

I took with me all the newspapers covering the release of Bayardo. I enjoyed the stories. 'A triumph for the poor people of Guatemala City,' they said. Well, in a sense it was true, but no doubt some of those citizens will recall those headlines and, if they happen to read this story, they'll realise they had a little prompting from behind the scenes.

On that flight back I reflected on my way of life. Up to that time I'd handled some fifty or so kidnaps and been fortunate enough not to have suffered a failure. How long would my luck last? How the hell had I started in this business? I decided it was time to tell the story.

CHAPTER

2

Author's note

Author's note
The metamorphosis from university undergraduate to kidnap negotiato
took me through a number of phases, each of which had a bearing on th
instinct I came to realise I possessed and the methods of operating whic
I developed. I feel it is important to briefly describe these phases and th
effects they had on my life.

THE memories never leave you, they continue to be conjured u
by the oddest things; the smell of roast pork in a restaurant, lam
chops on the barbecue grill or the buffeting from a sudden gust o
wind. The violent interactions of extreme pressures and counter
pressures are sufficient to suck muscle and tissue from the bone
the corpses near the eye of the explosion look peeled; then you
nostrils are assaulted by the smell of burning flesh.

The bomb at Trainor's Bar was my first experience of blas
injuries. They had been compounded by the effects of the resultan
fire. I will never forget trawling through the still smoking debris i
the hopeless search for survivors, surrounded by the local thril
seekers with their 'Oh's and 'Aah's and furtive nudges as the
spotted the bits and pieces of dismembered bodies; the wails o
the genuinely grief-stricken and the often ribald comments of th
soldiers in my platoon – a ribaldry which I knew to be a surfac
defence to conceal the sense of shock and outrage.

I remember being conscious of my feet suddenly beginning t
sweat profusely as the heat from the ashes finally penetrated th
rubber soles of my boots. When the RUC and the Fire Brigad
arrived, my duties reverted to those of setting up a cordon to kee

the spectators clear while the grisly task of putting the bodies into containers took place. Glares of hatred accompanied the insults as we pushed the crowd back to an acceptable distance.

Corporal 'Fang' Tooth nudged me back from the memories created by the sound of the distant explosion.

'Should be getting to the drop-off pretty soon, sir.'

'OK, Corporal, thanks.' Not for the first time I cursed the Saracen armoured troop carrier, unaffectionately known as the 'Pig'. It may offer good protection from snipers but, except for the two soldiers at the rear who were able to peer through the quarter-open back doors, those travelling within the dark, smelly confines of the vehicle were pretty well blind to what was going on outside. One of these was Sergeant 'Dusty' Miller a veteran of six tours in Ulster. An Irishman himself, he seemed to be totally unmoved by any aspect of the 'troubles'. I knew that like myself he was a Roman Catholic but this knowledge came from his records, not from anything he had ever said or any outward Sunday devoutness I had noticed; like many other professional soldiers of his rank, the Warrant Officers' & Sergeants' Mess was his church and confessional.

I suppose the best thing about travelling in a Pig is that within twenty minutes the various smells, ranging from the body odours (not all from the armpits) of a dozen tightly packed soldiers to the hot oily stink from the overheated gear box, make you damned glad to get out of it, whatever lies in wait. I had selected the corner of the Lurgan municipal sports field as my drop-off point. It gave me a choice of three different directions in which I could send my platoon scurrying for initial cover as we got out of the vehicle.

Tonight was one of those exceptions. We would have willingly stayed inside the steel cocoon, smells and all. The reason was not the job we were about to begin but the atrocious weather. It was absolutely belting down with rain. Forget the modern equipment of today's soldier. The only reasonably water-proof items issued in Ulster were the poncho and the 'jackets, foul weather, colour, black'. The poncho renders efficient weapon handling impossible and the jacket is so noisy that even a small section of men can be heard fifty yards away, their coming signalled by the harsh, unmistakeable rustling noise given off by the garment at every movement of the body. The only realistic answer was to accept getting wet and take comfort from the fact that if 'Paddy' was out looking for mischief then he was bloody wet as well.

The cumbersome vehicle squealed to a halt a good fifty yards past the point I'd given the driver and as the brake lights, which should

21

have been disconnected, illuminated our exit, I resolved to let the MTO (Motor Transport Officer) know my feelings when I got back. I allowed myself the luxury of a moment's anger as I pictured him taking his pint of beer in front of the log fire in the Mess. 'Unfair' I thought. I knew that Mick had been one of the Regiment's best RSMs before he was commissioned and I could picture his frustration as he watched the platoons going out night after night knowing that he could do the job better than any of us young subalterns.

We were immediately and thoroughly soaked. Conscious of the brake lights which had been on throughout the seconds it took us to debus, I headed the platoon to the one point of cover which had a good all-round view of the area. This was the sports pavilion tucked away in the corner of the field, close to a small copse. We positioned ourselves around it, getting temporary respite from the rain as we tucked close into the wooden shack and took advantage of the overhanging eaves. We crouched quietly and watched to see whether there had been any reaction to our deployment.

I knew we were invisible in our camouflage suits darkened even more by the rain as we waited against the black backdrop of the building. All was quiet. The decision to move was going to be unpopular with everyone except Dusty, who would be chomping at the bit and wanting to get onto the streets. I risked his sarcasm by hanging on. It wasn't a sense of foreboding or a reluctance to carry on with the patrol which kept me there. It was simply that I didn't relish getting out into the rain before I had to. Squatting on my heels, back against the wall, I looked down at the puddle of water swirling in a mini-whirlpool as it disappeared between the paving stones under my feet. I was mesmerised by it; it was flowing away quite fast. I was interrupted by a harsh whisper from Dusty.

'If you've finished dreaming about the blonde bint with the big tits, sir, don't you think we ought to go and do our bit for the Queen?' For once I was ready.

'Come here, Sergeant,' (I'd never yet dared to call him Dusty out loud). 'There's something a bit odd.'

I could see his eyes rolling in exaggerated disbelief as he silently made his way to me, seemingly oblivious to the rain.

'What is it?' he demanded in the same whisper.

I showed him the water which was still draining away at the same rate.

'You're right, lad. There's something under there.'

He forgot protocol in his sudden interest.

He reached to his right and flicked the ear of a dozing soldier. It has always amazed me that the British soldier can kip under any conditions.

'Wake up, you twat. Pass me your bayonet.'

Simpson made a very brave gesture of defiance.

'You've got one Sarge, why not use your own?'

'Because mine's bloody clean, laddie. Now pass it over before I forget your tender soddin' youth.'

The Irish brogue which could be so disarming was also capable of veiled threats, never explicit but sufficient to warn off the most hardened soldier. The bayonet was passed and Simpson's attitude took on a new, and for him, alien alertness.

Dusty slipped the bayonet into the groove between the paving stones and it passed easily around the whole slab. He started to pry upwards. I grabbed his wrist and shook my head as his eyes snapped up to meet mine.

'No. We may have been seen. We'll move out and return when we're absolutely sure there's no-one around.'

I thought he was going to argue, for we'd almost certainly stumbled onto a cache, but I knew my orders made sense. I left unspoken the thought that the damned thing could have been booby-trapped.

'Aye, you're right, sir. I suggest we leave the bugger until just before first light.'

He gave Simpson his bayonet back and passed around the platoon, nudging them and preparing them to move. I knew the significance of his remark about first light. Whoever located a cache or 'hide', as the common expression was in those days, had to report it immediately and then place an extended cordon around the area until the forensic boys came to examine it. We were going to get even wetter tonight anyway but far better to be mobile and then report the hide at the last moment when we were due to be replaced on the ground by Simon's platoon.

Dawn was breaking as we returned to the pavilion. I had taken the precaution of reporting the suspected find half an hour earlier under the assumption that the Glory Boys would not move without a hot coffee. I was right. We still had almost an hour to wait before they appeared. The rain had stopped; they looked warm and comfortable as they moved in to meet me. I showed them the slab which looked quite innocuous now that the water had drained away. There was just the clean junction line around it which would probably have escaped notice by the casual observer.

We were hustled away from the hide. It was no longer our

responsibility and the self-important forensic squad made this quit
clear. This was their moment. Simon's platoon arrived, none too
pleased with the prospect of spending most of their duty perio
keeping a cordon around an operation which they were not even
going to be allowed to witness.

'Thanks, James. I'll do the same for you.'

It was my platoon's first find and I was pleasantly surprised at th
sudden lifting of morale. I recalled that the training the battalio
had done prior to this Ulster tour had included nothing abou
locating such hides. Certainly, the battalion was aware of the Irish
Republican Army (IRA) and the Ulster Defence Association (UDA
methods of caching or hiding weapons in various places; we ha
specialist search teams trained by the experts in the Royal Engineers
but these were primarily aimed at the searching of houses either on
suspicion or after a sniper incident as the cordon tightened. It wa
food for thought even though our current tour was almost at an end

Two weeks later saw us back in Colchester. It was the practice o
the time for the battalion to be met at the railway station and marcl
back to the barracks behind the Regimental Band. I remember on
this occasion the students of the nearby Essex University welcomin
us home with catcalls and a few well-aimed stones and bottles! On
vastly different scale I could sympathise with the returning Vietnan
veterans in the USA. During the relatively relaxed life of regimenta
duties I often wondered at the perversity of human nature whic
made me decide, on leaving university with a degree in commercia
art, to join the army.

The Royal Military Academy, Sandhurst, caused my emotions t
swing like a pendulum between a sense of the sublime and th
ridiculous. I have always enjoyed the past and so the studies c
history appealed. But pomp and ceremony are wasted on me. Ther
may be sound traditional reasons for an adjutant to mount the step
on horseback, but all it raised in me was a desire to laugh. I couldn'
equate the sheer expense of mess dress and lavish male-only banquet
with modern soldiering. I'm a loner by nature and though I'm a
ease in the company of others, I do prefer to keep my own counsel
My hobbies of collecting Victorian watercolours and also, at tha
time, a keen interest in vintage motor cars didn't require the presenc
of others for enjoyment. An unremarkable student at Sandhurst ca
normally expect to lead a fairly quiet life, not being hounded t
exploit a sporting prowess nor being held up constantly as a shinin
example of officership. But standing as I do at six foot three inche
there are penalties. It is difficult to evade the hawk eyes of a dri

24

sergeant, for example, and the profile is easily spotted during the interminable tactical manoeuvres while trying to master the leopard crawl and other such methods of moving between two points in a manner supposedly invisible to the enemy. This ease of recognition gave me many moments of extreme vexation.

I enjoyed actual soldiering and the tactical exercises. That was challenging; it was not only my military skills which developed! I was not one of the privileged few with the benefit of an allowance, and the mess bills, many of which were divided on a pro rata basis, could be a struggle to pay. On exercise I noticed how quickly young, wealthy officers devoured their rations, often with a speed which left them short for the final few days or hours of a manoeuvre. I was able to capitalise on this weakness by stocking up at the beginning of an exercise with Mars bars and other such attractive goodies; by carefully hoarding these until the optimum moment I was in a position to command premium prices from the drooling officer cadets. There were certainly no hard feelings as a result of this; indeed exercise budgets were often individually set around my prices. I did after all accept the burden of responsibility for carrying the extra load.

I passed out of Sandhurst and into the Royal Regiment of Fusiliers and very quickly found myself in Northern Ireland getting to grips with grass roots soldiering. This was far more interesting to me, even though I recognised at an early stage that my long-term future did not lie with the army. The basis of my battalion before the unpopular unpheaval of the British army (a Petronius-like reorganisation) had been the Royal Northumberland Fusiliers, which meant that the great majority of my platoon were Geordies from the North East. With their ready wit, tempered by an uncompromising outlook on life, their utter loyalty to the battalion and 'wor gaffer', they were a great bunch to work with and life was more than tolerable.

My day-to-day problems militarily were drastically reduced by Sergeant Miller leaving me with concerns of a more personal nature. In the main these revolved around how to keep my Morgan on the road despite the fact that as I didn't have a driving licence, I was unable to tax or insure it! I managed it for quite a long time but all good things come to an end, which is another story; suffice to say that an understanding Commanding Officer and an imminent tour in Ulster enabled me to stave off any real punishment. On that tour I like to think that I became a useful officer and the cache find, last time around, accidental though it was had given me a resolution to look deeper into this facet of 'peacetime' soldiering in the province.

Preparations for an infantry battalion moving out to Northern Ireland for a tour of duty are both necessary and realistic. Custom-made facilities now exist where the battalion literally goes 'on operations' for a period of about two weeks. Most aspects of active service in the province are covered with the different companies taking the role of enemy for each other. Battalion and company headquarters are set up properly and the intelligence and communications systems are shaken down into good working order; signal networks are practised until they are as competent and secure as possible, and orders and briefings groups follow the same format as they will in the months to come.

Soldier meets rival soldier in enthusiastic street riot and rural ambush; junior officer pits himself against junior officer in competitive appreciation and planning sessions. These lessons have stayed with me right up to the present day – I have never yet been faced with a problem which could not be analysed and put into perspective by the application of the military appreciation system. In this exercise environment, platoons and sections of infantrymen are faced with sniper attacks; screaming 'Irishwomen' played by enthusiastic service girls abuse the squads as they patrol the street of simulated Belfast and Londonderry. Republican music blares ou from the windows of the tenements and drunken revellers spill from the bars.

It is a good preparation phase and not without its share of injurie as the lads enter wholeheartedly into the spirit of it. Still noticeably missing, though, was any type of formal training on specifically hunting for terrorist hides. I am not contending that locating these hides has any great impact on the war. The terrorists are to well supplied. The only thing which is of any great moment is killing the terrorists or having the ability to intern them for long periods. I have never known the finding of a hide, no matter how big, to slow down IRA operations; in fact it can have the opposit effect. When one or two gunmen fall in action, however, o are successfully brought to trial and convicted, that is a differen story.

Despite this, a battalion at that time could go through a complet three-month tour and not have a single incident. Patrolling all too often consisted of 'showing the flag' in hard republican areas, placing soldiers at risk for highly questionable returns. It was in my min that if a determined attempt was made to locate terrorist caches, i would make life a damned sight more interesting for the platoons o the ground while still being a very useful contribution to the overal effort. If hides were to be found often enough it could have an unsettling effect on the enemy.

I count myself extremely fortunate at that time to have had Colonel 'Biffo' as my commanding officer. As a soldier, he had 'been the route', he had served two tours with 22nd Special Air Service Regiment, one of which had given him the opportunity to command a troop in the jungles of Malaya during the Emergency; even so, information on those periods had to be drawn out of him. He was a stocky man with a pugnacious, highly mobile, expressive face which could switch quickly between obvious good humour, anger and a beguiling, disarming smile which usually meant he was about to hit someone! Hit he certainly could; a good rugby player, he was deceptively agile and very powerful. Above all, he was a tremendously well-respected leader and totally dedicated to his command. A relaxed and easy man to talk to, though he didn't suffer fools gladly.

I am not sure where the nickname Biffo came from – almost certainly awarded by his comrades in the SAS (I can guess why). It was not a question you asked and if you wanted to stay upright as a junior officer you certainly didn't address him by that name! The only man I ever heard use it to him was Spike, a soldier with lengthy SAS service who had joined the battalion on being commissioned. When he used the name they were deep in conversation about some mystical operation or other. I never knew at the time which one of them floored the SAS 'pretender' who tried to muscle in on their deliberations! Spike once told me that for a number of years after he joined the SAS his mother thought he was part of a special postal service which went round the world supervising the packaging of delicate military cargoes. Those two were my first real acquaintance with the SAS and though I didn't know it at the time, they were not to be the last.

I talked to the Colonel about my ideas and not surprisingly I found an interested and alert listener. After hearing me out, he related to me the process by which the SAS had set about finding the jungle camps of the Communist Terrorists (CTs) during the Malayan campaign. They knew what component needs the CTs had when making a base. They needed water (their methods of piping water along seemingly accidentally or naturally fallen leaves and sections of bamboo were cunning in the extreme); they needed physical cover – they liked to be surrounded by difficult terrain or undergrowth which would make a close approach by the enemy noisy; they had to be within reasonable proximity of a line of communication such as a track or a river by which to take their supplies and messages from the Min Yuen (a supporting Chinese organisation); and they needed an escape route in the event of an emergency.

A careful map search could narrow down the possibilities significantly for the searching SAS patrols and a detailed ground study coupled to intuition could do the rest. In this way, allied to their infinite patience and superb jungle craft, they scored a great many successes. This conversation had the obvious effect on my thinking – it encouraged me to set to work calculating all the requirements necessary to an operational hide of weapons. I tried to put myself into the mind of the Irish terrorist. It was a stimulating study and I kept it totally to myself. If any rewards were going to be reaped then the lads in my platoon were going to be the harvesters.

This was not a jealous or disloyal attitude; after all there was an even chance of failure. If the process was that simple then why hadn't someone else done something about it?

In the following days, as we prepared to move to Ulster, I did not have much time to devote to the searching business. One fact had pleased me enormously: we were going to Gough Barracks in the city of Armagh with an area of responsibility which stretched down to the border. This was bandit country with a very active terrorist unit which indulged in both urban and rural operations. It was theoretically the best possible place to put my ideas into practice. Changing over with the occupants of Gough Barracks took but a few days and then the normal process of familiarisation patrols began. By this system the maximum number of men in the battalion get to know as much of the ground as possible before settling down to their own patches. My company, 'C' Company, drew a rural area which included a nice slice of the border territory which was gratifying to say the least.

Between the patrols, ordered as a necessary part of the battalion plan, I spent as much time as possible studying the situation. I was initially tempted to begin by analysing the past records of all hides (or finds) in the area but I decided that this might unwittingly lead me down the wrong trail. A map study of a grid reference would not, I felt, necessarily show me what I wanted and so I followed the obliquely given advice of the Colonel. I worked out in detail what I reckoned a terrorist would look for when establishing a weapons hide.

My list looked something like this:

- A recognition feature which could be unmistakeably described verbally to a second party.
- Close to a road, track or railway line.
- An area not likely to be investigated by domestic, digging animals such as pigs or dogs.
- A covered approach.
- An area which it was easy to watch prior to a pick-up.
- A site which was easy to recognise at night.
- If possible, not on a regular military patrol route.
- Possibly an area which was under permanent observation from a farm house or the like.
- A site which offered natural hiding places such as ruined buildings, walls, the roots of large trees or thick hedgerows.

Many of the above requirements could not be determined from a map so I began the process of studying the files and taking such details as had been recorded about previous finds. From this I was able to visit the actual sites and see how many of my requirements for a hide actually fitted the ground.

I concentrated only on significant hides and discounted the small finds of single old weapons and the odd small box of ammunition. I was pleasantly surprised to find that most of the sites had all or the majority of the pre-conditions which I had worked out. I now briefed my platoon on the findings and got a vigorous response. We told no-one that we were deliberately trying out the theories, though I think the Colonel suspected what we were up to even in the early stages.

We had a variety of different types of patrol to conduct in those days. We might be tasked with putting in an ambush as a result of intelligence; we could be despatched to a particular area to chat up the locals, hoping to glean information, or we could be given the task of supplying part of a cordon in a major search operation. We would occasionally be required to set up an observation post on a suspected terrorist meeting place or border crossing point or even used as escorts for visitors.

All these types of patrol would be constantly interrupted by emergencies; a sudden street riot, a bombing or other incident which required the company or even battalion to deploy in strength. There was one other sort of patrol which was my platoon's favourite. This was the free-wheeling charter which simply gave us the task of following our noses in a particular area; this was tailor-made for the business of seeking hides.

I could not have had a better platoon for my purpose – a fair smattering of country lads with poacher's instincts and eyes sharp enough to spot the oddly placed branch or the hump in a hedgerow which didn't seem natural, and city boys with their natural street-wisdom and alertness. Dusty Miller was as keen as I was and we quickly built up a healthy competitive spirit between our sections. We quickly learned the sort of markers which were being used in our operational area and began to regularly locate hides of different types, both long-term well-constructed underground caches and short-term hides where weapons in transit or laid ready for use were simply put into easily located temporary positions.

We began to build up quite a reputation as the 'Finds Platoon' and the boys were cock-a-hoop. We discussed the techniques we used willingly and openly now but we seemed to have the anchor on success. I realised that I and quite a number of the platoon were beginning to have a feel or instinct for the business. We could go into an area and sense that there was something there and we invariably found it. It was during this tour of duty that I was given the somewhat unglamorous nickname of 'Sniffer' which the platoon immediately adopted for themselves.

In the latter stages of the tour we adopted the habit of deliberately missing hides. If we were trawling along a suspect hedgerow or wall and one of the boys spotted a probable site, we would deliberately ignore it and perhaps make a play of rooting around in the under-growth some distance away in case anyone was watching and then retire in obvious defeat. This line of thought had occurred to me after we were told that we were being successful enough for the IRA to suspect that they had an informer giving away hide locations. I deduced that by appearing in the area of a hide but failing to find it, we might give observers the notion that we were acting on infor-mation but were simply not clever or alert enough to locate the site. The principle was that we or another platoon could then ambush the position that night in the hope that the terrorists would appear on the scene to move the contents of the hide.

For some reason we had no success in this particular tactic. I can only assume that the terrorists thought that as we had missed it the first time round we would assume that we had been given false information and they obviously felt that the weapons were secure where they were.

At the end of the tour I was instructed to write a paper outlining the successful methods my platoon had used. This was for general dissemination to those units beginning their Ulster tours. I heard only of limited successes as a result of this and began to feel that the instinct was perhaps a reality. This business of applying lateral thinking techniques and trying to get into the terrorist's mind was to stand me in good stead later, though I did not know it at the time.

During my next (and last) tour in Ulster my platoon, which was relatively unchanged, had similar successes, and to our pleasure we were often sent into other unit patches at their request to search particular areas where they suspected the presence of hides. It invariably led to success but not always where the unit had indicated – we would usually try to spend some time on a map study of the patch in question before moving out and this paid dividends. If we were directed into an unfruitful area, we were able to suggest to the local commander that we may as well look at grid square 'X' while we were there.

I tried very hard during this tour to persuade the army to adopt the tactic of using the media to put across the information that acting on intelligence we had successfully located a hide containing 'X' weapons and explosives near the village of 'Y' or whatever in a deliberate attempt to feed IRA suspicions that they had an informer in their midst. If nothing else, it could have caused the terrorists to begin a major overhaul of their cache system, leaving the army with a good chance of springing successful ambushes. I don't think the tactic was ever used, at least not in my time.

We were not long in the United Kingdom after that tour before we were moved out to Cyprus to become part of the United Nations emergency force defending the British Crown property during the Turkish invasion. It was a total contrast to Ulster and a sheer delight to be patrolling in warm sunshine with the added incentive to good soldiering in the form of the occasional stray bullet passing overhead.

On return to Colchester from Cyprus, I was summoned by the Commanding Officer and told that I was being loaned to the SAS to assist them in a study of some sort. I was mystified but very keen to work with the organisation, which I did for some months. The work was fascinating and obviously not for public airing; it is mentioned only because as a result of this attachment, I was to meet a number of people who were to play a part in my eventual decision to become a negotiator.

The time had arrived for me to make up my mind whether to remain in the army or try my luck outside. I was then a Captain with a good record of service much boosted by the tours in Ulster, but I recognised that in the long term I would not be fulfilled in an army career. I did not appreciate it at the time, but I had learned a lot in the army which was to come in very useful. The patience and discipline which comes from long, uncomfortable hours in ambushes and surveillance positions; the analytical appreciation processes; the sifting and collating of an endless stream of seemingly disjointed information, turning it into tactical intelligence; the hours spent listening to the personal problems of the diverse characters who made up my platoon; all these factors and a score of others prepared me well for the future.

Shortly before I was due to disappear into the melting pot of civilian life and try to pick up the traces in the world of commercial art, I was invited to meet an ex-SAS officer who was forming the operational nucleus of a company called Control Risks Limited.

I listened with interest as the company's background and proposed operation was outlined. A basic idea by Julian Radcliffe, then working with a prominent group of underwriters at Lloyd's, had captured the interest of Timothy Royle, an executive with the blue chip company Hogg Robinson. The intention was to offer a loss adjustment service in the kidnap and ransom field. At that time underwriters at Lloyd's were writing some US$40–50 million worth of business out of a world total generally reckoned to be about US$70 million.

It should be made clear that Lloyd's do not actually pay out ransom money. Their policies cover reimbursement which is set at a figure which the client could reasonably afford to pay in the event of a kidnap. The service to be provided by Control Risks was designed to check that an actual kidnap had taken place, that the insured had complied with the policy demands and that the ransom money had been paid – exactly the same role as loss adjusters in any other form of insurance.

Royle and Radcliffe had read a business plan or proposal, written by my interviewer, for the formation of a security company. They had been impressed and saw a need for his type of experience in their own operation and so he was recruited into Control Risks. Shortly after, the services of Simon Adams-Dale, another ex-SAS officer, were similarly attracted. The Cassidy Davis syndicate was at that time writing most of Lloyd's kidnap and ransom business and it was to them that Royle and Radcliffe turned. The syndicate agreed to pay fees for the service.

Shortly before I was interviewed, a further ex-SAS officer joined the organisation, Arish Turle, who was later to become the Managing Director. The work which had been offered appealed to me and I gave a commitment to join the company after I had finally severed my contract with the army. Boots, sleeping bag and other essentials having been handed back into the care of the Quartermaster, I returned to London to take up my appointment.

I eventually reported for duty in the Crutched Friars headquarters in the City of London. Turle had already seen the potential for expanding the service into advisory areas before and during the event of kidnap and calculated that by offering this, it ought to be possible firstly to reduce the risk and secondly, by ensuring a structured negotiation, reduce the actual sums paid out as ransoms. This idea was gelling in the minds of the board of directors. That was the situation in 1977 when I joined.

Turle and Adams-Dale were in South America at the time when we were hit by half-a-dozen simultaneous cases in Italy. A couple more consultants were recruited and I ended up overseeing the response to all those cases. While this was happening the two men in South America had the misfortune to be jailed for their troubles. In itself this led to a rapid rewrite of Standard Operating Procedures (SOPs). I think in that first year up to early 1978, we advised on something like twelve or thirteen cases and the fees were flowing in to everyone's satisfaction.

It would have been about that time that Julian Radcliffe proposed an approach to the underwriters to elicit a retainer above and beyond the fee system. I remember the meeting in his country house when this matter was raised. In typical ex-officer fashion, then untutored in the ways of the City, many of us thought this was a very daring idea – the fact that the astronomical figure of £10,000 was to be suggested filled us with mirth.

Not surprisingly, with the wisdom of hindsight, a retainer was established which eventually ran into millions of pounds, though this is likely to be less nowadays with the decrease in kidnapping. I progressed to become Head of Kidnap Negotiations. Turle and Adams-Dale took up executive positions and life went on apace. After three very busy years with the organisation, I decided that I would rather be master of my own destiny.

I wanted to stay in the kidnap business; it interested me, I was good at it and I had my own ideas on how to operate. I wanted flexibility. There was a big market and I was not afraid of competition. I launched myself in the simplest possible way. I made an offer to an Italian lawyer which he just could not afford to refuse; he was to become my link man on the ground in that country. He would uncover the cases and introduce me to the families.

I set up similar representation in South America. The system worked well and I got an increasing amount of kidnap consultancy work and eventually decided to form my own company, which was subsequently retained by another syndicate of underwriters who covered kidnap and ransom policies. As my workload increased I was forced to take on other consultants and I began to realise the difficulty of finding and training good, reliable people.

A fair number of potential consultants came from an SAS background, which was not surprising. Such men are highly saleable and tend to have a security-based background revolving around counter-terrorism, the care of VIPs, overseas embassies and the like. They are well versed in intelligence collation and analysis. Despite these factors I have always had reservations about the use of ex-SAS people. True, they have the right security background, they are confident and self-contained, usually honest and loyal. But personality plays such an important part in kidnap consultancy and this is where I uncovered a shortcoming. I suppose it was the fact that they had lived in an environment where it was essential to be close-mouthed that so many of them were taciturn and introverted in attitudes. This does not equip them at all well to deal with the emotional Latin temperament. An exception can be the young officer who has done his single tour with the Regiment, but often he then lacks the underlying experience and stability necessary to success.

In South America I selected Arturo, whom I have briefly mentioned in connection with the Ruiz case, and he served me very well over the years. Since I have reduced my own business commitments, he has acted as a consultant himself on a number of occasions and often phones me if he wants to discuss a particular problem with a case. In Italy I was less fortunate. I got plenty of cases but I eventually found to my cost that all lawyers are not necessarily honest. When I found my representative to be dealing from both sides of the deck during a particularly fraught case, the parting of the ways was inevitable. I describe the scene later in the book.

My company was running very profitably, achieving a high level of business from both the insured and uninsured markets, as well as becoming more and more involved in straightforward preventive, advisory business. But I was still having great problems finding the right calibre of consultant. In the intervening period I had married Maria and was rapidly becoming disenchanted with the amount of time I was spending away on cases. At that time I had been involved in over sixty cases and felt that the time had come to change direction.

I suppose I was also getting tired. I decided to pare down drastically the kidnap and ransom consultancy business and set up in an equally challenging area of the security market which led to the formation of my current company. I am still called upon from time to time and asked to advise on cases. This is usually the result of a word of mouth recommendation from a past client and, depending upon what type of case it is and what my commitments are at the time, I will either attend to it myself or commit one of a couple of trusted, experienced friends and assist them remotely if they require it.

The business still fascinates me. It is an extension in many ways of the systems I used in Ulster back in those early army days when the challenge was to get into the mind of the terrorist and adopt his thinking processes. This, plus the fact that each case presents its uniquely different aspects, will always interest me and I cannot see a time when I will ever completely divorce myself from the challenge of kidnap and ransom negotiations.

The pattern of setting up a case response is quite simple but some of the tactics and the reasoning behind them may initially be confusing. I have therefore set out some details which explain my method of operating and will help in an overall appreciation of the business.

The events I relate are true. Where requested I have hidden the identity of some of the clients in the interests of their continued security. This is an absolute necessity. An alert fiscal authority may decide to investigate. A skeleton could fall noisily from the family closet or – even worse – a once-thwarted kidnapper could well decide to strike again!

CHAPTER

3

Author's note

Kidnap negotiations can be long and protracted. There are many technical factors to appreciate. There are a bewildering number of tactics which can be used by kidnap gang and deprived family alike. In this chapter I give an overall view of the business in order that the reader can more easily put into perspective some of the actions taken in the case histories which follow.

THERE is no great mystique about the crime of kidnapping; it predates the Holy Wars of Richard the Lionheart and Saladin and the principles involved have altered little over the centuries. The greatest evolutionary change has been the transformation from the purely political crime to straight-forward commercial extortion for money. There are a number of reasons why kidnap is shrouded in mystery which are important to understand. In many cases, where the super-rich are involved, the source of personal finance can be questionable, not least to the fiscal authorities of the country concerned; very intimate and potentially embarrassing family details may be uncovered; the sensitive issues of insurance policies (sometimes illegal) may have to be hidden and it is not surprising that the families of victims shun any form of publicity and are often reluctant to collaborate with law enforcement agencies. In some countries the abilities of those police organisations can be suspect and families are unwilling to pass on any information which may tempt the security forces into a rescue operation which could go wrong with tragic results.

For a variety of socio-economic reasons there are certain kidnap centres in the world; these can be loosely defined as the Middle East,

Italy and South America, with the Orient (to include Thailand, Hong Kong and the Philippine Islands) straggling some way behind in third place. Europe is a relative late-comer onto the scene. I dislike statistics, but to put the business into perspective Italy has had over 600 kidnaps for ransom in the last sixteen years; South America has had somewhat more than half this number and the rest of the world has seen about one third. These crude figures discount political cases though not necessarily terrorist motivated kidnaps.

The Middle East deserves special mention. There is virtually no demand for the private consultant as there is no ransom demand by the captors. A number of factors are at work in the Beirut type situation. Victims are not necessarily taken because of their individual status. Indeed it can take months or even years before the kidnappers build up any perception at all as to the relative values of their victims. Essentially they have only one indication of the victim's standing in his country of origin and that is the publicity the kidnap receives.

There is a great deal of inter-connection between the 'gangs'; this spreads across ideals, philosophies and tactics. None of them are short of operating funds; the families of the victims are rarely possessed of the sort of wealth which would enable them to offer more than would be considered as petty cash. To consider that Muhammer Ghaddafi is alleged to have put US$50,000,000 at the disposal of General Noriega in order for him to continue to pay his army is a sobering thought and it puts the funding figures into perspective.

The prisoners in Beirut have their ransoms paid by the governments and news media of their own countries in regular publicity. It is interesting to observe how when concern for a kidnapped individual may be fading, there will be a press release often in the form of a video tape in order to snatch the world headlines again. An appeal from the Archbishop of Canterbury for the release of Terry Waite is worth far more to 'the cause' than a few thousand dollars.

It was principally the enormity of the Italian and South American figures which inspired Lloyd's of London to seize the opportunity of getting into the market with policies offered to insure companies and wealthy, private individuals against the risk of kidnap and ransom. Lloyd's, with its estimated 65 per cent of the world market, was reported to have control over approximately US$60 million worth of annual business during the peak days of kidnapping in the 1970s. Obviously such figures require a method of loss assessment or adjustment in order to exercise any degree of control and it was from this need that the negotiator came into being. Some would contend that negotiator is a misnomer as the actual role of people such as myself is to advise. I shall continue to use this term because, unlike many, I am willing to accept executive status in a case.

The question of the morality of kidnap insurance continues to be raised periodically by journalists, sociologists and governments. Some countries have made it illegal but it continues to flourish even in those places. I have preferred to work on uninsured cases without the pressures from the underwriters on me but I have no really strong feelings about such policies. For every question which raises doubt there is an answer which at least calls for serious debate. If a person's property is at risk from burglary or fire he can insure against that risk. If the threat lies in the possibility of kidnap then why should he not also be able to insure against that risk?

Generally kidnap cases which are in the hands of experienced negotiators should be safely settled at lower figures than others thus releasing less money into the criminal fraternity. Doubts are occasionally raised in connection with terrorist inspired incidents. A private company or consultant, retained by underwriters to respond to cases within their portfolios, has no choice but to take part in the negotiations or be in breach of contract.

The Don Tidey case of 1983 was reported in the press to have culminated in £2 million being credited to an IRA bank account and this resulted in EEC countries taking a close look at the legalities of the underwriters' involvement; even if the decision was to outlaw it, how could such a law be enforced? The business would simply move to the USA which is already the seat of Lloyd's fiercest competition.

An insurance policy is only a safeguard if the knowledge of its existence is a closely guarded secret. I am certainly aware of an uncanny 'coincidence' in Italy when a significant number of insured victims on the same broker's list were hit in close succession. If a kidnap gang is certain that the target victim is insured then it will be pretty confident of getting a reasonable settlement. If this is the case, the gang is also going to be sorely tempted to continue to hit the 'golden egg' in the same family or corporation. The underwriters are aware of these dangers and their security is of a very high order but in a business where the ransom figures can be staggeringly large, corruption (in some parts of the world) has to be a serious consideration.

In my opinion kidnap is one of the lowest forms of crime; it is simply not possible to imagine the savage rape of emotions involved when a loved one is suddenly, and often brutally, snatched from the midst of a family. The ensuing fear, shock and uncertainty is a potent weapon for the kidnapper and it is his hope that this emotional disruption will be sufficient to make the family capitulate immediately they receive his demand for payment.

It is a common tactic for the gang to remain silent for a time after the snatch in order for the family to sink into the pits of despair. The more frightened and disoriented they are, the more likely becomes a rapid success for the gang. I count myself lucky if I can get involved in these critical early days as this is the period during which I can start to educate the family about what to expect.

Barter is the essential ingredient of kidnap negotiations – with the obvious difference that a human life is involved. As with all business discussions, regardless of the commodity concerned, there is an element of give and take whereby both parties start from a fixed position and move towards an accommodation acceptable to all. The victim is reduced to the role of merchandise while both sides discuss, argue, cajole and threaten their way to agreement. Now, it is fine for me to explain that standpoint from my detached view but my clients, who are directly involved in the threat to life and possible financial disaster, are thrown into a maelstrom of bewildering nightmare and suffering and the basic negotiation process can become totally obscured. It is my first duty to explain the whole process of kidnap and settlement to the family.

As far as briefing the family is concerned, I always make the initial assumption that we are dealing with a professional gang. Amateurs can be a real problem to the negotiator but there is no point in even discussing this until it becomes a reality. After all I am trying to put the family as much at ease as possible in these early stages.

There are exceptions to every rule, indeed no two cases are ever identical even if the same gang is involved, but generally kidnap negotiations are viewed by the kidnappers as a process of arriving at a satisfactory price for the commodity they hold. The majority of gangs accept that their victims (the remaining family) will pay what they can genuinely afford without wrecking or seriously endangering the whole family's financial security. In most cases the price is a matter of the maximum amount that the family can raise in cash by way of existing liquid holdings added to subsequent bank loans.

True professionals will have spent considerable time (and money) on research into the victim's financial situation and will not normally expect major assets to be sold. This, they know could attract attention from the police or other similar organisations, which is the last thing they want. Experienced gangs have learned that there is a price bracket which is affordable by their victims beyond which most families cannot or will not move.

While it is easy to see that the gang holds the major card – the victim – the family holds an equally important asset – the money. After all, this is the sole reason that the situation has occurred. So we have a sole seller and a sole interested purchaser, each with the strengths and weaknesses imposed by such a position. The gang knows well that the process is one of bargaining with threat and they will attempt to dominate the proceedings from the outset as this will give them the best chance of success. The greatest threat they can use is to kill the victim but this is a total contradiction, as it is an implicit statement that they are going to destroy their source of income! There have been occasions when these threats have been carried out but generally these have been at the hands of amateur gangs, gangs faced with a totally intransigent negotiator, or for political reasons.

As with many other businesses, market forces are at work in the kidnap game. A 'going rate' will have been unofficially established above which of course there is no limit but below which there will often be little scope for compromise. It follows therefore that in order to achieve a working discipline, a budget has to be set. This budget is absolutely critical and is the dominating force in the negotiating process. Too high or low a budget will invariably lead to complicated, prolonged and dangerous negotiations. In essence the process revolves around the budget which is set and the manner in which it is offered; outside these two factors most of the other considerations are incidental. It is important for the family to realise from the very outset that everything which occurs during a nego-tiation on the part of the gang is calculated to extract the maximum amount of money. All the communications received will be geared to squeezing the buyer forever upwards to a point which is acceptable (i.e. in the area of the 'going rate').

A negotiation will be successfully concluded only as the result of two factors: firstly, that the buyer's offer is within the 'area of acceptability' and secondly, that he has realistically demonstrated to the gang that no more money will be forthcoming. It is usually pointless to give the impression that there is no more cash before the 'area of acceptability' has been reached. It has to be remembered that professional gangs have a vested interest in maintaining or even increasing the 'going rate' – this is their livelihood and they will appreciate the complication in their own market if a settlement is too low – all subsequent victims will try to settle at a similar figure.

If the process is as simple and clear cut as this, why the need for a negotiator? Surely the family merely offers a sum within the area of the going rate and makes the exchange. If only it was that simple! Any market trader will confirm that if the acceptable offer comes too quickly then he has either under priced the commodity or the buyer has a special reason for wanting to close the deal quickly. In the case of a kidnap, the gang leader is in a position to apply even more pressure if it is suspected that the above is true.

He has a number of options open to him: he can threaten death or mutilation knowing that he has a more than fair chance of squeezing more money from the family; he can simply take the money on offer, refuse to release the victim and the whole process will start again; or he can 'sell' the victim to another gang. This is the nub of negotiation. I have to impress on the family that they will be squeezed like a sponge. I have to prepare them to adopt the attitude that a threat can be viewed as a good sign. It indicates a last desperate effort by the gang to administer the last squeeze – to get the last 'drop of water'. These are the gang's actions which the negotiator will forestall by carefully analysing the situation, advising the family on tactics and counter-tactics so that when the settlement is eventually reached, the gang will be in no doubt that the family is unable to afford a single penny more (whether this be true or not).

The art of negotiation is to maintain momentum and achieve the position where the gang is reacting to the client's moves rather than vice versa. Everything revolves around communications, both from the gang and from the client. Every communication from the gang has but a single purpose – to ensure the maximum financial return. Even the provision of proof of the victim's life is to reassure the family in order that they will continue to negotiate without delay. I have found that once my clients realise that there are no messages, only pressure tactics, they are more likely to understand the process of negotiation. It is my role to reduce all communications from the gang into component parts. I take the threat, show what lies behind it and what can be read between the lines, then, after this analysis I give advice on the next move with its advantages and disadvantages followed by an indication of what the next communication is likely to contain.

Communications from the gang can be in various forms, each calculated to bring the maximum pressure to bear on the client. In the main kidnap countries the majority of negotiations are conducted by telephone. This form of direct contact is a prime method of impressing the personality of the gang's negotiator on the client; it is usually possible at an early stage to determine the level of expertise of the gang by the way they use the telephone.

As the negotiator, I am constantly asking myself the question: 'Who is out there?' I am forever looking for indications of experience. It is always a possibility that the gang may be led by someone who has been a minor figure in other kidnaps where he may have seen certain tactics used from the viewpoint of a person back at the base. He may have seen letters written and tapes made but he has no experience of telephone handling. I have to try to get into his mind and ascertain just how much he knows about the business.

An experienced professional will confine his conversation to a series of grunts or short expressions such as, 'Tell me, eh?' 'Speak'. All he is interested in hearing is the amount of the latest offer and nothing else. He will spend thirty to forty-five seconds only – he will be aware that the phone may be tapped and he doesn't particularly care as he knows how long it will take the police to trace the call and he will rarely use the same phone twice.

These calls may be made directly to the family home but frequently they are made to relatives or business associates as this way there is a better chance that the family will not tell the authorities. The recipients of the calls are often given instructions on security, told to go directly to the family of the hostage and not to use the telephone. An amateur is more likely to call the family direct and his calls have been known to last as long as fifteen minutes. It may well be possible to engage him in conversation and though it is unlikely that anything concrete will be learned, it is a way of beginning to turn the tables psychologically.

The usual purpose of a telephone call is for the gang to hear the family's latest offer and to pass on a threat when that amount (as always) is insufficient. A brisk, commanding voice is the norm in order to impress upon the family that they are dealing with an uncompromising professional.

It is not unusual in Italy, for example, for the gang to use two or even more negotiators on the phone; one will conduct ninety per cent of the proceedings, with others of an apparently more aggressive and intolerant nature being brought in from time to time for impact on the family. The purpose then of telephone calls is to give verbal instructions as to where a letter or package can be picked up; the provision of proof that the victim is alive; to obtain financial news; to initiate aggressive tactics generally by direct threats but sometimes using tapes made by the victim and to pass on instructions regarding the making of payments.

As a rule, letters are used as tactics, to send proof or to give payment instructions. The number of letters in a case will vary from none to many but an average case will see four or five letters of some description. The recipients are often acquaintances of the victim or his family with the choice being non-obvious in order to reduce the chance of a police surveillance operation. If this is the chosen method then the recipient will be given instructions to deliver it personally to a selected member of the family and he will be given some basic security orders on how to behave such as: 'Behave normally, don't inform anyone else, do not use your telephone, deliver only to "X"'

Letters are frequently written in the victim's own hand even though they will be produced by the gang. In most cases however they are typed. The contents of all letters (with some notable exceptions) will originate with the gang. They may simply dictate or they may give the victim a list of points to include and tell him to use his own words to give the letter maximum authenticity. The gang will often attempt to give the impression that the victim has been permitted to write the letter as an act of humanity in order to assist in persuading the family that the contents are genuine. Delivery of the letters will usually be by hand to a location such as a telephone box, waste bin, petrol station etc., which is close to the house or office of the person instructed to collect it. This is another safeguard against police interception; it will generally ensure that the intended recipient arrives on the scene first. The spot chosen must be such that it is possible, within the duration of a very short phone call, to pass simple, clear instructions which will enable the target to find the letter without delay. It is not normal to use the official postal system due to the possibilities of interception and the unpredictability of delivery times.

Letters are likely to be used to convey direct orders from the gang, handwritten notes from the victim, newspaper cuttings with the victim's signature on it as proof of life, maps with routes for payment delivery, or a personal item which the victim may have been wearing or carrying at the time of the snatch, the latter being a method of establishing the gang's credibility. Letters will sometimes contain a photograph of the victim and various ploys may be used to upset the family. The victim may be cosmetically made up to appear very ill or made to look as though he has been savagely beaten by the judicious application of tomato ketchup to simulate blood. The photographs will often show the victim holding a newspaper where the headlines are clearly visible as proof of life. This cannot be taken at face value. I am aware of one extreme case where such photographs were regularly delivered to the family but it later transpired that the victim had been killed some time previously and stored, in a sitting position, in a deep freeze cabinet. The cadaver was extracted from time to time to be photographed with a newspaper!

Another common form of putting pressure on the family is to send tapes of the victim's voice. The gang will often go to great lengths to make the victim sound ill or very despondent. This may be the result of many rehearsals or indeed they could well beat the victim just prior to taping the message which they will invariably dictate. Tapes are of course purely a tactical weapon though the effect on the family is naturally traumatic. In Italy, tapes are being used more and more and they are usually delivered in the same manner as letters.

Packages are another form of communication, passed on by the normal means of pre-arranged drops close to the family home. This is perhaps the worst form of instruction the family can receive; a letter is innocuous and cannot contain much of a sinister nature, but a parcel? This could hold anything and the family will go through agonies until it is collected and opened. They can contain a number of items depending upon the purpose. A favourite in Salvador and Guatemala is to use one of the many companies which make home deliveries; various types of 'present' may be sent to the family and in the past boxes have contained such items as blood stained clothing identifiable as the victim's, and even severed fingers!

Bombs have been used on occasions when the gang has felt that the family needed jolting out of following a specific line or policy which was undesirable; for instance the gang may suspect that the family is co-operating with the authorities or not offering enough money. Such bombs would generally be designed to destroy family property such as a car or building and not specifically used against individuals.

Telegrams are uncommon although they have been used in one or two cases. But they seem not to have served any real purpose.

In the cases described in this book there will be many mentions of silence – this is a tactic used frequently by gangs and it can be described as a form of communication because the gang are most definitely sending a message by NOT communicating. When negotiations suddenly stop, it is a most unsettling thing for the family. Uncertainty and fear begin to take over again if they do not fully understand the reasons for the silence. The gang know this. They are demonstrating that they have all the time in the world and that they are simply not prepared to talk until the family begin to make more reasonable offers. Having said this, there are factors to take into consideration, for example in a rural case, periods of silence may be enforced by the sheer difficulty of communicating. Publicity during the Richard Starr case showed how it had been necessary to communicate with his captors who were hiding out in a deep jungle camp; there were weeks, sometimes months between letters.

Silences are often used at the very beginning of a case; there have been examples of initial silent periods running into six or seven weeks in order to reduce the resistance of the family. To my mind this is a waste of time as there are far quicker methods of achieving this objective. On the whole it is better to prevent silences by keeping the momentum of negotiation realistic. There are various ways of ending a silence which will become apparent later.

So much for the communication systems open to the gang. What about the family, how do they get their messages across? There are essentially two types of communication from the family; those messages which are stipulated by the kidnappers and those initiated by the client. Taken from the gang's point of view, they must have a simple way of holding regular contacts at short notice while at the same time maintaining control of the initiative in the negotiations. In most cases the gang stipulates a method via which the family can let them know that they wish to speak.

The methods used are often connected with the press whereby a public notice in the form of an open appeal can be inserted by the family which requests the gang to make contact. The gang will decide which newspaper is to be used. The other form of notice may be a specifically worded advertisement such as, 'Lost in Rome, District 14. Two-year-old Irish Wolfhound. Big reward for information'. Knowing the gang's preferred newspaper, it is easy enough for the family to place an advert or notice couched in the correct phraseology to catch the gang's attention if they wish (as they often do) to make an unsolicited statement.

With carefully thought out 'scripting' it is possible for the family negotiator to get messages across during telephone calls which the gang may make.

What I have said so far illustrates the type of information which I have to get across to the victim's family; in essence they have to be educated and armed with the knowledge that this is a business as far as the kidnappers are concerned and that every letter, telephone call, package or photograph is nothing more than a tactic designed to heighten their concern and pressure them into an early, high settlement. I have to convince them of the dangers of early settlements at too high a figure – the risk of the double (or even treble) payment which in the end will probably only extend the length of time which the victim will spend in captivity. I will explain to them the aim of the negotiation, which is 'to achieve the safe release of the victim in the shortest possible time at the least expense'. Having done this I must put into perspective the demands which will be made on the time and resources of the family.

Before I begin the process of family education, I first have to gain their confidence. I achieve this by beginning with a full personal briefing. I tell them about my background covering my time in the army and my involvement with counter-terrorism. I give them a synopsis of my experience in kidnap negotiation consultancy. I explain my method of operating showing my files, charts and graphs. I explain that many of my past clients have allowed me to keep tapes, letters and recordings of various telephone calls between gangs and families which I intend to use from time to time during their case. This sets the scene, establishes my credentials and leads me into advising them on a script to be used in the event of a sudden call from the gang and from there into the organisation of the negotiating team.

Their business lives will be disrupted by all manner of duties to the negotiation and I demonstrate to them that the most effective manner of handling these demands is the creation of a negotiating team. The team will be the foundation of the negotiation process, it will make all the critical decisions as they are called for and my initial input to that team will be that of consultant/adviser (though it often escalates to an executive role as will be seen later). Circumstances will cause the team to differ from case to case but there are essential elements and duties to be performed and if the onus for these can be placed on individuals then so much the better. Many occasions will arise when there is a need for a vote to decide a course of action and therefore to avoid deadlock it is often best to have an odd number. No better action can be devised than to give a casting vote to the chairman.

The chairman of the team is not necessarily a member of the family although he may often be related or at least a good friend. The quality required of him is the ability to take decisions objectively. This is no mean thing in a kidnap case where he may literally be dealing with life or death situations. The area of responsibility and the decision-making scope of the chairman must be agreed by all members of the team at the earliest possible stage.

Second in importance to the chairman will be the negotiator, the man or woman who will actually talk to their opposite number in the kidnap gang. The negotiator needs certain qualities which are not easily found. It is essential that he (or she) be able to follow instructions to the letter. As will be seen later, the negotiator's script will be worked out prior to an expected call from the gang. He must be sufficiently sharp to take advantage of unexpected extra time gained on the telephone which he can use to his advantage to reinforce the credibility of his message. It will be obvious that the negotiator has to be fluent in the language of the country – he will have no time to ask for repeat instructions or the like.

It has happened on some occasions that an intermediary has been required by the gang to take part in face to face meetings (this is more likely to occur in rural cases). In that case he must have the physical stamina and courage to enact the part. It is a great advantage if the negotiator is not a senior member of the family. This gives him a built-in excuse to stall for time by telling the gang that he cannot make decisions himself, that he is acting in a reporting role. There have been occasions where skilful negotiators have been able to establish a rapport with their counterparts in the gang by blaming the head of the family or the team for dragging their feet when pressure has been applied to them.

In some countries liaison with various organisations can be of fundamental importance to the safety of the victim. We take Italy as our example here. In that country the judiciary is involved in any known kidnap and a judge will be given the onus of responsibility for the investigation of any case and will personally task the police in their efforts to locate the gang. As a further complication it is illegal to pay a ransom in Italy but at the same time the judge can agree to this law being broken provided that it can be shown that the ransom payment will save the life of the victim. Thus it will be seen that it is generally in the victim's interests that the family establishes and maintains a good liaison with the appointed judge. From all points of view it is better that the person responsible be a properly accredited member of the team. It may well be a suitable role for the family solicitor.

Police liaison is definitely a matter dictated by the country in which the kidnap has occurred. Generally speaking there is more to be gained from co-operating with the police than there is to be lost. Nine times out of ten they will become aware of the kidnap soon after it happens and will take an interest anyway. If it is remembered that there is no disparity of interest until the point of the ransom payment then it will be seen that it is generally better to have them on one's side. They will be in possession of all the up to date information on kidnaps in the area and this can be of significant value to the team in making their decisions, as will be seen in some of the cases covered later. The family will have been instructed by the gang (probably under threat) not to have anything to do with the police. Therefore liaison should be handled with great care and the person chosen to be responsible, although he may be a member of the team, should not have a direct link to the family in case he is under surveillance by the gang.

The value of press manipulation has already been demonstrated, albeit in a somewhat obscure form in the case of Doctor Bayardo Alvarez Ruiz in Guatemala City. This powerful organ should be the subject of close liaison. As well as assisting, as in the case of Ruiz, misplaced newspaper articles can be very damaging indeed. Where possible the press should be persuaded to keep silent in the interests of the victim's safety. But another aspect to bear in mind is the fact that many of the communications from the family to the gang will depend upon inserts in the newspapers. It can be most useful if a rapport is established whereby editors will take advertisements at short notice or during shut down periods. It is often better if the delegated press liaison person is a member of the family as this makes it somewhat easier to play on the finer feelings of editors and journalists. All this is not to say that the press should get no more than 'No comment'. In itself this is dangerous and guaranteed to arouse at least curiosity if not antagonism. A party line should be decided on at an early stage and it should be as close to the truth as possible while remaining innocuous.

It is always worth considering appointing someone specifically to act as the security controller. Although everyone has the basic responsibility for security and should be very conscious of adhering strictly to the 'need to know' principle, there are occasions when the stresses of team duties are inclined to make people careless and if there is a responsible person whose main task it is to keep an eye on this facet then so much the better.

There is a further aspect of security which can be overseen, the physical safety of the remaining members of the family. Double kidnaps are rare but they have happened and it is relatively simple to alert people to the basic security principles – as an offshoot it also helps to keep their minds off the case. The same security man can be used to advise the various liaison persons on how to travel to and from their meetings and how to conduct themselves in order that gang surveillance of the house does not show them up in their true roles.

A corporate kidnap may well throw up the need to involve personnel with other specific duties but the tasks I have mentioned are certainly the most important. In many family cases there may not be enough trusted people around to fulfil all those listed duties. If this is the case then obviously some doubling up is recommended. So long as the functions are not neglected it is not important.

The consultant's role within the team is purely advisory as I have mentioned but his importance is paramount if the members of the team are going to be able to function as normal businessmen. If you consider that cases can last for periods well in excess of three months (sometimes over a year) it will be seen that the members cannot devote their full time to the team. The consultant is the man who will apply his experience to the analysis of all messages and other factors and work out realistic tactics for the team to discuss. He will carefully balance all options and list the ramifications of each. In other words he will present the team with a well ordered basis for discussion and decision. 'The camel is a horse designed by committee'. Within that statement lies one of the greatest dangers of any committee. With both hearts and minds affected by the kidnap there is a natural tendency for discussions and arguments about any single tactic to go on for interminable periods. This serves no purpose except to exhaust the team members physically and mentally and rob them of the ability to think clearly. The chairman has to show his strength on these occasions and the consultant has to be prepared to help him where necessary.

We now have a team but there is an essential process to go through before we are ready to begin negotiations. The first action is always to prepare a holding script for the negotiator in case the gang should make an unexpected telephone call before a strategy has been decided. This will be a simple list of points dictated by known events at the time and designed to hold the situation. It is very important to do this to avoid an unprepared negotiator or family member making an irrevocable statement if caught by surprise or before they fully understand the situation.

I will then conduct a detailed examination of the kidnap. I explain that in order for me to properly advise them on a strategy, I must have as much information as is available on the case. Tired though the family are, this is an essential exercise as the details will provide the basis for future decisions. It is most important to have the whole team present during this initial interrogation for two reasons; firstly much of the information which will come to light will be of great use to the members in their individual responsibilities of liaison and control and, secondly, it is the beginning of the process where I start to mould the members together to form a team in the truest sense.

The basis for any workable strategy is intelligence and at this meeting the team will gather together all the known information on the factors which affect the working plan. I usually start by examining the family. This has a two-fold benefit; it will show me how the victim came to the attention of the kidnappers in the first place and by looking at the amount of publicity the family has had and what sort of details on their wealth may have been accessible to the gang, I can form a picture of the gang's cash expectancy. It is also an ideal opportunity for me to see the family reactions in this sensitive area of financial exposure and get to know a little about their characters and their feelings for the victim (not all families are desperately concerned!)

We have to discuss whether it was the visible signs of wealth which first attracted the gang's attention, whether there are public sources which would reveal the company or family accounts or indeed whether or not there could have been a leak from the inside as a result of a disgruntled employee or a jealous family member. We need to be able to consider the victim from the same perspective as the kidnapper in order to assess the likely level of ransom expectancy.

I want to know as much as possible about the victim himself. What sort of character is he? How will he stand up to the stress of capture? Is he in good health? Have the family ever discussed the possibility of kidnap before and have they arranged any secret codes to be used in proof questions or in the event of letters from the victim? How much does the victim know about the true wealth of the family? Is the victim the sort of person, for whatever motive, who would try to take a hand in the negotiations himself from the 'inside'? I ask the family to try to make a list of everything the victim was wearing and may have been carrying; particularly important is any document he may have had with him which relates to the business or bank accounts which the gang could use to give the impression that their knowledge is greater than it really is. It is essential to conduct this part of the exercise at the earliest opportunity before details are forgotten and imagination takes over.

Now we must look at the actual kidnap. I am always surprised how much information seems to come to light especially if the victim is snatched from the vicinity of his place of work (as many are). Eye-witnesses will come forward some time after the event, often shamefacedly, but always with helpful information. This intelligence will assist in two ways. It will help me to make an assessment of the gang's level of experience and it will help with the next step which is gleaning information from the police and perhaps past kidnap victims by a comparison of modus operandi which may 'fingerprint' the gang and give the team assistance in formulating future tactics. This is the time for the members responsible for police and judiciary liaison to begin establishing the necessary rapport with their opposite numbers.

Building up a picture of the kidnappers themselves is critical. It is also the most difficult aspect at the beginning of the case. Information will be scant and the team will be asked to contact those families who have suffered similarly, dredge every bit of information from the police in order to collate an overall picture on a country-wide basis and this, added to my own files, will contribute to the opening of my case or field log. From this point on every bit of information, every communication, every nuance in speech during the gang's telephone calls will be noted down in chronological order in carefully tabulated sections of the log. This will generally have at least the following sections:

- The kidnap
- The family (notes on character, strengths, weaknesses)
- The team
- The daily log
- Judiciary
- Police
- Press (including press treatment of old cases)
- Communications from the gang
- Communications from the team
- Demands and offers (budget notes)
- My assessments and appreciations (daily or at every new occurrence)
- Negotiator's scripts
- National notes on kidnap – past settlements
    - known gangs
    - past tactics

This is not a definitive list, I will add whatever becomes necessary by way of additional reference material. This constantly updated log allows me to compare events and reassess the situation at any given time and it is also a tremendous boost to family morale to see the picture of the case slowly building up in such a useful way.

I said earlier that the objective of the team was to secure the safe release of the victim in the shortest possible time at the lowest possible cost. These three factors will now form the basis upon which all strategy is calculated. It is surprising how often the team meetings seem to be mainly motivated by money rather than the safety of the victim and this is not always a natural subconscious safety valve coming into play. It seems that the longer the victim stays out of sight the more used to this the team becomes, and begins seriously to deal with the matter as a straightforward business. This is healthy from one point of view but I have to constantly stress the possible effects of any given tactic on the victim's safety. The importance of these three factors will become clear later in the book.

If we continue with the business theme it is now time to look at the negotiating facets of both interested parties. On the kidnappers side their initial demand, although it will be way above the going rate can be considered as being much higher than the figure which they anticipate getting. Although the going rate is not carved in stone it does help tactically to know what this national average is at the start of the case, because from this the team can crudely determine the gang's level of expectancy. This will invariably be within a few hundred thousand dollars of the average. Surrounding the level of expectancy will be a 'loop' which can be described as the area of acceptability. The size of this area is determined by numerous factors such as the length of time negotiations are taking and the pressures on the gang. It has to be appreciated that conducting the kidnap reconnaissance, effecting the snatch and the after-care of the victim is an expensive business. On top of this the organiser may well be working through a series of cut-outs to enhance his own security and this will add to his expenses. He can, in a protracted case, become fearful of police activities which may cause inner tensions in the gang. All these factors may well persuade the gang to accept a lower level of payment. Looked at diagramatically it might appear thus:

US$	2,000,000	Initial demand
US$	500,000	Expectancy
US$	400,000	Acceptability

As will be seen in some of the cases to follow, the above configuration of ransom payments is also affected by the character and experience of the gang and their willingness to engage in sensible negotiations.

The facets controlling the success of the family negotiations are somewhat simpler on the surface, though as will be seen later, complications can set in. In essence the solidity and resolve of the team is a critical factor coupled with the ability of the negotiator to convince his counterpart in the gang that he is telling the truth. It is action, not speech which gets results. For example, if the team wished to make a small increase and the negotiator was instructed to say: 'We have a further $2,000.' I would have no indication whatsoever what measure of interest this had raised in the gang, regardless of how his answer was phrased. If however the negotiator said: 'There is only a little more – so small I know you're not interested.' If this were to lead to the gang's spokesman saying: 'How much?' It would be an indication that he was interested. Lastly, not always obvious as a factor, is whether the family is actually willing to pay an acceptable sum for the release of the victim.'

Although there are general principles of organisation and negotiating actions, there is no rigid formula for the handling of a kidnap. Characters, personalities, national factors, the kidnappers' experience, the apparent and actual wealth of the family and the behaviour of the victim all play their part in the game. Threats will escalate, unforeseen difficulties will arise and the options will frequently change, but if the team remains resolute and stable there is every chance of a successful conclusion to the case.

It will have become apparent that underlying all these factors and principles there is a further need in terms of the consultant's ability. Advising on a kidnap is not a mechanical act; it requires a deep knowledge of the business, the ability to analytically appreciate an often fast moving situation and above all, an instinct, an intuition as to how the mind of the kidnapper is likely to react in given scenarios.

The team now has at its fingertips all the relevant information which can be amassed at this stage. It has an idea of the format the negotiations will follow, at least in principle, and it has the records and experience of the consultant at its disposal. It now needs to consider two more important things before it is ready to face a long negotiation. The first requirement is to set the budget and the first point which I make as a consultant is that the budget is flexible. At this stage of events there is no way of telling how the negotiations will go but the setting of this figure will allow the team to make the second decision, which is the initial negotiating strategy.

It is worth considering strategies, and the first thing to note is that every strategy must be capable of a change in response to the gang's tactics if it is assessed that the victim's life is being endangered. Flexibility is a by-word in this business.

There are two basic strategies and it must be appreciated that the gang will be as aware of these as the team – the secret is to fool them into thinking that they are imposing their will on an unsuspecting family. The first line is that of apparent acquiescence. This is the production of a negotiating façade which suggests to the gang that the family has accepted that the kidnappers hold all the aces and that they are trying to do their best under enormous difficulties to give the gang exactly what they want.

The alternative is of a much more offensive nature and hence more dangerous to the victim. It relies on trying to reduce the resolve of the gang by refusal to carry out all or part of their instructions; by constantly demanding proof that the victim lives; by insisting that their demands are ridiculous – that the family simply cannot afford such figures.

At the start of a case, the first approach would be favoured although later appreciations and assessments may dictate that a switch to more aggressive tactics may be called for; both approaches have their merits and demerits as will be seen. Both strategies are designed to reach the level of ransom which the family wants (or can afford) to pay in a realistic time frame. I have found it useful in the past to draft a series of budgetary options for use by the team in calculating the timing and amounts of their offers.

There are certain dangers in this. As the CMT (Crisis Management Team) becomes more resolute in its actions it is always a possibility that the team will begin to consider these written tables as immovable and I have to constantly stress; flexibility, flexibility. Such tables will have different totals which will be in line with the possible strategies and may appear like this:

	Course A		Course B	
	Increase	Total offer	Increase	Total offer
Offer a.	150	150	210	210
b.	100	250	180	390
c.	80	330	110	500

Do not read anything into these figures other than that they are demonstrative of one system which may help the team. They will be finely calculated against the kidnappers' demands, the going rate and the amount which the family sets as the budget. One point is worth making here, if I am dealing with an insured case and let's say that the premium provides cover up to US$1,000,000, I will clearly say to the family: 'Your cover is for one million dollars and that is what you have paid for. At the end of the day that is the figure which you do not willingly want to exceed.' This will establish that I am on their side and not controlled by underwriters who want to cut their losses. I am then obliged to go on and repeat my earlier warnings about the dangers of paying too much too soon and the possibilities of double and treble demands which may occur.

Once these essentials are attended to, the team is ready for action. Action may well have interrupted this sequence of examination anyway and if this is the case I am in the position of having to think on my feet and advise the family as events unfold even though they may not be fully psychologically prepared. At some stage, however, all the basic working details will have been collated and I then step back into my consultancy role. My appreciation of the situation will be drafted each time a communication from the gang is received. Before I make any of these appreciations, though, my first act on receipt of a message from the gang will be to formulate a holding script for the negotiator so that he is never taken unawares by a sudden telephone call.

My appreciations are important documents and they are always written out in full and always recorded in my field log. This is not a form of self-protection but an important means of being able to cross-check the history of a case in full at any stage of the proceedings. The papers will begin by clearly identifying the objective of the document. This is required to give the team a clear statement of what they must discuss at the meeting; if this is not done it is quite easy for a 'Chinese parliament' to ensue (depending of course on the strength of the chairman). All the relevant factors, no matter how small, will be listed and summarised. I will then, rather in the manner of a military tactical appreciation, list all the options open to the gang and the team. With each option will be a complete list of all the advantages and disadvantages of adopting that course.

I will always give my personal recommendations along with the pros and cons. I am being paid for my services by the family and it would be dishonest or cowardly in the extreme not to give such recommendations. The team is under no compulsion to go along with my ideas at all. These appreciations are critical to the overall case analysis and they are always of great psychological value in reducing the effect of the kidnappers' threats. In the paragraphs concerning the possible actions of the kidnappers, I am often able to predict the type of threat which will appear next from the gang; if and when that threat does appear, couched in similar terms to those which I have already described, the family is able to view it in perspective for what it really is – a tactic.

How all these machinations fit into the overall scene will become apparent as I relate specific cases. The only other aspect of a kidnap I want to mention at this stage is the after-care of the victim once he has been released. This can be a very traumatic time for both the victim and the family, especially if the case has been a long one.

The victim may well be in a sorry physical condition, in ragged clothing, stinking from lack of bathing facilities. It is essential that no revulsion is shown by whichever member of the family first meets him. He could be suffering from mental stresses of a nature which make him question how the family could have treated him so badly. How could they have forestalled payment for so long knowing what his conditions were like? It is not unknown for quite violent displays of hatred during the early post-release stages. I advise the family of all these potential problems and often use the explanation of the Stockholm Syndrome[1] to illustrate the point.

My advice is to have a doctor on hand and to allow the victim to clean himself up before he is put into the presence of well-loved people such as his wife or children. They should then arrange for him to move out to a quiet location with close family members for a recuperation period. An often difficult but very necessary task is the detailed debrief of the victim which must be done as soon as possible after his release while his memory is clear. This is infinitely useful to both the police and to myself as a consultant for future cases, and I have never yet known a family or victim who have been through a kidnap to refuse to co-operate.

So long as they are given an assurance that none of their personal details will ever be given away without their consent there is every willingness to assist. After all it has been clearly demonstrated to them how the files relevant to past cases have helped them through their crisis.

[1] *The Stockholm Syndrome.* A phenomenon whereby the hostage builds up a relationship with the captor which develops into a feeling of trust, often manifesting itself in a dislike of the police/family who are trying to effect the release. First notified in August 1974 during the siege of a bank in Stockholm which involved four hostages.

The actual phases of negotiation and the critical handling of the ransom payment will all feature in the cases described in the book. It will be seen how every case has a different twist. Though the general principles remain the same or at least similar, intuition plays a major part and the differing factors give rise to a need for constant flexibility.

Chapter

4

Author's note

The most important factor in steering a family through the minefield of a kidnap negotiation is having access to all the facts of the case. Only then can I be certain that my appreciations, assessments and advice are correctly based. If information is withheld from me, for whatever reason, then my analysis of the situation is hindered; it may even be flawed. For reasons which will become obvious, I have had to change the name of the client in this case.

SOMETHING was wrong. Signora Romero was not telling me the truth. She was looking me in the eyes, her face was now calm and she never faltered. Call it instinct if you wish, but she was hiding something and I didn't like it.

Eva Romero and her husband, Paolo, were among Rome's most fêted social personalities. She was beautiful, highly intelligent and very, very wealthy. Her breeding was in evidence now. Paolo had been kidnapped but there was no sign of strain, no hint of tears or concern; I couldn't believe that this façade was genuine.

Rodrigo Arenas, who had been recommending me to such families ever since I'd taken on the Cano case a few years ago, had called me to Rome and given me some basic background on the Romeros. They were a fascinating family even by extrovert Roman standards.

Juan Carlos Romero, patriarch and a phenomenal success in the office machinery business, ranked among the richest men in Italy. In truth he was of Spanish extraction, his family having moved to this country after his father, sensing the advent of the Civil War, had sold off massive land holdings in Spain. An engineeer by instinct rather than training, Juan's father, Don José Romero, had assessed the huge financial returns available in Northern Italy.

He had purchased plant and facilities wisely and, apart from a recession during the Second World War, the business had flourished. Indeed, the aftermath of the war and the building of the new commercial and industrial Europe had secured his fortune. By the time Juan Carlos was forty his father's company, by then under Juan's leadership, had adapted and grown to become one of the largest manufacturers of quality computers and associated electronic components in the country. Now in his late sixties, Juan himself was thought to be anticipating handing over the reins.

They were not a political family in the true sense of the word; they had no aspirations to that sort of power. But their immense wealth drew them into the same social clique as Ministers and Premiers. They were well known as the chosen hosts to members of visiting royal families and senior political dignitaries, in whose company guests could relax without having their private conversations misinterpreted or called to question by the press the following day. They were trusted – they were Italy at its most serene and hospitable. They seemed to be a happy family well contented with their lot.

Paolo Romero was the apple of his father's eye; he was the managing director of the company and was being groomed for the position of chairman. Rodrigo had provided me with a number of newspaper cuttings about the Romero family and the pictures of Paolo and Eva, who were hounded as much by the paparazzi as any film stars, showed a tall, slim, black-haired and exceedingly handsome man always with laughter in his eyes. As a couple they were devoted; still childless, but never a breath of scandal had been attached to them. A seemingly perfect couple with a perfect life.

Their idyll had been shattered eight days before with Paolo's kidnap in the city. Rodrigo's telephone call had told me little (as usual) but I knew him well enough to take the news seriously.

'This is sensitive, James, very sensitive. Not a word of the family name. The police are as yet unaware of the case and that is how it must remain for as long as possible.'

The call had come within two days of the snatch. It's amazing how men like Rodrigo have a nose for such events. If I'd not had such good service from him, I might have been suspicious, but in all our dealings he'd been scrupulously honest and I was aware of how tightly knit the avvocatos' network was in Rome. I flew out as soon as I was able and I arrived on the ninth day of the case.

I enjoy travelling and in particular, I love to visit Rome. But I have one pet hate: I can't stand the interminable waiting at airports for baggage and the subsequent customs checks. For this reason I travel very light, taking only one bag which is small enough not to cause me any hassle as hand luggage. Generally I'm out of the airport within minutes. Rodrigo and I have never met openly at airports or stations: there is always a police presence at those places and Rodrigo is well known. I have no desire to be linked to him officially. Despite my many cases in Italy I'm pretty sure that at that time I'd never been formally identified as being associated with him.

From Fiumicino Airport, I took the Acotral bus into the Stazione Termini and from there I disappeared into the crowd and made my way around the corner into Via Marsala and started walking slowly south east towards the San Lorenzo Gate. I had covered no more than a couple of hundred yards when Rodrigo's Maserati nosed itself out of the pea soup of Rome's traffic and drew alongside me. Within seconds we were weaving erratically through the mechanised morass Rodrigo drove like any other Italian, hand on horn and with a continuous stream of harmlessly barbed insults on his lips.

We turned off along the Via Tiburtina and then north west into Regina Margherita.

'I've booked you into the Lord Byron, James. OK?'

He knew it was OK, I'd stayed there before and had a great liking for the place. Set in Via Guiseppe De Notaris, in the quiet Villa Borghese. It is a small hotel which looks to outward appearances like a private club. Having only forty-odd rooms the service is personal and excellent and the restaurant is superb. Although the cuisine in Rome is nowhere near as good as that in Northern Italy it is still possible to dine extremely well in a few places like the Byron. They also know me well enough not to insist on retaining my passport overnight on arrival.

Rodrigo stayed silent as I knew he would after his remark about the hotel, and I sat back and enjoyed the vista of Rome. The contrast in this, the eternal city, never fail to amaze me. It's an unbelievable mixture of ancient and modern; signs of both religious devoutness and profanity abound in scenery which is at the same time serene and chaotic. It's a city constantly on the move, vibrant and alive Where else in the world would a traffic policeman ignore the mounting chaos of impatient commuters in order to give his total attention to the beautifully mobile buttocks of a passing woman?

I studied Rodrigo from the corners of my eyes as he helter skeltered through the gaps in the streams of cars. He looked com posed even though I knew he was excited. To be working for the Romero family would certainly do him no harm; in Rome an avvocato's business is contact-based and he would already be mentally exploiting the potential possibilities after the case. I knew he wouldn't even be considering the eventuality of failure – it simply never occurred to him.

I realised I knew little about him. I'd met him socially in the old Control Risks days, appreciated the strength of his contacts and approached him with my proposition when I decided to go private. So far I had no cause to regret it. He was discreet in himself and he looked after my own security. He seemed to be trusted within police circles and the other legal professions which was very useful and he had a real nose for kidnappings. How he uncovered the cases long before there was any publicity was a mystery to me but there it was, he'd brought me a lot of business.

I don't think Rodrigo was a Roman. From his shortness and slightly coarsened features, I guessed that he came from the south, perhaps Calabria, from peasant stock. I knew that his success was based more on animal cunning than on academic qualifications. When excited his accent would thicken but generally he comported himself as an upper middle class Italian from the city. He was not a handsome man but his brooding, bushy-browed features must have held some appeal to women if the companions I had seen him with from time to time were anything to base the assumption on. He was pale; in common with many Italians he took great pains to stay out of the sun. He would never walk down the sunny side of the street if there was shade across the way and as crossing a road in Rome is not without hazard it says something for the vanity of this nation.

Rodrigo didn't enter the Byron with me. I left him with the promise that I would be in the Via Gravina an hour later. It was only ten minutes walk from the Byron and I took advantage of the time to buy four or five shirts and some lightweight trousers to complement my meagre travelling wardrobe. A quick refreshing shower and I was ready. I checked my briefcase and made sure that my files were in the correct order. I took sidestreets up to the point where I crossed the main highway, Via Flaminia, but I was not being followed. Indeed, I didn't expect to be but it does no harm to check these things – it's a habit which has stood me in good stead in the past.

When Rodrigo picked me up this time he was driving a nondescript Fiat and without the heavy steel cocoon of the Maserati to protect me I felt even more vulnerable as he zigzagged his way through the

61

back streets. We were heading south towards Old Rome, and as I knew from the news clippings that the Romero villa was in the northern suburbs of the city, I guessed that we were to meet the family in one of their city apartments.

We turned off south west just short of the Forum and crossed the Tiber on the Ponte Garibaldi. I lost my bearings as we criss-crossed Trastevere. It didn't matter, I was never more than fifteen minutes walk in any direction in this city from a point which I would know.

We were ushered into the drawing room by the butler whom Rodrigo referred to as Giorgio; seated in leather chairs which had the appearance of being casually scattered around the room were four people. Though they had the outward appearance of being very relaxed, they looked expectant and I could feel the undercurrent of tension. They were seated in a manner which suggested that they had been chatting prior to our arrival, and the air was heavy with tobacco smoke.

I recognised Juan Carlos immediately, deduced that the young woman was Eva Romero and shook the hand of the man who introduced himself as Luis Fernando, the family solicitor. He took my elbow and steered me towards the patriarch's chair.

'Signor Romero, this is Signor March.'

The old man was impressive, tough looking and fitting the image of a Godfather. He was tall and, though bulky, he was not fat. His full head of iron grey hair was still naturally wavy and his eyes were unblinking as he stood up and welcomed me to the household. His handshake was firm and he bowed slightly as he spoke.

'Signore, it was good of you to come so quickly. I hope you had a pleasant flight. Is your hotel satisfactory?' Without waiting for my answer he took me across to the younger man.

'This is Enrique, my second eldest son.' Enrique was very like the press photographs I had seen of Paolo. Tall, slim, impeccably dressed and apparently at ease. He was very brown and I guessed he spent a lot of time outdoors; with his wealth it was probably a sporting pursuit rather than work. He stood up almost languidly and as he put his hand out his face took on an ill-disguised sneer.

'So, Signor March, you come to the rescue in our hour of need. No doubt your pearls of wisdom will be as expensive as the pearls of the oyster, heh?' He seemed amused at his own attempt at humour and sat back down, dismissing me without a second glance. Juan Carlos grimaced and moved across to the woman, Eva it was. Unnecessarily she stood, shook my hand and welcomed me.

'Forgive Enrique, Signore, he is upset. We are glad to see you.

Luis has spoken to the Torlettis who praise you highly. Do you remember them?'

She was taller than I had imagined, graceful and quite lovely. Long jet-black hair, casually brushed back, framed a stunningly beautiful face. She was pale-faced, so white that her skin was almost translucent and this gave an added depth to already bottomless dark brown eyes. I noticed the way her hand strayed to Juan Carlos's arm and the answering squeeze he gave it. They were obviously fond of each other.

'Thank you, Signora. Yes, I remember the Torlettis well. A fine family.' I made no mention of the actual case. 'Rodrigo told me of the introduction. Yes, Signore,' I addressed myself to Juan Carlos, answering his earlier question, 'I had a good flight and I'm staying at the Lord Byron which suits me very well.'

He nodded approvingly. Whether this was because he knew that the hotel was in the upper expense bracket, whether he, like me, found the food and surroundings exceptionally good, or whether Franco Torletti had told him that I'd used it in the past I don't know.

Romero spoke again. 'Signore, it is easier if I call you James, no?' Without pausing he went on: 'You know the problem. I suggest we begin by giving you the details.' I raised my hand, stopping him.

'No. Let me first tell you something about myself.' I went on to relate my background in the army; how I'd joined a large company and then decided to operate alone. I told them of the cases I'd been involved with (without identifying them) and of the fact that they had all been successfully concluded. As I talked I spread out the various charts, graphs and files which I always carry, on the coffee table in front of them. I produced specimens of letters, tapes and photographs of packages.

'These are all records of past cases, copied with the clients' permission. Later I'll use these to demonstrate some of the kidnappers' possible tactics. I must tell you at this stage that you are under no pressure to do as I say; I am an adviser. I know this business well but at the end of the day it will be the family's decision on which course of action to take. If you can accept that kidnapping is like any other form of business – like the electronics industry for example. If you have a buyer wanting your product,' I was addressing myself directly to Romero now, 'you will ask for the highest possible price. He in turn will try to knock your price down and make a counter-offer. You will resist, perhaps you will argue that the quality of your product is the finest in Italy, that your delivery times are the fastest and so on. You will bring into your argument all the selling points you can think of and the client will produce as many reasons as he can as to why he should not pay your price. In this manner you will eventually reach an equable position and the sale will be concluded.' I had their interest.

'A kidnap situation is exactly the same in principle in that we have, on the one hand, the gang holding the commodity which you want; on the other hand you have the cash which they want. The difference is that they are able to play on your emotions in a much more effective manner than the potential electronics components purchaser could. They'll use deception, they'll use threats and they'll use silence to unbalance your thinking. If you think of these as marketing tactics, where every letter, telephone call or other contact is designed to put pressure on you in order to extract the maximum amount of money, you'll understand the business and it will help you through the days ahead.' I sat back. There was a long silence and then Enrique stood up.

'James, I have behaved badly. I can see now that you are sincere and that you are very experienced. I apologise for my bad joke. There will be no problem with fees. We want Paolo back safely.' He extended his hand again and I took it with an answering smile. There was no need for comment.

'I have to make one further statement. You must trust me. In order to be effective and give you the best possible advice, I must have access to all the facts. You must believe that this information will be treated in the utmost confidence.' They looked at each other, again the tension, the slight stiffening of Eva's shoulders and the reaching out to Juan Carlos's arm for comfort.

'Now, we have a little organising to do. Just in case the kidnappers make contact before we are finished you must be prepared. What was the last message you had?' It was Eva who answered.

'Just a very brief call to say: "We have him, do not notify the authorities or it will go badly for him." That is all. That call came the morning after Paolo disappeared. It sounded like a very hard man.'

'Good,' I replied, 'if they call again, no matter what they ask, just start demanding proof that they are the people who have Paolo and that he is alive. That's all – don't be drawn into talking about money. The call, if it comes, will be short, they will not take a chance on the telephone location being traced.'

I collected my files together and addressed them once more. 'In the days to come you'll have to make many decisions. Some of these

64

will be hard. Your emotions will be subjected to great stress and it's essential that such decisions are arrived at clinically, with all factors and options having been properly analysed. For this reason I suggest that you form a negotiating team. Now, any team needs a leader, a chairman in this case, who will have the final say. It must be a person whose judgment you respect and he or she must have access to all the facts. It's often easier to select a trusted friend from outside the family so that he's removed from the emotional pressure. Is there such a person?' This time I looked at Juan Carlos as the head of the family and his reply was not unexpected.

'James, even though I am Paolo's father, I have been in a family business for a long time. In order for my company to achieve its position as the largest and richest exporter of electronic components in the country, I have had to make many decisions which have affected members of my family. Many of these decisions have been hurtful to their pride but that has not dissuaded me from putting business first. You have explained that kidnapping is a business. I can fill the role of chairman.' I looked around and there was no sign of dissent – rather of relief, I thought.

'Very well, it's the family's decision.' I went on: 'You will also need to appoint a negotiator. This is an important position. This is the person who will take all the incoming calls from the gang. He will need to try to develop a rapport with their spokesman. He will need to have the discipline to stick to the agreed scripts but also have the ability to get the gang's negotiator talking if that is possible. He will need a cool, clear head at all times.' Enrique stood up.

'It is for me to do this. I am the next in line in the family.' Juan Carlos held up a hand. 'No! Enrique, you are too fiery. You would never be able to resist the last word. It is your temper which has prevented you rising further in the firm. I suggest that Eva is the best choice.' I expected Enrique to flare up but he merely gave a wry grin and put both hands in the air in mock surrender.

This confirmed the strength of Juan Carlos and I knew he would be a firm chairman. I looked across at Eva. It wasn't normally a good move to have a person so closely involved with the victim as the negotiator. I'd seen it before and it had worked but she would have to be strong.

'Signora, you had best consider that you may have to listen to snatches of tapes of your husband over the telephone. These will have been doctored for effect but nonetheless they could throw you off balance if you hear them unexpectedly. You will have to adopt a reporting role. The negotiator cannot admit to being able to make a decision. You may have to listen to threats and you may well get outbursts of unpleasant and foul language.' Romero threw his head back and laughed.

'James, she is made of steel. Do not let a pretty face fool you. Many businessmen have made that mistake. She is one of my secret weapons.' Even Enrique was chuckling now.

'Again, it is a family decision,' I said. 'The other person we shall need is a liaison man. Someone who can talk to the police when they eventually become aware of the case, as they surely will. Someone who can make visits to the bank, to the newspaper offices, collect messages or any other task which may be directed by the gang and where public exposure is necessary.'

'Why not Enrique?' demanded Juan Carlos. 'This does not seem to be a job requiring coolness though I can see the need for tact.'

'Because to expose another member of the family to a task where we may be following the directions of the gang, perhaps into the back streets of the city in order to collect a letter or package, could be playing into their hands if they are planning a second kidnap victim. Such a tactic is rare but certainly not unknown.' Romero nodded thoughtfully.

'A good point, James, forgive me for not having considered it. How about you, Luis? Would you consider acting for us?' Luis inclined his head in assent though he looked uncomfortable. I resolved to keep an eye on him.

'Good. We have our negotiating team. Now, before we discuss the case, let me talk about security. It's your decision whether or not you tell the police. I can give you all the pros and cons if you wish but again, it is a team decision. As a family you must begin to observe some personal precautions. I'll give you a small aide-mémoire later. Of immediate concern is the matter of telephone security. Even if you do inform the police, you will not necessarily want them to know about every communication from the gang. This is particularly important when we get to the closing stages. When the police do find out that Paolo has been taken they will almost certainly put a trace on your telephone. You will not know that this is the case but you must assume it. The gang will also be aware of this and they may well ask you to do exactly what I am about to suggest.

'You should find an unlisted telephone or one which could not be linked to you in any way. You may have access to an unused property, a trusted friend's vacant apartment or an unused business telephone. Anything which will not be easily identified with the Romeros. It

66

should be accessible to you quickly – within five minutes if this is possible. At the first opportunity you must get this number to the gang and say that it is to avoid the authorities listening in to your conversations. This can now be added to the holding script we discussed earlier. When they accept that, you must tell them that as the telephone is not in this house, they should arrange to call you at set times so that you can guarantee being there. Tell them that you will be at that telephone for a set period each day. Stick to those times otherwise you will be letting yourself in for some lengthy waits on occasion and this will not help the negotiator mentally. Tell them also that if you have any suspicions you will change the contact point. This will help to establish in the gang's eyes that you are behaving as they wish and not co-operating with the authorities.' I paused. They seemed to see the logic of this. I continued.

'As far as contacting me is concerned, we'll arrange a simple code which fits in with my cover for being in Rome. If I wish to call you, I'll adopt the guise of an old friend, probably arrange to meet for dinner or tennis or some such pretext. As far as our meetings are concerned, I suggest that they take place here rather than your villa as the approaches are easier. For the next few days we should consider meeting daily at a time to fit in with your business commitments.' Ignoring the beginnings of a protest, I went on.

'No, you should carry on with your normal life as much as possible. It is part of the discipline of conditioning your thinking to accepting that the kidnap is a business commitment which has suddenly been added to everyday events. It's also necessary to preserve security as long as possible. Don't worry, the gang will also accept this reasoning. These early meetings will give me the chance to improve your knowledge of kidnap tactics and explain the types of events which will almost certainly take place. This will help you to be less afraid of the threats and assist you in making your decisions clearly and as a team. Once I've passed on everything which I need to, we can then fall back on having meetings at greater intervals or as events unfold.'

Romero stood up again. 'James, thank you. You have been a great comfort already. May I suggest that you and I go to my study and discuss some personal details then perhaps we could continue over dinner?' I agreed after adding the caution that over the evening meal we should not talk openly about the case in front of the domestic staff. I was assured that they all knew anyway and that there was no fear of them chattering out of turn. They were loyal and Paolo was a popular member of the family while Eva had clearly charmed them all. I accepted this and went off with Juan Carlos who obviously wished to discuss the fees.

Rodrigo excused himself, slipping me the telephone number o where he was spending the evening. We agreed to meet for breakfas in the Byron the next day.

Now that the team was established, and particularly in these earl days, I didn't want to talk about the case with individual famil members; everything had to be open although I knew from experi ence that once the pressure was on I might well be faced wit those same people seeking comfort from personal explanations an discussions.

Dinner gave me the chance to look over the family in more detail Even though the servants were aware of the kidnap there was n discussion on the topic. Conversation was confined to question about inflation in Britain, about the striking miners, police attitudes the royal family and other generalities which in each case wer compared with life in Italy. It was during this dinner that I dis covered that the Romeros had in fact played host to members of th British royal family.

They were a well-informed assembly and listened intently to m replies. Interspersed among the mundane topics were comments an observations on their own business. Their English was fluent an they stayed with the language; I don't think this was just for m benefit. It was possibly practice time.

Juan Carlos, at the head of the table, ate as he acted, decisively cutting his food into regular portions, deliberately chewing it we and rhythmically then washing it down with large mouthfuls of win which he swilled around the inside of his cheeks before swallowing His hands were big, and the blue veins made islands of the brow liver spots of age. He used his fork in the impossible British fashion curved aspect uppermost. Each minuscule piece of fat was carefull cut away and placed at the side of his plate, each in line with th other. It was as though he would make an account of the calorifi saving at the end of the meal.

Enrique ate like an American, cutting his food into portions the laying aside his knife and using his fork which he loaded by pushin the food on to it with a crust of bread. He didn't initiate any part o the conversation, contenting himself to responding to questions. H seemed quite relaxed now though he looked at his watch frequently He was unmarried so I assumed he had a date; he'd certainly hav to be among Rome's most eligible bachelors.

He was soberly dressed except for an enormous set of cuff link which appeared to depict a family crest of some sort. They were gaudy, probably very expensive, but out of keeping. He saw me looking.

'Terrible aren't they? They are Paolo's.' He resumed eating as though this statement explained itself.

Eva pecked at her food like a small bird. A quick dart with the fork and a swift movement to her mouth. Down with the fork and sitting upright on her chair she chewed, swallowed and took a small sip of wine. A long pause and then she would repeat the motion. She wore little jewellery. A thin, gold chain around her neck, a matching thin bracelet and a simple band of gold on her wedding finger. She'd somehow poured herself from the afternoon's casual sweater and trousers into a simple, clinging, light-coloured tube of a dress; low cut, it hid little of her figure. It had long sleeves and she looked totally composed, an attitude belied by the slight damp patches of perspiration under her arms. She was conscious of this. It showed in her movements and probably accounted for the way she put down her fork and sat upright with her hands on her lap after each mouthful. I put this down to the tensions of losing Paolo.

It was darkening rapidly now and the butler lit the candles. In the flickering light her eyes looked deeper than ever. Whenever our gazes met there was something unfathomable there. Was it a secret? Was it a carefully calculated pose to attract men? Whatever it was, it was effective. She was one of the loveliest women I'd ever met. I forced my mind back to the table. The fare was simple but delicious and even though I don't really care for alcohol, I was able to appreciate a very, very good wine.

The table was cleared and we were served coffee at the side tables. Juan Carlos lit a cigar, drew deeply, held the smoke in his mouth for a moment or two, and expelled it with a noisy, forceful breath.

'James, we had better tell you what has happened.'

At this point Enrique stood up and, ignoring his father's frown, excused himself. 'James, I know no more than anyone else. I am not part of the decision-making team. I have an appointment and I must go.'

'It is for the family to decide whether you are part of the team. You don't have to have a formal role in order to play an important part. Everyone is able to contribute with ideas, questions and suggestions.' I knew that as far as he was concerned it was the right thing to say. His look showed his appreciation.

'You may go, Enrique,' said Romero, 'but I suggest that you time your appointments in a less binding fashion until we have Paolo back.' The old man's eyes twinkled for a second or two as he turned to me. 'What a delight to be a young man in Rome,' he said as Enrique closed the door behind him. 'A rich young man at that.' He chuckled at some private memory and then the pain returned and he became brisk again.

'Now, Eva, perhaps you would give our account to James. Allow an old man to listen while he enjoys his cigar.' He leaned across and patted her hand.

'May I suggest that we sit at the dinner table.' They were surprised but I didn't elaborate. I wanted them to get into the business frame of mind as quickly as possible and the best way was to treat this as a board room meeting. Sitting at the table automatically instilled a discipline of sorts and it also gave me the chance to spread my files and pass around bits and pieces instead of moving from chair to chair or bending awkwardly over the low coffee tables and losing fluidity of action and speech.

I took out my note pad, turned towards Eva and she began.

'Nine, no, ten days ago, Paolo was late back for dinner. In itself this is not unusual. He is often late but it is his custom to let us know. We were not unduly concerned, he had been working on a takeover bid for a small company in Toscana. It was an important deal to us. We need to expand our printed circuit board manufacturing facilities. This is an experienced company and it can go into production very quickly.' It was interesting to note her switches between past and present tenses.

'We knew that Paolo would stay with the negotiations until the deal was concluded but it was still strange that he had not told us he would be delayed.' She paused. 'When midnight came we began to really worry. We considered calling the police but decided to wait until the morning. Juan Carlos and I sat up all night. In the morning at about eight-thirty, the call came which I told you about.' Her eyes moistened and I thought she was about to cry but she held the tears in check.

'We were shattered. Every wealthy family in this country lives under the threat of kidnap but like so many others, we never thought it would actually happen to us. The caller did not ask for money. He simply said: "We have him". We spoke to Luis and he suggested that we approach the Torlettis who had suffered a kidnap last year. Luis represents many families and so we asked him to speak to them first for advice in order that we keep Paolo's kidnap secret for as long as possible. The Torlettis mentioned the assistance they had had from you and advised Luis to contact Signor Arenas. James, you know the rest.' She sat back and her shoulders suddenly slumped. Once again the comforting hand of Romero reached out to her.

'In one respect you have been lucky. The gang has called you and you know that Paolo has been kidnapped. This is positive. It's been quite common in Italy for the kidnappers to leave families in silence for long periods in order to confuse their thinking. Indeed, it's possible that you may wait some time before there's another contact. If this proves to be so, as I mentioned earlier, look on this silence as a marketing tactic. The principle behind it is to get you into such mental turmoil that the relief of receiving news, even if it is a cash demand when it eventually does arrive, will be so great that you will pay at once.' Romero interrupted me as I was opening my briefcase.

'James, we will pay. Of that be certain. We want Paolo back as quickly as possible.' His brows furrowed with the beginnings of anger.

'Of course you want Paolo back. So do I. Please, consider for a moment the position of the kidnappers if the full ransom is paid immediately they request it. What are they to think? Have they misappreciated your true wealth, do you in fact have much more than they had thought? You have paid so quickly without protest that the amount must be a pittance! It's too easy. So, what do they do? Think about it.' I could see it dawn on Romero's face.

'Of course. They will ask for more?'

'There is certainly a good chance of it. Double payments are very common in this country and they are usually the result of having arrived at too high a figure too quickly. As with your computers, there is a going rate. Sure it's a generality, but the kidnappers will have an expectancy based roughly on this rate and although they would like more, they could become very suspicious if they got it too easily. They will expect you to bargain.'

'How can we ascertain this figure?' Despite the trauma of losing his son, Romero was getting interested in the techniques. A good sign? It could be.

'First things first,' I replied, 'Let's look at what we have. Not much, but it does give us a guide as to what could happen. Firstly we're pretty sure that Paolo has been kidnapped. Secondly it looks as though it could be a professional gang. The initial call was brief, blunt and timed to hit you at a low emotional ebb after a probably sleepless night. One of two things is likely. There'll be a period of silence which could stretch into weeks or, and I think this is more probable, you'll have contact within the next few days demanding a ransom. I don't expect any severe threats at this stage but it's always

71

possible. I think if a long silence was intended, it would have started from the beginning. I don't think you'd have had that early call. The rules aren't written in stone, however, so be prepared for either eventuality.' They sat silently waiting for me to go on.

'What we have to do at the earliest opportunity is to establish the safe telephone which I mentioned and get proof that Paolo is alive. It's unlikely that he's been harmed but we must never assume this. It wouldn't be the first time that negotiations have been conducted over a dead body.' I wasn't deliberately trying to shock them, though I could see that I had. It was important to get them into the habit of considering all possibilities when faced with the need to make decisions.

'Eva, may I call you Eva?' She nodded with a faint smile. 'That first telephone call is important. No matter what they try to tell you, you must get the new number across to them and override everything they say. You won't have much time. Ask them to prove that your husband is alive. Act as though you're bordering on the hysterical. This will be expected once they know they're talking to Paolo's wife. Don't worry about trying to remember exactly what they say, you must record all the calls so that we can analyse them at our meetings. Is this clear?' She nodded again.

'Once we have that proof we can plan our campaign. It would be no bad thing for me to leave you with something to think about tonight after I've gone. In order to exercise discipline over the negotiations we ought to set a budget for the ransom. Businesslike again, you see.' I smiled to take any sting from the statement. 'You should consider how much you can afford to pay for the return of Paolo and also decide upon a figure beyond which you are not prepared to go. This sounds harsh but you will find that there is such a figure.

'Are you for instance prepared to give up everything you have worked for and become peasants or paupers for the sake of Paolo's life? It will not be easy but you must have this business attitude in your minds, otherwise your thinking will become impossibly clouded. You could let me have the figures tomorrow and we can begin to organise the budget. Now, I suggest that I return to my hotel and let you think about the matter. What would be a good time to meet tomorrow?'

'Any time at all,' said Juan Carlos, standing up and coming over to my side of the table.

'No!' I said sharply, 'Remember what I said about following the normal course of business. You must do this. I suggest that we meet either two hours before dinner or just after. Either of these timings will give you the opportunity to discuss, as a family, your confidential financial matters. You can then tell me what the telephone arrangements are going to be and the ransom position.'

I gave them my telephone number suggesting that they invite me for dinner or tennis, whichever was appropriate to the time of day, if the kidnappers made contact before our planned meeting. I declined the offer of a lift back. I wanted to get to know the routes between the Byron and the apartment. I left by the back entrance and struck out northwards. It wasn't long before I found myself on the hairpin bend of the Via Garibaldi which I knew. From there I took a cab back to the hotel along a similar route to my earlier one with Rodrigo.

Back in my room, I placed a call to Maria and briefed her in our own version of veiled speech about the situation. Other than what I had told the Romeros, there were no conclusions to be made at this stage. I thought about the Romeros' attitudes; the interplay of looks and the tactile signals between Eva and Juan Carlos were easily explained as the mutual comforting of daughter and father-in-law who were obviously fond of each other as well as being deeply involved in business together.

It certainly looked at this stage as though there would be a competent team at any rate. I spent a little time refreshing my memory on the recent ransom figures in Italy ready for the next day and fell asleep within minutes of getting into bed.

I had a light breakfast, an omelette, and then went back to my room where I began to make out the new proformas for the Romero log. I carefully ruled the columns and lines I would need for the various sections of the file. The letters I used for the column headings were deliberately large in order that the team could read them easily. Communications (from and to the gang), a daily record of events, demands and offers, notes on the family and then the all-important appreciations section. In this I wrote my first sparse assessment of the case. It contained little more than I had told the family the night before. I compiled notes on the family personalities and gave everyone including myself a code name. Such detail is important for many reasons. It gives confidence to the family when they can see the professional, painstaking approach; it is an instant and very useful aide-mémoire when balancing the factors in order to advise the family on the pros and cons of various decisions; it gives me a quite secure means of transmitting information to London and, against the possibility of anything happening to me, it is a detailed brief for another consultant to take my place and immediately begin to operate.

I browsed through all the city newspapers, particularly the advertisements, and I reckon I spotted indications of at least two more kidnaps going on in Rome at the time. I refreshed myself on recent settlement figures by chatting with Rodrigo over lunch and then I joined the Romans in a short siesta.

The Romeros usually had dinner at nine o'clock and so I timed my walk to the apartment to arrive just before seven that evening. Giorgio greeted me cordially and took me straight up to Juan Carlos's study where some movement of furniture had taken place in order to install a table large enough to seat half a dozen. Both Enrique and Luis were there. They both got to their feet as I was escorted in.

'Good evening, James. I have no appointments tonight.' Enrique was friendly and relaxed on the surface, but the quick, nervous puffs at his cigarette bespoke the underlying strains. 'Help yourself to coffee while I tell father and Eva that you are here.' He pushed over the silver tray and left the room. Luis made a great play of studying the newspaper. He obviously didn't want to talk so I left him alone and walked around looking at Romero's collection of miniature water colours. They were superb. I was interrupted by their entry, Juan Carlos closely followed by Eva. He looked serious, rubbing his hands together as he moved over to me. Eva looked strained around those lovely eyes. My guess was that the financial discussion had not been to her liking.

'Welcome, James. Sit down. Shall we start? Ah, come in, sit down Enrique.' He sat at the head of the table and we all half-turned to face him.

'James. The telephone. We think the best idea is to use the telephone in the apartment of my youngest son, Alvaro. I bought the place for him earlier this year and he has not even set foot in it yet. I doubt if anyone outside the estate agent's office knows that it is owned by the family.' He saw my inquisitive look and explained. 'Alvaro is in Heidelberg, at the university. In fact I called him today and told him about the problem. Of course he wanted to catch the first flight back but I instructed him to stay where he is. There is no point in disturbing his studies at this time.'

Privately I thought that the old man should have kept quiet. The boy's studies would certainly have been interrupted by the news. Still, that was a family affair, not mine.

The telephone system seemed reasonable enough and I indicated my agreement. Romero, pleased with himself, carried on.

'With regard to the budget. We have decided that our top figure will be ten miliardi. We do not consider this to be "written in stone" as you say, James. We will go further if we have to, but that seems a good figure to base our actions on.' As he finished his sentence I noticed Eva's head jerk up and then suddenly her whole body slackened in relief. 'Yes, Eva, I changed my mind as I began to speak. We cannot put a fixed price on Paolo. How does that seem to you, James?'

So I'd been right. They had argued about the principle of a top figure. It was interesting to see that she had accepted it, though. This team would be all right.

'That's fine. I know that ten miliardi has actually been the first demand in a couple of cases at least, but let me assure you that I don't think we'll be paying that much. It's a good enough basis to start from.'

I spent the next couple of hours furthering their education on possible tactics which we could encounter and the reasons for them. I told them how we could consider breaking the silence in a number of ways if it stretched on too long and generally chatted them easily through a couple of past cases. After this I suggested that I return to the hotel and that we should meet at the same time the next evening.

I declined their offer of dinner. I didn't want them to question me too far in advance of events. A confident CMT (Crisis Management Team) is one thing but there is always the danger that if they feel they know the whole business they can be tempted into precipitate action without fully considering the effects.

I left the way I'd entered and decided to walk back to the Byron. I took a slightly different route, enjoying the stroll through the streets which were beginning to liven up as Rome went out to eat. Over my own dinner in Le Jardin, I considered what sort of picture the gang would have on the Romeros' true wealth. The business was high profile, as it is in most product-dependent enterprises, and this would give a crudely calculable indication of wealth. The Romeros didn't, to my knowledge, live life to the full, at least not in the eyes of the public. They were quite low profile, but the occasions when they hosted foreign dignitaries were well publicised and this would confirm their wealth in the minds of the kidnappers.

A family in that position would not be expected to indulge in the great Roman pastime of tax evasion and so it was possible that we may be able to lower the gang's expectations slightly by claiming that excessive taxes had robbed the family of ready money. We would have to find some plausible way of doing this and I resolved to discuss it with Romero the next evening.

When I called Maria she reported that all was quiet. She had lined up two people for me to interview on my return. I was looking for likely men to assist me as trainee consultants because if things carried on at the current rate I was going to see precious little of my own family. I mused over the possibility of flying Maria out to Rome for a few days later on if the case looked like being a lengthy one.

Before turning in for the night, I called Rodrigo and asked him to meet me for breakfast, warning him that I wanted to talk about Luis. I didn't expect him to say too much about a brother avvocato but I might get some sort of line to explain his taciturnity. I wasn't tempted by Rome's night spots and after spending a little time browsing through Idris Shah's *Thinkers of the East*, which I carry everywhere, got another early night.

As planned, Rodrigo joined me for breakfast. Over the bowl of fresh fruit I asked him about Luis Fernando. He thought for a long time before he answered me.

'James, it is not done for avvocatos to talk professionally about each other unless it is to recommend. You understand this? It is the same in the occupation of consultant, is it not?' An interesting distinction, I thought, between occupation and profession. However, I nodded in agreement.

'I have known Luis for about fifteen years and he is a good avvocato and a friend. There is something about him in this case, though, which I find disturbing. Nothing that he has said, rather what he has not said.' Rodrigo looked more hurt than puzzled and I cast my mind back to Luis's reluctance to talk the previous evening. It wasn't an Italian characteristic, let alone an avvocato's.

'Do you think he is hiding something?'

'I cannot think what it would be, James. The Romeros are an impeccable family on the surface. I have learned something in my years as a solicitor, though, and that is that there is a skeleton in every broom closet – a very good English saying, that. Very descriptive. It is usually a matter of taxes, an affair of the heart or ethical questions in the various professions. But I cannot see any of those things here. I am having lunch with Luis today and I shall try to find out more.'

He obviously wasn't going to say any more, at least not yet, and the conversation dwindled into questions about Maria and my family. In response to my joking query as to when he was going to settle down and marry, Rodrigo just laughed and quipped: 'Not all of us Italians want to start a dynasty, James. My life suits me very well as it is at the moment.'

When I sat down to update my notes and appreciations I was forced to conclude that the family was not telling me everything. There was nothing concrete to confirm this and I considered all the conversations we'd had to date. The one thing which didn't fit in with my past experience was that very little had actually been said about Paolo the man. All my questions about his character and how he was likely to react with his captors had been answered briefly and succinctly. That was it, you see; usually there would have been little anecdotes and reminiscences; photographs would have been thrust into my hands and there would have been outpourings of love. Was this significant? I just didn't know. The attitudes I had met from the Romeros so far could have been ascribed to the normal and well-controlled instincts of a family united in business as well as love. I would just have to ride it out and be alert for nuance and facial expression.

My telephone rang.

'James, how about coming round for a few sets of tennis before it gets too hot. I was going to play with Enrique but he has had to go into the city. Come as soon as you like.'

'A good idea, Juan Carlos. You realise that I shall probably win again.' To maintain the agreed cover I spoke with familiarity in the manner of old friends.

I took a cab as far as Via Calandrelli and walked the few hundred yards to the apartment. Giorgio opened the door before I had the chance to knock and led me straight to Juan Carlos in his study. He motioned me to sit down as he continued almost nervously to pace up and down as he spoke.

'They called about half an hour ago. The man said: "This is Restrepo. . . ." Eva did not give him the chance to continue. As you suggested she shouted: "Show me that Paolo is alive" and she continued by telling him of the telephone to be used. The man then said: "Go there now, I shall call in fifteen minutes." Then he put the phone down.'

His voice was calm enough, certainly. 'Enrique drove straight to Alvaro's apartment with Eva. I am now waiting for them to call.'

'They must never call this number from the apartment again. If the call is traced then the number has lost its value.' I thought they had understood this from my briefings.

'It's OK, James, the police know nothing about the kidnap,' Juan Carlos protested.

'Maybe not. We cannot be certain and in any case the discipline of security must be adopted as from now,' I explained.

When the call came, some one and a half hours later, Juan Carlos merely said: 'Come home,' and put his receiver down.

I prompted Romero to contact Luis. Whatever message Eva and Enrique returned with would require the attention of the full team. He did as I asked. Son and daughter-in-law arrived with Luis only minutes behind. Juan Carlos stopped them talking until we were seated around the table and the door was closed by Giorgio, who was instructed that there were to be no interruptions.

Eva began.

'We waited in the apartment for almost an hour. When the kidnapper called it was the same man, Restrepo. He said we had been sensible with the phone number. I interrupted him and asked if Paolo was alive. He told me to shut up and listen. He said: "Go to the Ristorante Marsala. Outside there is a bus stop. In the top of the litter bin is a packet of Marlboro cigarettes. Take it home. Be at this number at seven o'clock tonight." He terminated the call, James, I could not even begin to tell him about the times we planned to be at the phone. The call took only a few seconds.' She was plaintive as though she thought she had somehow failed us.

'Don't worry. They seem to be professional. They keep their calls short and say only what they want to say. You'll have another chance to get the times across to them. Do you have the recording?'

Juan Carlos interjected. 'There has been no time to fit the tape recorder, James. We had planned to do it tonight.'

'In that case, Eva, write down the conversation exactly as it took place so that we can refer to it later if necessary. Please do it now while it is fresh in your mind. Luis, do you know the Ristorante Marsala?'

'Yes. It is very close to here, maybe three or four minutes walk.' I remembered the place now. I'd passed it the evening before – small, intimate looking, the bistro type of café which abounds in Rome. 'Does that mean they have been watching the house?' Luis was certainly ill at ease.

'It's quite possible but I generally find that messages are left close to the house. You see if the police are tapping the telephone then the closer the dead letter box is to the home the better. It gives the police less chance to organise surveillance. To make sure there are no mistakes, a man probably hired by the gang will drop off the package as he sees you approach but don't try to spot him. I suggest it is collected quickly.' I looked at Juan Carlos for approval. He was the chairman, after all, and the instruction must come from him.

'Yes, go right away, Luis, be careful. Do exactly as we have been told. Do not hang around or try to identify anyone who may be observing.' Fernando opened the door and Eva left at the same time, saying that she would organise some coffee.

I browsed through my file as we waited, watching Juan Carlos covertly. He paced up and down and every few seconds he looked at me from under brows beetled by the furrows of his frown. He was very tense but that was to be expected. We were about to get a package and we had no idea what it would contain. The coffee arrived, brought by one of the maids, Ana, a well-built woman whose looks were beginning to fade as the pasta took its toll on her figure. She poured the coffee, fussed over the placement of the cream and sugar and left. Eva didn't return and I assumed that she was spending the agonising waiting period in privacy somewhere.

I got up and walked over to the study window which overlooked the main street. Double glazing deadened the sound and gave the passing streams of traffic an almost surreal dimension as the cars scurried around like foraging ants below me. I noted Fernando's red Peugeot nosing into the kerb and carried my coffee cup back to the table. It took Luis a very long time to come to the study, considering that he parked right outside the front door. When he appeared it was with Eva. She was carrying a small tube of paper and the distinctive red and white Marlboro packet. She handed both to Romero, giving him an almost imperceptible nod.

He unrolled the tube, which turned out to be two sheets of paper. He read and reread the notes and then put them in front of him. He sat with head in hands until Enrique said: 'For God's sake, father, what does it say?' Juan Carlos passed both papers over to him. I waited in silence. Sooner or later they would give them to me. Romero shook himself, stood up and said tersely: 'Give them to James.'

There was a note from Paolo, handwritten, dated the day before and couched in fairly standard terms.

> Cara Eva,
> I am alive and well apart from some small bruises. I do not know how long this will remain so. These men mean business. Please do as they say. I am being kept in a small, very dirty room. You know how much I hate this. Already they threaten to disfigure me if you do not do as they say. Entreat with my father to get whatever money·they ask for.

Whatever has happened, forgive me for I love you, Eva
Please do not fail me now.
Yours forever,
Paolo

The other note was from the kidnappers. It was typed and to the
point.

> To: Signora Eva Romero
> You will know that we mean business. The note from your
> husband will prove he is alive. Do not go near the authorities
> if you wish him to live. To get him back is simple. You will
> tell us when you have collected together ten miliardi. To do
> this you will place an advertisement in *Il Messagero* which
> will say: 'Wanted. 1938 Maserati. Contact Box Number 171.
> We will then contact you. If you do not do as we ask, we
> shall take one or more fingers and then release news

The letter was grammatically correct with the punctuation marks
properly placed except for the missing full stop at the end. The
paper wasn't torn, though it was shorter than the standard A4 page.
I read through the notes again and I asked Eva for the cigarette
packet. It was passed over and I examined it closely; there was
nothing else inside it or trapped behind the silver paper lining.

'What are you looking for, James?' I looked at Romero. 'It seems
to be incomplete.' He frowned and glanced at Eva. 'What do you
mean?'

'The letter from the gang is incomplete. There is no closing full
stop. There is no deadline for you to work to. A threat is not a threat
unless there is the pressure of time, real or implied. The last portion
"and then release news" doesn't make sense. Are you sure there was
nothing else?' I asked the question of Luis. Before he could reply
Eva cut in.

'There was nothing else. It makes sense to me. They will release
the news of the finger to us. What else could it mean?' Her cheeks
were compressed with emotion. I didn't press her as she continued.
'Paolo is alive. We can do as they say. The money is the same as we
had calculated.' Taking a deep breath I countered her.

'That note could have been written a dozen days ago within hours
of Paolo's capture. The date means nothing. I assume from your
certainty that it is Paolo's handwriting?' She nodded tightly. 'Good,
that's a start. Now what do you make of his statement: "You know
how I hate this"?'

'Paolo has claustrophobia, he cannot tolerate being in small rooms. The kidnappers must know that this will drive him crazy.' There were droplets of moisture forming in the corners of her eyes.

'Not necessarily. It is normal to keep captives in the smallest possible place. It is easier to guard them and it would weaken the will of most people over a long period of time. No. They don't necessarily know of his claustrophobia. What about his reference to "Whatever has happened". It's an odd phrase. What do you think he means?' Again the sideways glance at Juan Carlos who took over from her.

'It is simple. Eva and Paolo had a quarrel shortly before he was taken. It was nothing, a lover's tiff. It has probably assumed greater proportions in his mind because of his captive state.' Eva clutched his arm and gave him a weak smile. She lit a cigarette with a trembling hand and inhaling deeply, she turned again to face me. I looked away from her to Enrique and then to Luis. They were both looking at the table top in front of them. Only Juan Carlos and Eva met my gaze.

Something was wrong. Signora Romero was simply not telling me the truth. She was looking me in the eyes, her face was now calm and she never faltered. Call it instinct if you wish, but she was hiding something and I didn't like it.

First things first, I thought. We'd get to the bottom of it sooner or later. I asked them all to sit down and began to advise them on the immediate requirements.

'Despite what the letter says, you could get another call from the gang at any time. You'd better be prepared for it. Eva, you need a holding script, some working notes. We must have that proof of life. Think of a question which only Paolo could answer. Make it a question which he will easily understand and which will not tax his memory too hard, avoid dates. He is under stress. He may not be able to concentrate on details and if by mistake he gave us the wrong answer we would be no further forward. If the gang calls, refuse to discuss money. Insist on getting the answer to the question and then try to get the telephone times across to them. Be prepared for them to make threats but try to ignore them and fix your mind on the question and the timings. Are you happy with this?'

She was smiling again. Relieved, I suppose because I had stopped asking questions about the letters. This was a temporary respite for her, I assured myself, as I turned to Juan Carlos and said: 'We

should consider the counter-offer to make to the gang. Have yo
any thoughts?' I wanted to get him thinking along business line
again.

'As Eva said, we had already considered ten miliardi but I accep
the need to bargain. What do you think about eight miliardi?' Hi
pencil was out and he pulled the writing pad towards him. I though
about it. Ten miliardi was 10,000 million lire[1]. The going rate a
that time in Rome was about 700–800 million lire. Given the know
facts about the family and the gang's apparent professionalism, the
would be expecting somewhere in this region at the end of the da
They would try for more of course; they might even accept less.

My concern was that I was now pretty certain that the Romero
were hiding something from me. Whatever that something was, i
was bound to affect my appreciation of the case – everything doe
It was not unusual for the first communication to contain a deman
though it often came after the family had been well and truly softene
up. I could not understand why, after all my briefings and cas
histories, Juan Carlos was contemplating such a large offer. If I wa
right about something being hidden, I could only surmise that thi
was because the Romeros thought the gang had some damned goo
aces up their sleeves.

The family had to be hiding something from me. Why, for God'
sake? I had explained the importance of frankness in making accurat
appreciations.

'If you have told me everything, and only if you have told m
everything,' I paused and looked at them each in turn, 'then m
advice would be one thing. If you have hidden anything from m
which affects the negotiation then that advice could be dangerous i
many ways. I can only base my suggestions on the full facts.'
paused again. There was some shuffling but no response. I repeated
'If you have told me everything, I would point out to you that th
current going rate is about 800 million lire. It will be somewher
around this figure where we could normally expect to settle.

'We need negotiating space in order to use our own tactics but w
can't afford to ignore the dangers of making an opening offer so lo
that the gang would feel insulted. This could precipitate action of
type we don't want. I would suggest that you consider a figur
around 400 to 500 million as an opener.' They looked alarmed.

'So low, James, surely this will anger them?' Romero seeme
genuinely worried.

'Unless they have a card in their hands about which I've been tol

[1] At the time, this would have been approximately US$8,000,000.

nothing, it shouldn't alarm them, though they will certainly make noises and threats.'

'Can we take some time to think about this? Can we be sure that they will respond to the advertisement? If we place it and then when they call we say that we are only offering 500 million what will happen?'

'Firstly, they have not given you any deadline and they would expect it to take you some time to collect large sums of money without attracting the attention of the authorities. You don't have to react immediately. After a suitable period – we can discuss that later – you can insert a modification of their advertisement such as: *Wanted, 1938 Mercedes. Unable to pay full market price but dearly love that model. Contact Box Number 171'*. If they have no special trump cards they may wait some time before answering or even wait until you raise the offer. If they have a special card then they will probably make contact very quickly to make sure you understand its value.' I'll swear they were looking sheepish but they made no mention of my constant harping on about trump cards and special cards.

'James, if there is no hurry we would like to discuss this in private. Perhaps you could call round tomorrow before dinner?' I was being politely dismissed. I had no objection to this. I like the negotiating teams to work things out independently. I reminded Eva of the script and took my leave.

I had a very real feeling of déjà-vu as I scanned the *Il Messagero* over dinner that night. My worst fears were confirmed. There, half way down the advertisements column was: 'Wanted, 1938 Maserati, Contact Box Number 71'. They hadn't even implied a lower offer. The bloody fools! I tried to get Romero on the phone all evening but there was no reply. I suspected this was deliberate, and contemplated calling Alvaro's apartment. But on balance I decided to wait until the appointed hour the next day.

I was angry, I admit it, but no client is obliged to take my advice. What on earth was the secret they were hiding from me? It had to be a powerful argument indeed. I was convinced that Romero, the whole family in fact, had accepted the sense of my briefings so far. I spoke to Rodrigo but he had heard nothing from Luis.

As I passed through the foyer of the Byron the next morning I was passed a message. I opened it before going in for breakfast. It was a short note from Romero.

James,

I regret that we cannot keep our appointment for dinne
tonight. We have spoken to our clients and offered one fift
of the asking price for the property. They have accepted
Please do not leave Rome as we wish to thank you properl
after this is all over.

Juan Carlos Romero

I think under normal circumstancés I would have replied with
note and politely made my excuses before returning to England.
was disappointed in Romero's actions and my instinct told me tha
the outcome would be a great shock to them.

Out of a real sense of duty, I did try to contact them again but th
servants who took my call merely said that the family were out c
town for a short time. I wanted to advise them on the dange
relevant to the drop-off of money and make sure they were properl
organised. If they wouldn't speak to me I was powerless. I decide
to stay for a week and again considered asking Maria to join me. A
it turned out it took less than a week for the Romeros to contact n
again.

CHAPTER

5

Author's note

Double ransom payments are not uncommon, though I have usually managed to avoid them. Once a 'double' payment has been demanded, the danger to the victim is increased in direct proportion to his perceived value. The gang has already taken delivery of an amount of money which was probably within their area of acceptability – the second demand will be a bonus. If the gang also has a bargaining ace in their hands, the process of ensuring the safety of the victim becomes even more difficult. Since this case was resolved, 'Juan Carlos Romero' has given permission for some unique aspects of the case to be discussed.

AS usual Giorgio was ahead of me and the door opened as I reached out to the bell push. In the study they were all assembled, Juan Carlos, Enrique, Eva and Luis. There was an air of abject despair as Maria the maid tuttutted her way through the smouldering volcanoes of cigarette and cigar butts on the overflowing ashtrays. No-one spoke until she had left the room with a promise of coffee to follow at Eva's order.

I shook their hands in turn and sat down, raising an eyebrow at Juan Carlos. He cleared his throat noisily.

'James,' heavily, 'You were right.' He held his hands out in my direction, palms uppermost as if in supplication. 'We obeyed instructions to the letter when we dropped off the money. At the appointed hour there was no sign of Paolo. The money was paid three days ago. Two hours ago Luis collected this package from a pazzatura can, a garbage can a few streets away.' Hurt and vulnerable, he held up a grimy milk carton and a single sheet of paper. I held out my hand for it.

'No. Let me read it to you. It says, "Signora Romero. You hav
paid the deposit. Now we want the real money. Be at the telephon
at eight o'clock tonight. You know the consequences should yo
fail." That is all.' He folded the paper again and put it in hi
document case.

'Eva. Enrique. It is time to go to the telephone.' They ros
Enrique steadied Eva as she stumbled to the door. Her face was se
jaws clenched so tightly that the facial muscles stood out, ripplin
under the chalk-white skin.

'Stop,' I said. 'Whatever has happened, and you can tell me late
don't forget; it is now even more important to get proof that Paol
is alive. Have you a question in mind?' She nodded. 'Then insi
above all else that the question is answered before you agree to eve
talk to them again. It is very important. Do you understand?' Agai
the jerky nod. 'And don't forget the recording.' A glance at Romer
and they left.

I made no apology for assuming command at that point. Ther
was no time for debate and they all knew the reasons for m
insistence.

'Let me see the note, please.' I stretched my hand out to Romero
document case. He, apparently absently, put his hand over it an
began to talk.

'Let me tell you what happened. Restrepo called the day after th
advertisement was placed. He asked if we had the money. Eva tol
him that it was not possible to raise that amount without alertin
the authorities through the banks. The best we could manage wa
two miliardi. Restrepo cursed and put the phone down but he calle
again within ten minutes and said that because Paolo's health wa
suffering and they were humane people, they were going to accep
our offer. He told us where to collect instructions which would b
ready within two hours.

'We collected them. They were in a doughnut wrapper. Th
papers gave us detailed orders on the type of car and routes t
follow – much as you had explained to us in the beginning, Jame
It said that Paolo would be released the next day. Set down in
remote part of the city with enough money to get a cab to th
apartment. James, we did exactly as they said. They did not releas
Paolo as you now know.'

Dammit. I wasn't surprised. Two miliardi, it must have been on
of the biggest payments made in Rome. Well over twice the goin
rate! The gang must have thought all their birthdays had arrive
together.

There was no way that I was going to say: 'I told you so.' I had to find a way to boost their confidence again. I had warned them of the dangers of too much too soon. They realised that, of course. Indeed, Romero had admitted it. They had to tell me what they'd been withholding from me. I wasn't going to tackle Romero alone. I wanted them all to hear what I had to say. I tested him.

'May I see the note, please.' Again he feigned deafness and walked over to the window with his document case tucked negligently under his arm affecting a pose suggesting a businessman's habit and not a deliberate action. I gave up rather than reach an embarrassing impasse. There would be time when the others returned.

By nine-thirty Eva and Enrique were back. Their expressions said it all. They sat down. Eva, lips trembling and hands shaking, began to relate the news.

'Il Porco. The pig. He was so rude – so foul-mouthed. It was Restrepo again. All he would say was "We have the deposit. We want the rest of the money. Quickly." He will call at the same time tomorrow and he wants a new telephone number to be given to him then. I kept repeating the question for Paolo. He called me "puttana" and other foul things.'

She was fighting back tears, but knowing her background in business from Juan Carlos's comments, I found it hard to believe that it was just the foul language which was causing the stress. Again, something was being hidden.

'Did he accept the question, Eva?' I asked. 'Can we hear the tape?'

She sighed. 'There is no tape, James, we never did get around to fixing it up. It seemed so unimportant when we knew that Paolo was going to be returned to us. Yes, he said the question would be answered on the new telephone.'

Juan Carlos started to speak but I cut him off gently.

'First thing, remember, you must be prepared for Restrepo to call without warning. You must be ready for this. If he calls, it will be for one of two reasons probably. To answer the question you put to Paolo or simply to press home the demand for the rest of the money.

'If he answers the question he will follow it up with money demands. Eva, if this is the case, you have to say that this is out of our control. That you have to refer to Juan Carlos; that you know there will be difficulties in getting more cash in secret; that you know how angry Juan Carlos is at their betrayal of your trust. You did exactly as they ordered, you have not told the authorities, you delivered the money in good faith and they let you down.

'Don't be drawn into discussions on figures. If the question is not answered, continue to maintain that you can do nothing as Juan Carlos will not even speak about the matter until he has positiv proof that Paolo is alive. The call will be short but try to get as much as possible across to them. They will be listening to you. Can you do this?'

'Yes. I can do that but when do you think he will call?'

'Probably on schedule as arranged but you have to be prepared for the unexpected in order not to be caught off balance.' She nodded understandingly. She was looking a little calmer again. It's amazing how just the process of thinking begins to reduce the stress. Juan Carlos shifted uncomfortably at the head of the table. He poured coffee for all of us, opened his document case, staring at it unseeing as he picked up from my last interruption.

'James, I have already apologised for our treatment of you. We were wrong to ignore your advice. What do you think the outcome will be?'

'Juan Carlos, you don't have to apologise to me. Any decision which has to be made is for the family, the team to make. I'm an adviser only. You are in a less than perfect position now but you must accept it as it is. It's certainly not a unique situation, many families in this country have been faced with double payments for one reason or another. What is important is that you fully understand what is happening and why it has happened, the options open to the kidnappers and the options open to you.' I was tempted to play on the fact that they were still hiding something from me but I decided to take it a bit further first.

'In what I'm going to say I imply no criticism but it's vital to your understanding of the business. Put yourselves in the kidnapper situation. They asked for ten miliardi and they probably had a expectancy of up to say 800 million lire. To their surprise, and I do believe it would have been a surprise, they were offered two miliardi. Two miliardi as the opening gambit! Their immediate reactions were very understandable. They would conclude that you knew little about the business of negotiating in a kidnap case. It would streng then their belief that the threats they had made to you were effective

'They could also believe that this situation could change if you took professional advice. Therefore they did the logical thing and took the money as fast as possible, hung onto Paolo and then sa down to think things through.

'The fact that you produced such a sum so quickly also intimat that it was no problem to obtain it. If that was the case then you could surely get your hands on more, even though that may take ttle time. Right, they thought, hold onto the victim and let's have ome more. For security they may well have changed location and aid off their leg men, the men who laid the messages for you to ollect and possibly the men who were guarding Paolo at first.

'Now, the options which are open to the gang must be appreciated y the team.' I was now going to deliver some shocks.

'Firstly, they can continue to hold Paolo for an indefinite period ntil they've extracted what they assess as being the maximum mount of cash from you. The advantages are obvious. The main isadvantage is that they become more vulnerable to detection each ay they hold onto Paolo and use up more funds in looking after im. This will have been calculated in the first place before the natch but now they may have some internal pressures from gang nembers who want to take advantage of their good luck so far and ut and run.

If they decide to cut and run, the question will pass through their ninds: "Why not kill the victim? He's worthless to us now and why hould we take the risk of him giving information to the authorities vhich could incriminate us"?' There was a gasp from Eva. The point vas not lost with the others either. They all braced themselves lightly. I held up my hand for continued silence and carried on.

'Another option to make more money from Paolo is to sell him to nother gang.' This was too much for Juan Carlos and Eva. They oth stood up protestingly.

'Sell him, James, sell him? What is he? A bag of oranges?' Juan Carlos was shaking with anger.

'He is exactly that.' I spoke quite sharply. 'I told you when we rst sat down last week that this is a business. Your son, Juan Carlos; our husband, Eva, is nothing more than a commodity to the gang. Ie represents to them only a means of acquiring money. If it seems reasonable alternative to holding him longer or killing him, they vill even consider selling him and he is very saleable because of the ase with which they've already made money. I told you this isn't a nique situation. Victims have been sold under similar circumstances.

'The third option is simply to kill him. It's because of these options reated by the current situation that at all times you must insist on aving proof of Paolo's survival. Not just once but every time a new ecision or demand is made.

'Now, the options open to you are somewhat more limited. You'll ave to conduct some careful negotiating towards a point where the ang can see that their best interests are served by keeping Paolo

themselves and continuing to deal with you. You'll almost certainl
have to spend more money but you must have control over it other
wise you'll lay yourselves open to the gang's fourth option – t
reproduce exactly the same situation and go for a third payment
Each time they go through the payment stage they increase thei
risk of detection and this is proportionately reflected in the risk t
Paolo's life.' I paused and sat back, looking at them. Before I coul
begin again, Eva spoke up.

'James, are you certain of all this?'

'By no means. There are no certainties in kidnap cases. Based o:
my experience, I believe I've given you some of the options open t
the gang. There will be many possible variations on the basic theme
as you can imagine. Remember, you're still in business. About to b
committed to a game of move and counter-move and you must know
the worst and best cases. In the best case, the gang have their fift
option – it's also the most unlikely one – simply to release Paolo
Unlikely but not unknown. It's just possible that their presen
demands are a cover to keep you from the authorities while the
make good their escape leaving Paolo with the means to free himsel:
Most unlikely.'

'Will you stay and continue to help us, James?' This was fror
Enrique. I kept silent for a long time, gazing from one to the othe
before answering.

'I will, of course I will.' They appeared relieved but I once mor
stopped them talking.

'You have to realise that my advice is based only on the informatio
which I've been given by you. Consider the effect on my thinking :
anything's been hidden from me. It will be like working in
sandstorm. I have to half-close my eyelids to keep out the blindin
sand in order to see a way ahead. I take the best route I can detec
and fall into a hole. A hole I would have avoided if I'd been abl
to open my eyes just a little bit more, to broaden my perceptio
marginally; if only the sand weren't so thick I'd have seen that hol

'I'm now going for a short walk to clear my head of the tobacc
fumes. I suggest that I return in about thirty minutes and we ca
discuss the next moves. Eva, don't forget what you have to get acros
to the gang if Restrepo should call. Oh. Yes. You'd better thin
about the instruction to find another telephone.' Without a furthe
word, I got up and left. I deliberately left my file on the table. I'
never complained about the tobacco smoke before. They knew wh
I was going and if they cared to look at my notes they would see th
constant queries as to what was being hidden from me.

As I walked, I thought over the long dissertation I'd just delivered. I'd tried to shock without numbing them. I'd tried to get the message across that they'd been pretty foolish without demeaning them or lessening the authority of Juan Carlos. I'd tried to show them that there was still a good chance of getting Paolo out without hiding the dangers. In short, I'd tried to bring them back into the business of negotiating with hope if not confidence. Had I succeeded? I'd know very soon.

I actually walked past the Ristorante Marsala, where the first message had been left. It did nothing more than remind me how hungry I was. Glancing at my watch I saw that it was eleven-thirty and I debated calling the Byron to book a table for a late night dinner. I decided against it. I could be set for a few more hours' work if things went well. Was I going to stay if they didn't come clean? I didn't know.

A negotiating team isn't obliged to follow the consultant's advice but it's not a particularly good thing to be linked to a case which could prove to be disastrous if they continued to act in such an arbitrary fashion without considering the penalties. No, I decided I wouldn't pull out, whatever happened. Even if they didn't confide in me there would always be the chance that I could save them some grief at a later stage. Having made the decision, I turned and slowly retraced my footsteps.

When I returned to Romero's study there was a mouth-watering smell of chicken and various spices. While I'd been walking they'd also felt the pangs of hunger and a hasty but delicious array of light snacks was arranged on the table. This was a good sign. If they had decided not to tell me then surely they'd have opted for their usual semi-formal dinner using it as an excuse for not talking business. We'd see. Meanwhile at Eva's invitation I tucked into the dishes scattered haphazardly around the table. Not exactly filling, but it certainly took the edge off my appetite.

There was little or no conversation over the meal. Without exception they looked worried. Eva had been weeping and had made a very bad job of disguising it; there were still streaks of mascara at the corners of her eyes. Not until the plates were cleared away and the coffee had been served amid the statutory clouds of smoke did Romero clear his throat and open the meeting.

'James, when we first met you told us that anything we said was in confidence. You said that all the tapes of past cases we listened to and all the letters we read had been cleared by the families concerned.' I nodded at the implied question.

'I accept that you are a man of integrity but I now want your handshake as a man of honour. I want you to promise that you will never relate to a living person what we have to tell you. There is nothing illegal. On that you have my word.' He raised his eyebrows. I said nothing but I reached out to shake his damp hand.

His eyes were anguished. Whatever he had to say, and I couldn't imagine what it was, he wasn't going to find it easy. I looked across at Eva. She dropped her head the moment our glances locked. Enrique sprawled back in his seat, one hand deep in his pocket, the other nervously twisting the cigar about with no regard to the falling ash. Luis ignored me and looked out of the window.

'For a time,' began Romero, 'we thought you had not noticed that we were misleading you. No. Not misleading you, lying by omission. We thought you had believed the explanations about the first letters. Believed the story of the lover's tiff between Eva and Paolo. Yes, we had cut off the bottom of the first letter from the gang, the one which you so quickly noticed ended without a full stop leaving the odd phrase referring to the "finger" and the "release of news". Yes, there was more in the note. What else made you suspicious?'

'Not just suspicious, quite certain. It's not difficult to appreciate that you could have installed a tape recorder within minutes, yet you didn't – or at least said you didn't. You have two in this study alone, one of which is custom-made for recording telephone conversations.' I indicated the machines alongside the hi-fi radio.

'When Luis went to collect the message from the Marsala I saw his car return and yet it took him twenty minutes to get to this room from the pavement. Twenty minutes during which Eva was still out of the room. Plenty of time for her to cut the last part of the message away leaving it much shorter than the normal commercial stationery.

'After asking twice to see the message in your document case, you still pretended not to have noticed my request but it wasn't just these obvious signs. When you've been in the business as long as I have you notice the little personal interchanges of signal. The nuances of voice and expression all tell their tale.

'Let me say one thing. This isn't a new situation. At first some people are reluctant to pass on confidences. This is quite natural and often quite unimportant, but in this case I suspect that what you haven't told me is a fact of some sort of which Restrepo at least is aware and this fact, whatever it is, represents in your minds a powerful lever in the gang's hands.

'You have my absolute assurance that the matter will remain between us unless you yourself, Juan Carlos, decide one day that i may be of use to some other family. Now, what you're about to say to me will be important but first, in case we're interrupted by Restrepo, have you sorted out a new telephone?'

I could have said more, but what was the point if they were going to come clean? I knew that they'd arranged a new telephone, I'd heard them discussing it but I wanted to set a perspective here – let them know that though what they had to say was of great interest to me, at the same time the priority was keeping the business of negotiation under control.

'Yes. We are going to use the apartment of a friend of Luis who is on a sabbatical in America.' Juan Carlos paused again and fussed over the coffee pot; rang the bell and asked for replenishment. Using every excuse he could to delay the inevitable, he waited until it had been served and paced around the study a few times before clearing his throat yet again.

'James, this is very delicate. If word were to get out it would cause great embarrassment to the family, to the business, to our government and probably to some of our past guests, many of whom were here for diplomatic purposes at the highest levels of politics. In itself it is not so unusual. Very, very distasteful but not so unusual. It is our particular circumstances which make it so difficult as Restrepo knows.' He paused again; he looked quite tragic, unprotected and forlorn.

'For God's sake, father. Bloody well tell him. Paolo is omossessuale, froscio, finocchio, queer, a bloody puff.'

Enrique was standing and shouting, red-faced and belligerent. The sudden, stinging slap from Romero staggered him and he left the room abruptly, slamming the door violently. Eva was hunched in her seat, head in hands, and I could see tears coursing between her fingers and down her arms. Blue-black mascara streaking runnels of contrast along that ivory white skin, twisting and forking as they were resisted by the fine golden hairs. I felt for her and thought back to the photographs in the news clippings Rodrigo had given me. Hard to think of the affectionate Paolo as a homosexual as he held her close to him posing for the cameras.

Romero's precipitate action in striking his son had lifted him into anger. He stalked around the room talking loudly.

'To think I can trace my family back to the Conquistadores, soldiers, men. My uncles fought in the Spanish Civil War. God, they were men. My father and I both fought for our countries in times of war. Now to find that Paolo is a woman in a man's clothing. It is unforgivable of God. What have we ever done to deserve such disgrace?' He wasn't asking the question of me so I remained silent. Far better to let him burn his anger out.

He carried on in the same vein for two or three minutes and then suddenly became aware of the effect he was having on Eva. Full of contrition, he stood behind her and placed both hands on her shoulders, drawing her head back against his chest. He stroked her hair and made crooning noises. They both began to relax and I idly wondered if they'd ever been lovers. There was certainly a great bond between them. I mentally shrugged. It was of no concern to me; it had no effect on the case.

I began to think about what he had told me and what it meant. I decided that the first thing I had to ascertain was whether or not it was true. At the risk of starting Romero off again, I asked:

'Juan Carlos, I have to ask you this. Are you certain or is there a possibility of it being some sort of trick by the gang?'

'No. It is not a trick. I have to tell you though that until Paolo was kidnapped neither myself nor Eva had any inkling whatsoever of Paolo's, what shall we call it, "other life". Eva I know has found him a good husband in every sense.' Stress on the 'every' I noticed wryly. 'No-one in the family could ever have guessed at it.'

"How did you find out?' I was curious rather than seeking necessary knowledge but it was keeping Romero talking and the more he talked the calmer he was becoming. Eva had stopped crying now and she excused herself, gesturing to her face as she left to carry out repairs.

'When the kidnappers made the first call on the morning after Paolo was taken, they told us to go to his apartment downtown. They simply gave us the address. At the time we didn't even know he had an apartment. Stupidly I took Eva along. I am saying stupidly but she had to know sooner or later I guess. When we arrived it seemed like an everyday apartment. Comfortable but not luxurious. On the face of things the only indication that it belonged to Paolo were a few items of clothing scattered around and his briefcase which we recognised.

It all appeared very normal. We started to look around, you know, opening closets, wardrobes and drawers, feeling very much like thieves in the night. After all, why should a man not have an apartment? To tell the truth I was beginning to respect Paolo even more, thinking that this was a refuge he had found to escape to now and again with the occasional mistress. This is part of life in my country as you know, James. I don't think even Eva was too upset at that point.

'We began to find odd things; items of female underwear, perfumes and the like. Well this fitted in with what we were both beginning to think. Paolo had a mistress or mistresses. He was certainly handsome, wealthy and the subject of much flirtation. We then began to find photographs, disgusting photographs. Paolo with men. No! Not even men but young boys.' Romero's voice cracked and his shoulders shook. I felt sorry for the proud old man and I made to stand up but he stopped me.

'No, James, let me finish. Let me purge myself. Some of these boys were street urchins, not even clean. The effect on Eva was devastating as you can imagine. It is one thing to find that your husband has been deceiving you with another woman. That is after all a risk in life, a potential factor in any marriage. A matter which a wife can do something about if she wishes. To find that he has been guilty of such depravity with males is too much to bear.

'Again, I do her an injustice. She has borne it well, James. Today was the first time she has cried. Can you believe that? She tells me she still loves the animal. God, what charity women in love are capable of. I don't know whether I can ever look at Paolo again. I cannot show you the photographs, we burned them. I would not have shown you anyway. They were vile.

'Perhaps the hardest thing to take is the manner in which Paolo was kidnapped. A young boy from the streets was used to lure him to the apartment. Imagine it! Such was his need that he was diverted from a most important business meeting in order to slake his lust on a boy. I vomited, James, when I found out.'

Eva returned, still strained but with the confidence of a woman who knows that she looks more than acceptable. What a tonic make-up can be at times like these.

'I have told James everything, Eva. Everything. You do not need to say more. We must now look to the way ahead – if there is one.' He touched my shoulder, inviting me to speak, but Eva cut me off.

'I need to say one thing.' Her voice was low, husky from cigarettes and emotion. 'I do love Paolo, James, and I want him back. You may find this difficult to accept but I do want him back. Whatever he has done I forgive. I am his wife and it is for me to care for him until this sickness has gone. Don't worry, babbo,' she turned to Romero. 'He will change. In a few months you will have forgotten all about it. James, is it hopeless? If word of this gets out the family is finished in Rome, in Italy in fact. It is not so important for me but for Juan Carlos the business has been his life.' She ruffled his hair. 'He also has the pride of his ancestors and this would be the hardest part of all for him.'

I'd completely forgotten Luis Fernando, who'd been sitting silently in the corner of the study throughout. He rose, came to the table and contributed to the conversation for the first time.

'Signor March. Signore Juan and Signora Eva have neglected to tell you that Restrepo, in his early notes and in the telephone conversations, said that he had taken some photographs from Paolo's apartment, very explicit photographs, and that if we do not accede to his demands not only will Paolo be beaten but the photographs will be sent simultaneously to *Il Messagero*, *Il Tempo* and *Paese Sera*. Can you imagine what they would do with them?' I had of course guessed as soon as they revealed the truth that something like this had to be the threat.

'Look, nothing is hopeless. You are still in business. All you have told me is that the gang have an extra bargaining factor. So what? Your job is to analyse all this, mine is to help you, together we'll make an appreciation and from there plot our course of action. The bag of oranges, remember? Now if we're to have a meeting shouldn't Enrique be here?'

'I do not think we shall find Enrique much use right now,' Juan Carlos sat down again. 'If I know him he will be consoling himself with the bottle after which he will probably go to the city to prove his own virility.'

Juan Carlos smiled. Good. Things were returning to an even keel again. There was a visible relaxing now that the secret was out.

I'd made no reference to my feelings. No signs of shock, disgust or any other emotion. Only a clinical interest as befitted the revelation of an added business factor. As Juan Carlos had said it was not so unusual, the great difference was the family's social standing regarding the government and their status as international hosts.

In truth it was of no concern to me, though I was sad for Eva and Juan Carlos of course. As a consultant you simply cannot afford to get emotionally involved. God knows it's easy enough for that to happen. It takes all kinds to make this world of ours tick over; what I had to do was find the negotiating edge, find a way to get Restrepo moving towards us.

'Look, it's now two-thirty. You've had a mentally draining experience and you must be tired.' Eva smiled gratefully. 'I know what it cost you to talk as frankly as you did and I thank you for your trust. You've told me nothing which changes the points I gave to Eva earlier. We still need to know that Paolo is definitely alive. She must still not get tied down to figures. If there is a call behave exactly as I advised earlier. Do you agree, Juan Carlos?'

'Of course. It seems very sensible to me. You are right. We are all tired. What were you going to suggest?'

'That we break off for the remainder of the night. That we meet at whatever time you leave your business to take lunch tomorrow. This will give me time to make my appreciation and advise you of the course of action open to you. I am happy to carry on with this right now but I think tomorrow would be better.'

'Tomorrow is the Anniversario della Liberazione, 25 April. It is a public holiday. We can have as much time as you wish. James, come for lunch, I promise you a better one than even Le Jardin. After that we can meet and talk. Luis please also, you should join us for lunch.'

He was beaming now. Much of the tension had been lifted. I accepted but Luis claimed a prior appointment and promised to be with us by two-thirty. I shook hands all round and left. The eternal Giorgio was still there. This time as I went through the door he shook my hand warmly.

'Thank you, Signore.' Had he been listening? I suppose so. It's in the nature of trusted domestic staff at Giorgio's level to decide that they have a perfect right to know everything that goes on within their employer's domain.

I hadn't gone far when Luis's Peugeot pulled alongside and he motioned me inside.

'You did remarkably well with Signor Romero tonight, Signor March. I thought it would be a long time before I saw him smile again. Tell me, is there a chance?'

'There is a very good chance.' I looked at him. 'The family will have to take some hard decisions, though. Their strength will be tested to the limit perhaps.'

'Signor Romero and Signora Eva, they have the strength. Enrique will resort to his friend the "grappa". If it is suggested, Signore, let Enrique fade from the team. I could hint of this to Signor Romero. If he is out of it everyone will understand why.'

'Luis, please call me James. I'd thought of this after I saw Enrique's performance tonight but it must be a family decision. I leave it to them.' He smiled and I reckoned that it was unlikely that Enrique would be at the meeting the next day.

At the Byron I managed to persuade the night staff to get me some cold bits and pieces. Lord, but I was ravenous. It had been an interesting night, though, and I had to force the events from my mind to get some sleep.

I'm certainly no art expert but I am an art lover, and the next morning I walked the few hundred yards south east from the Byron into the grounds of the Villa Borghese. I spent a peaceful hour just browsing through gardens (gorgeous in April), past lakes, the famous water-clock and numerous statues. It's a marvellously quiet place with not even a hint of the frenzy of the Rome which surrounds it.

Into the Borghese Pavilion which houses the almost indescribable delights of the Borghese Gallery with its breathtaking display of Italian masterpieces. It's all there, Bernini's sculptures of *David* and *Apollo and Daphne*, there's Raphael's *Deposition from the Cross*, Titian's *Sacred and Profane Love* all rubbing shoulders with Rubens, Veronese, Botticelli, Caravaggio, Correggio and a host of others. Time stands still for me in such places but much as I enjoyed it, like the company of an old and trusted friend, my mind kept returning to the Romeros.

I went back to my room and made notes for the afternoon session at the apartment. What did I have? My preliminary notes appeared something like this:

THE TEAM

Weak link – Enrique. Eva and Juan Carlos likely to remain strong now they're up and running. Likely to follow advice but can't be certain. Luis – no problem. Want Paolo back.

FINANCIAL

Paid two miliardi. More cash (up to ten mil) available.

VICTIM

Probably alive. Probably unharmed. Probably scared.

THE GANG

Probably experienced. Possible internal dissent due to earlier payment. Restrepo experienced negotiator? Security conscious. Probably confident due strength cards held/early success. More likely go for double payment than kill or sell P. Possibly insecure location due early demand/drop-off of cash/possible change of leg men. Possible under time pressure or why early demand?

CASH EXPECTANCY

Can't say till next contact. Probably had more already than original expectancy. If edge found, should get second payment well under going rate.

PROBLEM

Get Paolo out

METHOD
Reduce gang's expectancy by lowering value of Paolo
HOW
1st – buy time. Proof. Proof. Proof.
Difficult to get money? Must be plausible – Careful, Eva!
Difficulties with Juan C? Dangerous!
Authorities on to us? Dangerous!
Publish and be damned!!!! Arthur Wellesley – Duke of Wellington! A Wellington variation? Will they wear it!. Eva/JC/Enr. – GANG?

Well, there it was, the Wellington option. I had to see if the family would go for it. I decided to walk to the Romeros. Apart from being a nice day it gave me time to think it through properly. What I was going to propose had its dangers but it seemed the best course. I would have to be tactful and persuasive, particularly with Eva. She was going to bear the brunt of it. Could she take it? Would she take it? I was feeling more than sorry for her but the more I thought of Wellington, the more I felt it could work; furthermore, it could work quickly if the Romeros were, convincing.

'Must remember to take out a policy against lung cancer', I remember thinking as I was welcomed into Juan Carlos's study. They'd really excelled themselves with their smoking this time. I coughed, I couldn't help it. I'm not actually averse to smoke but in that room it seemed to hang in heavy clouds and I could get quite light-headed after a while. They didn't seem to notice. Their mood wasn't light but despair was no longer dominant. Eva looked as though she'd had a decent sleep and Juan Carlos was as I'd first met him, confident and in control. I wondered how long it would last.

We had lunch in the long dining room and this time I had time to look around me properly and enjoy the Romero painting collection. All heavy oils in traditional ornate, antique gold frames, they were perfect for the setting, at least one original, a Botticelli. The Romeros had tried to recreate a piece of old Rome in this room. Heavy brocaded curtains draped in lavish abundance alongside the darkened glass windows. The fireplace was something to behold. The whole family could have got together inside and still have had space to raise their glasses in a toast. The huge cast iron heat reflector at the back must have been two hundred years old at least with a fine patina from the years of polishing. The relief work on it depicted one of the early Popes surrounded by his armed guard.

A slim shelf ran round the room, about ten feet from the floor. It held a marvellous collection of small icons, many of which I guessed to be Russian. The carpet was Persian and of the highest quality, quite possibly from Kermanshah. It was showing signs of wear in places and it was impossible to tell its age without a closer examination. On small pedestals running the length of the room on each side were figurines of all the Roman emperors from Caesar Augustus to Marcus Aurelius Numerius. I wondered why it stopped there, there was room for more. I decided that he had only collected up to the point of the East and West sub-division of the Empire in AD 284. I could have spent hours enjoying that room but out of politeness, I joined the conversaton.

Enrique was with us for lunch but as we stood to leave he came across and apologised for his outburst of the previous day. He was embarrassed but whether this was because I now knew about Paolo or whether he was genuinely ashamed at his lack of control, I don't know. He told me that he would not be joining the meeting. He didn't seem put out by this and I supposed it was quite normal for him to be barred from events where his temper may let him down. He was going, he said, to take a trip to Heidelberg to spend some time with his brother Alvaro. He did whisper 'Good Luck' to me, though.

Luis was prompt and the meeting began with Romero giving a resumé of the case to date. Turning to me, he asked: 'James, you have had your time to think. How do you see it?' I glanced at Eva.

'Have you a question prepared for the call tonight?' At her nod, I went on, still addressing Eva. 'Does Restrepo know that you are aware of Paolo's "problem"?'

'Yes. I have taken all the telephone calls. When he referred to the photographs after we had visited the apartment I made no comment so he must know that I am aware.'

'Have you spoken about the subject at all?' She shook her head.

'When the telephone call comes tonight there is no reason to change Eva's brief as it will consist purely of demanding proof that Paolo lives. I would, however, like to change the emphasis if you agree with a strategy which I'm about to suggest. Meantime, if a call comes during our discussion, Eva, stick to the brief.' They were looking interested now.

'I've explained the bargaining process already using comparisons to a commodity. I'll stay with that for the time being. The gang have Paolo but in addition to this they have the blackmail lever which has already proved effective.

'Consider, Juan Carlos, that you are marketing a large quantity of printed circuit boards to a prospective client. He's hovering and

100

you're not sure which way he's going to go so you throw in an extra temptation. You say: "But, Signore, these are boards from the most modern Italian factory, as good as any in the world." The client is enthused by this. It takes on great importance in his mind, it becomes the whole reason for him dealing with you. You close the deal.

'That night on the television news there is a release saying that a new American technique to improve printed circuit board manufacture has been discovered. Development has been under way in secret for some months and the company is taking orders right now. What is the effect? Your client loses interest in your product. Romero products are no longer the finest; no longer in great demand; there is a rival new technology. You, the vendor, have lost your bargaining edge.' I paused to let them consider. Romero's expression was of puzzled interest. Eva's face began to crinkle in alarm. 'Sharp lady,' I thought to myself.

'You see Paolo's problem can be likened to the marketing edge given by the established Romero reputation. It's the factor which immediately made you pay off a large amount of money. What happens if that edge is lost?'

'I see,' Juan Carlos was speaking cautiously. 'Paolo does not lose his value to us but the gang does not know this and loses a pressure tactic. Yes, I see that but I cannot conceive of how we can take that away from them. It is a marketing edge – one which we cannot remove. It is there. It is a fact.'

'Do you know the story about the Duke of Wellington during Britain's Napoleonic wars when he was threatened by an ex-mistress who had kept some letters from him which could at best be described as compromising? He received news that unless he returned to her, she would publish those letters. His reply is generally reputed to have been: "Publish and be damned".' Juan Carlos was on his feet.

'We cannot do that. It is preposterous. What if they do publish? I would in their position.'

'Hear me out. I wasn't going to suggest Wellington's solution, though in his case it did work. I was going to suggest a variation on it. No, we certainly don't invite them to publish. We don't even refer to the photographs. Put them out of your minds for the time being. After all, you don't even know if they have them. Remember when you searched Paolo's apartment you didn't find the photographs scattered about as you would have expected them to be if someone had found them and taken a selection. Put them out of your minds for now.

'Concentrate on Paolo's problem. Eva, you have shown a remarkably humane reaction to the discovery. Many wives would not have behaved that way. Their feelings would have been closer to Juan Carlos's. What if Juan Carlos had worked on your feelings, made you see the error of your thinking. What if your heart had hardened to Paolo and you'd decided that you never wanted to see him again. What if, when Restrepo calls tonight, he's totally thrown by your response. When he hears your voice, filled with disgust and loathing say: "Keep the vile creature. I don't care if I never see the offal again. You've taken two miliardi from us and he wasn't worth that. I don't know if he's alive or dead and I don't care. He will never return to my house or bed." You then put the telephone down. What will Restrepo think?'

'Supposing I did this. Would Paolo find out?' Concern choked her voice.

'Quite probably.' Now brutally: 'What does it matter? Time enough to sort that out with him when he is released. He's quite possibly thinking that could be your reaction anyway.' I couldn't fathom what was going through her mind. Her eyes locked with mine and she stared unblinkingly for a long time. It wasn't for effect, she was thinking, turning over the alternatives.

'No. If there is the slightest chance of Paolo finding out I will not do it. It could destroy him.' She stood up and faced Romero, a warning finger raised. 'No.'

After she left Luis said: 'I now see what you mean by hard decisions, James. Do you honestly think it would work?'

'I think it's the best shot. They've had more money than they expected to get. If Restrepo is reporting back to the gang, which he probably is (it's rare for the leader to expose himself by taking on the role of negotiator and spending time in phone booths which may be traced), then the gang will be quick to point this out.

'No matter how careful they've been, their security will have been weakened by collecting the ransom. This will be in their minds. I believe they'll only hang onto Paolo if they think they have all the aces. If their prime negotiating factor is weakened then they'll have to consider deeply the value of carrying on.

'Of course this isn't without danger. There's the risk that they'll simply kill Paolo. There's the risk that they'll maim him in an attempt to force your hand, but the value of the maiming threat is also reduced if Eva is obviously not interested in Paolo's return.' I was becoming more and more certain of the ploy but I didn't want them to ignore the risk factor.

'Leave Eva to me,' Juan Carlos was grim-faced. 'I see the sense of your suggestion, James. Does it have to be Eva who responds to the phone call?'

'It would be best. If anyone else takes the call Restrepo may just smell a rat. She'll have to be very convincing, though. Restrepo may not fall for it as a result of one call. If I were in his shoes, I think I'd pass it on to Paolo and make a tape of his reactions. Perhaps a beating to make him conform to a written script. Eva ought to be told this – if she agrees.'

'What do you think the alternative will be, James?'

'It's my guess that they wouldn't publish the photographs, if they have them. After all, what would they gain? They'd just be creating the very situation which we are trying to impose on them now. I think the alternative would be a long drawn out negotiating process to get to the point where we agreed a mutually acceptable figure. In other words a normal kidnap situation starting from the beginning. Impossible to say how long. It depends on how convincing we can be regarding the difficulty of raising more funds covertly.'

'I think you are right. Will you give us time alone please, James? You do not need to leave. I will have some coffee brought to the lounge for you. Luis, perhaps you will join James. I need to discuss some personal matters with Eva.' He was standing, summoning Maria to take us to the lounge.

We weren't kept waiting long. Within thirty minutes Luis was summoned back to the study and I followed ten minutes or so later. Eva was there and the look she gave me would have shrivelled the man who didn't expect it. A lot was being asked of her and I was the handiest object to focus the emotions on, I suppose, though she was quite frosty with Juan Carlos. She had obviously capitulated and I wondered how he'd persuaded her.

'It is agreed,' rubbing his hands Juan Carlos was pleased. 'It begins with the evening phone call. I have mentioned to Eva what you said about the possibility of a tape, James. Can you tell her more?'

I repeated more or less what I'd said to the others but I explained in more detail about how the tape was likely to be produced.

'There may not be a tape. I'm only saying that this would be a sensible move for them to make to test the truth of your statement. If they do use it then you must understand why and how it will be produced. You see, Eva, in order for the tape to be of value it has to put across the message which the gang wants. The only way they can ensure this is to write a script for Paolo. To get the right emotion into his voice they may rough him up a little. Consider a few things here; if there is a tape in response to your message then it means that Paolo is alive. It means that your acting has had the desired effect on the gang.

'When you listen to the tape I'm sure that you'll know it's scripted. The language will simply not be Paolo's and you of all people will recognise this. All this will be easier for you to bear if the tape is delivered somewhere for collection. If that's the case you can listen to it as many times as you want in your own surroundings before you need to respond to it.

'You won't get a tape in response to your actions tonight, of course, but there may be something of a general nature already recorded and you should be ready for this. It may be something to persuade you that Paolo is ill. Cast your mind back to just before the payment. You told me that the gang had said "because Paolo is not in good health and we are humane". They may have decided to press this point a bit further.

'If such a tape is played over the telephone, it will only be a snatch; indeed they may try to make you think it is actually Paolo speaking. It won't be him of course, they'd never take him to a call box. What you must avoid if this happens is any sort of reply, even a gasp, which may cause them to think you're bluffing.' A pause for questions. There were none.

'It's important that you record this conversation so that if a tape is used, you can study it later and assure yourself that Paolo is under duress. The tape of course may be accompanied by a threat of mutilation or death. Stand firm if this is said on the phone. If you're caught short and you have to fill a silence then fall back on saying that Juan Carlos will not consider anything until he has proof that Paolo is alive. Put the emphasis on Juan Carlos – remember, you don't actually care very much. Whatever happens on the phone tonight, it'll be short and sharp. You won't have to endure it for long. No more than a couple of minutes at the most.'

'Will you come with me to wait for the call, James? If they call back quickly as they did the other night I would like to be able to discuss it with you straight away.' She'd lost the venom. Probably Juan Carlos hadn't put the message across to her particularly well and now she'd heard a little more she was becoming convinced that the strategy could work.

'I can come, of course, but remember that it is Juan Carlos who is the chairman of the team. Between you, him and Luis you have to make the decisions. The gang know that you have to refer to Juan Carlos. If they say they're going to call back within a few minutes, try to get across to them that you can't return to the phone in less than one and a half hours. If you do convey this then you must stick to the time. It's the only way to make the process believable. I will come if you wish but please consider what I've just said.'

'Very sensibly put, James. I think that is the right approach, Eva. I will come with you myself.'

'No. Juan Carlos, you can't. What if the gang have someone watching this apartment. Eva would be caught out in a lie and she'd lose all credibility. Better Luis, I think.'

'OK. Sorry, I should have thought of that. Luis, you go, heh?'

Luis nodded, stood up and took Eva's arm.

'Come, it is almost time. We can rehearse a little on the way perhaps?' It was the right thing to say. Eva looked happier and I knew that Luis would keep her at it, take her mind off Paolo until the telephone rang.

'Remember,' Juan Carlos cautioned, 'do not call us from the apartment. We shall just await your return.'

After they had gone and Juan Carlos's cigar was once more glowing to his satisfaction, I asked him how he'd persuaded Eva to change her mind.

'It was not so difficult, James, she is after all a woman. A somewhat special woman I grant you, but she has the instinct to protect those she loves. I simply chatted to her, remember that she did not know why I was there talking. I just reminisced about Paolo saying what a great pity it was that I would have to dispense with his services in the business after this was all over. How I should not be able to tolerate his presence in the house any more.' The old man's eyes were devilish now, the humour was there in a way which I'd never seen before.

'You may know the business of kidnapping James, but credit an old man with knowing his family. You see, I let her persuade me. She made me agree to keep Paolo on as though nothing had happened and in return she would go along with our tactics provided that you still thought it was the best chance. I had no intention of letting Paolo go; he is the best in the business. True, our relationship will never be the same again but I have to consider the future of the company.'

The cunning old fraud. I had to take my hat off to him. He'd pulled it off. When I'd seen the expression on Eva's face as she'd given that emphatic 'No', I was fairly sure that she'd not change her mind easily. I congratulated him. We filled in the time talking over old cases and I played some of the typical tapes to him again, commenting that it might be a good idea to do the same for Eva and Luis when they returned. Doing this tends to take away the feeling of isolation experienced by all families when they hear a tape of the victim. I was by no means certain that a tape would be used, of course, but it still seemed the most likely ploy.

The avvocato was bubbling when they returned.

'Signor Romero, she was magnificent. She poured scorn down the phone. She even had me convinced of her hatred for Paolo. At one point she said: "Do not talk to me of the pig. If his stupid father wants him back after this and I cannot conceive why he should, he will want to know if the 'figlio d'una puttana' is alive." Magnificent, I tell you.' I'd never seen Luis so animated.

Eva spoke up. She was trembling, drained, washed out. 'It was horrible. I am not sure I could do it again.' She faltered. 'We are to be prepared to collect a package tomorrow morning at six-thirty. They will call with instructions.'

'Well done, cara,' Juan Carlos said, putting an arm round her.

She pulled away violently. 'You tricked me!' she accused. 'I have thought about it and you tricked me.' She stormed out of the room.

Juan Carlos laughed. 'Do not worry. When things begin to work she will forget all this.' I wasn't so sure but then that was for the pair of them to come to terms with in the future.

I suggested to Juan Carlos that when Eva had calmed down she be asked to stay with the script in the unlikely event of a call from the gang. Luis and Eva hadn't recorded the call but this time I believed their apologies; they'd just forgotten. There was nothing more to do and we agreed to meet just before six the next day. The package was on top of a coffee dispenser at Giovanni's garage.

I'm glad I was right; it was a tape. If it hadn't been I think there may have been problems with Eva. Luis came in just after six o'clock with the package which he handed unopened to Juan Carlos. It was in a polythene wrapping tucked inside a soup packet.

It was the most amazing tape imaginable. The gang had really blown it! They'd started to record, slapped Paolo's face and told him to read only what was written and started again. The trouble was they'd forgotten to wipe off the first attempt! There was no need to spend time convincing Eva, the gang had supplied its own proof of the written script. After that, the recording was only of academic interest. All vouched for the fact that it was indeed Paolo's voice, they had no doubts whatsoever. It proved that he was alive, or had been a few hours ago.

The tape was typical of its type, and ran something like this:

Cara Eva. I could not believe your indifference. It is too much. You have not yet heard my side of things. When you do, you will forgive me I know. Why is my father being so hard? He has the money, it is not a problem. Talk to him, cara, you must make him see sense. I am so ill. My chest, I think it is my heart, so much pain. You must do it, Eva, you must persuade him. I am cold, wet and hungry. For God's sake I cannot survive these conditions much longer. Get me out. Get me out.

The last sound on the tape was a sort of strangled gurgle as he was pulled away from the machine. Attached to the tape was a brief, typed note:

The Romeros.
You have heard him. He is not well. For one miliardi, he is yours. He is not worth less to us. Be at the telephone at eight o'clock tonight. Your failure is his death.

We discussed the tape and letter, playing the former several times over. Although she knew it to be scripted by the gang it was clear that Eva was getting some comfort just from the sound of Paolo's voice. I thought, not for the first time, that he was a lucky person indeed.

'What do you think, James?' Juan Carlos spoke, his face encircled by a perfect smoke ring.

'Well, they're responding to us in much the manner we'd hoped. The fact that they made such a macello of the recording means that they're either off balance or not as professional as we thought.' They laughed at my colloquial use of 'cock-up'.

'I think we've thrown them. It's a unique tactic after all. They've made a threat to kill Paolo but they've not set a deadline for this, only for the next call. They've reduced their demand from the balance of eight miliardi to one miliardi. I would guess that there could be some inside pressure to cut and run. I'd say they've almost swallowed Eva's story. They're still hopeful of getting a little more money but certainly not confident. This makes the next call critical. Now, having heard what I've had to say, what does the team think?' I threw the ball back into their court and hoped they'd come up with the same conclusion I'd made.

They chattered animatedly in Italian for about half an hour or so, voices rising and falling as they made their own points and acquiesced to each other's opinions. On balance they were pretty well agreed. It was time to step in.

'I think you're coming to the right conclusion. At the next call Eva has to be hard. She has to push home the message that she just doesn't care any more. She doesn't give a damn what happens to Paolo.'

'What about Juan Carlos though,' interjected Eva. 'The gang think that he still cares.'

'Do they? You haven't said so. All you've said is that he wouldn't talk to you unless he knew that Paolo was alive.'

'In any case,' asked Juan Carlos, 'you can have your revenge, my Eva. You can persuade me to ditch Paolo.' They both smiled and they were back to the tactile comforting of the early days. 'Smart cookie', I thought.

'Think about it, Eva. If we're right and the gang's in disarray and losing confidence, if you were simply to say "Do what you will, I don't care," it could swing the balance to us very quickly.' I knew what she was going to say but I wanted it to come from her. I was doing too much talking. The more they thought it through themselves, the greater their confidence would become.

'What if they take me at my word and kill Paolo?' She was worried and rightly so. It was a possibility.

'What do you think, Juan Carlos, will they kill Paolo?' I wanted the chairman to take control.

He considered his answer carefully. 'They could of course do just that. I ask myself why they should. They have more money than they had expected, thanks to our stupidity, so where would their motive be? They could kill him in order to preserve their security. We cannot assess this accurately because we do not know how much Paolo has seen of them and his surroundings. What do you think about that aspect, James?'

'If it is a reasonably professional gang, and I believe it is, Paolo will have seen very little. Those who are guarding him will have been hired through a cut-out system. They won't know the gang members. Paolo will not have seen a face. They'll have used hoods or masks at all times. This isn't just for security by the way, it all helps to keep the prisoner frightened and remote. He would've been blindfolded when he was taken to his prison. In short I don't think he would be much use to the authorities in tracking the gang down.

'Thank you. In any case we would not go to the authorities in a case like this. Why should we risk an investigation which may uncover Paolo's past? The gang will surely know this. The only motive I can think of for them killing Paolo is spite. If we accept this as being a realistic motive then if they have swallowed Eva's story it would be a much more spiteful act to hand him back to us.' He sat back in the chair.

He'd summed up exactly as I'd hoped he would. The others appeared to agree.

'I think this is correct. I do not think they will kill Paolo. Why add a murder charge to their crimes? They know that if we haven't told the authorities yet, and they will be quite certain we haven't under the circumstances, we can cover up a kidnap because it has only been a few weeks. There is no way that we could cover up a murder – Paolo's complete disappearance. It makes sense to me but, Madonna, I hope we're right.' I could see where Eva's business reputation with Juan Carlos had come from. She was thinking logically, not missing a trick.

'Bravissima. Let us do it.' Juan Carlos was delighted with Eva's speech. 'There is a risk but the odds seem to be in our favour. I say we go ahead.' The others murmured their assent.

They were sensing that the end was near and I spent some time telling them of things which could go wrong. We were after all making some assumptions which were not necessarily correct. They all agreed this and it was Juan Carlos who put it clearly.

'Do not worry, James, we have already been caught out by believing in our assumptions. We have thought this thing through as well as we can this time. If I were negotiating a business deal, I would deduce that I had the cards very slightly in my favour. No more than that. We think the risk, balanced against the possibility of a long drawn-out case during which Paolo could be exposed at any time, is a fair gamble. James, we are going to church. Why not come round at eight tonight?'

When a positive and possibly final action has been decided on, the waiting time is difficult. I was able to switch off by returning to the museums. I called the Byron periodically to check whether there were any messages. In this business you always cater for the unexpected. I had lunch with Rodrigo and briefed him on progress without of course any mention of Paolo's homosexuality. If he found this out from Luis so be it but I wasn't going to break confidence. I just put the whole thing down to the family acting foolishly in the beginning and now coming to their senses.

I was back at the apartment early, about seven-thirty, purely because I'd found myself wandering around the Villa Sciarra and there was no point returning to the Byron. I wished Eva and Luis good luck as they left then Juan Carlos and I were back to the interminable waiting. We didn't talk much but the relative silence was companionable enough and I browsed again round his paintings, icons and the Caesers.

'How did it go?' Juan Carlos shouted before they were through the door.

'I do not know.' Eva was composed but the dark rings below her eyes told their own story.

'I did as we agreed. All Restrepo did was swear violently and say: "You'll never see him again". I had just time to say: "Good" before he cut me off.'

'Excellent, Eva. Well, now we're into the waiting game again,' I said. 'There's nothing you can do except be ready if they should chance to call here directly. Maintain the same story. If they do call here, I suggest Juan Carlos answers the phone. They'll know he's here and the same tactic can be used. Straight from the horse's mouth as it were.'

We sat until the small hours of the morning and then I decided to go back to the hotel. I called them after breakfast; there was no news but I was invited for lunch. I sat down to write up my log and I don't suppose I'd been at it for more than half an hour before a jubilant Eva called me.

'James, he's back! He's back! He returned just a few minutes ago. He's filthy. How he persuaded the cab driver to let him in I do not know but here he is!' There was more, mainly effusive thanks, but what impressed me most was that she'd taken the trouble to call me within minutes of Paolo's return. With all that they had to say to each other she'd remembered that I was waiting in the hotel.

I saw Juan Carlos one more time. When I got to the apartment Paolo and Eva had left. After a quick clean-up she'd insisted that regardless of how tired he was they were going to the villa, away from the city, away from Juan Carlos and the returning Enrique. 'Some time alone', she'd said. 'Time to sort things out.' I hoped that one day he would realise the true extent of his good fortune in marrying Eva.

Juan Carlos promised to get as many details about the kidnap as he could for me and mail them to me in the UK. He didn't ask for it but I showed him my file – there was no reference to Paolo's 'problem' in any of my notes. It was simply referred to as a bargaining factor. After all, that's just what it was.

CHAPTER

6

Author's note
What happens when the victim is a young child? The stresses on the family
are even more intense, the emotions even more brutally ravaged than in
the case of an adult. Imagination runs riot, particularly when gruesome
mutilations are threatened. Add these factors to a kidnap by a gang with a
history of child snatches in which the victim has always been murdered
and the situation is very fraught indeed. How does the negotiator cope with
a family which is emotionally falling apart? The father's profession and
social standing make it essential to hide his identity.

OVERLOOKING the high mountain watershed into the Esmer-
aldas River, perched on a plateau guarded by the slumbering volcano
Pinchincha, is Quito. It's a marvellous sight from the air. The centre
of the city, disciplined into regular blocks by Sebastian Benalcazar
after the Spanish conquest in the early sixteenth century, has been
slowly encapsulated by a hotch-potch of untidy suburbs as the
Indian and 'mestizo' populace succumbed to the temptations of the
twentieth century and came, Dick Whittington-like, to make their
fortunes in the capital city.

Sadly I was once again in transit through Ecuador. It's one of my
regrets that I've never had the time to explore the city and the
country which are unique even in the ever-contrasting continent of
South America. I'd only two hours to wait for my connecting flight
and I basked in the mild sun. It's only about fifteen miles from the
equator but in mid-July at an altitude of 9,250 feet it was like a warm
English spring. I enjoyed it while I could. I knew what to expect
from the weather in Lima. I'd taken the Avianca flight from Miami

and was waiting to connect with KLM. Three airlines and two days was the fastest I'd been able to make the journey from London.

As we touched down bumpily in Lima the weather was as I'd expected. The city was in the grip of the 'neblina', the annual overcasting of dull grey cloud, a fine mist and the resultant uncomfortable rise in humidity. I remember reading an article that said the 'neblina' was the cause of acute depression in foreign residents and Limenos alike, the explanation being that the body chemistry senses there should be a rainstorm – a storm which never comes. This weather phenomenon is very local. A fifteen to twenty mile drive in almost any direction takes you into blue skies, sun and intoxicatingly clear Andean air.

The drive into downtown Lima from the airport is an education in urban growth. Avenida Faucett takes a route through scenes of abject poverty in the shanty towns (though those who occupy them would view them as permanent), up through old Lima which is still the business centre with its colonial-style office blocks interrupted regularly by huge circular plazas in memory of some long forgotten Spaniard and impossible traffic, then, in my case, into the smart residential areas of San Isidro, ending at the hotel El Condado in Miraflores.

Like Quito, Lima is a city which was planned in a very orderly fashion with avenues and streets carving it into neat squares. But the influx of population has had an even more dramatic effect as the city has spread right across the Rimac river in a sprawling undignified, uncharted shambles. It's understandable when you appreciate that in the space of only fifty years the population has increased from half a million to about six million. The whole is based on facilities and an infrastructure catering only for the initial inhabitants. Not surprisingly, drinking water, sewage disposal facilities, power and other services are in a perpetual state of chaos.

El Condado is a good hotel much frequented by foreigners. It's possible to be totally anonymous there and still enjoy good food and service. I was lucky enough to get a room at the back of the hotel, away from the incessant noise and petrol fumes of Alcanfores. I wondered idly if I'd bump into any of the Control Risks operators. I had been told that they were in the city at the time training some local security men and this was one of the hotels they sometimes used. I asked the receptionist to send up the package from Arturo. He'd been unable to wait for my flight as he had business in Bolivia but he'd be back in a couple of days.

I'd operated in Peru only once before, about a year earlier. I wasn't one of the recognised centres of kidnapping. In those days the ease with which money could be made in the drugs trade, even by small-time operators, tended to focus criminal attention in that direction. The main terrorist group at that time was the Sendero Luminoso, with the Tupac Amaros (not to be confused with Uruguay's Tupamaros) rapidly catching up. Even those groups tended to look to the drugs trade rather than kidnapping or other more conventional crimes to procure their operating funds. I knew of only one political case, and that was debatable.

Arturo's notes were succinct:

Victim:	Teresa Arenas (11 years)
Family:	Father, Fernando Arenas, 48 years, successful in timber export trade, hardwoods and furniture, seems well controlled, business reputation is hard, efficient Mother, Isabel, 42 years, very emotional Brother, Acevedo, 21 years, excitable Friend: Andres Salazar, 62 years, close, trusted friend. Himself a kidnap victim 6 years ago, *knows it all***, great influence with Fernando
Police:	Captain Uribe, head of kidnap squad, aware of case, not yet been to see family, competent but no resources, badly trained men, poor equipment
Others:	Servant, Luisa, 17 years, nervous, claims to have been followed since kidnap, may be just wanting attention
Kidnap:	6 days ago, Teresa snatched while returning from school, unreliable eyewitnesses, Fernando has details
Gang:	No contact yet, be aware 3 cases of child kidnap in Lima in last 6 months, *all victims killed*, Salazar has some detail
Financial:	Family very wealthy, low profile life style in

	city but visible indications from villa, cars and business advertising, assess wealth as plus of US$10 million, gang not able to assess true wealth
Contact:	Phone 416 808, (San Isidro), further villa in Santa Maria del Mar, expects you to call as business friend, UK export/import
Self:	Expect return Friday, will call Condado, may have more info
Settlements:	Always in US$, going rate about 200,000 US$ no problem to client

Arturo had been in a hurry. His priorities were out of order in the notes, not that it mattered. He'd given me enough to make a start but I spent a bit of time on the details and up-dated my own files. I knew something about the child kidnappers but they'd all been insured cases. The fact that all the previous victims had been killed wasn't good news but I'd reserve judgment until I'd spoken to Salazar. I remembered his case. I'd have to look up the details and compare notes with him. Peru is a backwater as far as the European news services are concerned and events can roll along without the international press getting hold of them but between Arturo and my UK and American sources I was usually aware of the cases which were going on at any given time.

If the kidnap had taken place six days ago, why hadn't Captain Uribe been to see the family yet? That was curious. The police would normally have been quick off the mark with their telephone taps and exhortations to co-operate. From my records I'd have put the going rate at nearer US$250,000. Still, maybe Arturo had been thinking solely of the child cases. There wasn't too much point in spending any more time on the notes. They gave me enough to get an initial feel for the case. Arturo hadn't said who'd recommended me but I could get that from the Arenas.

I called the number and was directed to Avenida Coronel Pedro Portillo in San Isidro. The Arenas had the penthouse apartment, I noted, which would be setting them back a fair sum of money; not much fun for an eleven-year-old child living on the nineteenth floor. Their home security was good. There was no exit from the elevator until the occupant had been inspected by the apartment owners, the

114

control button was on their side and as the box came to a halt I heard the closed circuit television motor cut in.

'Quien es? Who is it?' a disembodied voice inquired through the grille.

'James March for Don Arenas.' This term of respect is still very much in use in South America.

I was let in by a young attractive girl whose sightly flattened features betrayed her Indian blood. Luisa, I assumed. She led me into the lounge which was empty, went out and almost immediately re-appeared with coffee.

'Don Fernando will be with you in just a few moments. About ten minutes.' Her Spanish was harsh-sounding and unnatural, though grammatically correct. I thanked her for the coffee and walked across to the window which almost spanned the length of the room, about forty feet in all.

Below me the vista of Lima stretched out to the north east. Just across the way I could see the rear of the villa of the Adams family, just off Avenida Pezet. English names are not uncommon out there even though the family was Spanish through and through. The windows were open, there was no balcony and the only thing between the room and the dizzying drop to the street below was a low wall, about three feet high. Ridiculous with children around, I thought. To the north east I looked straight down the length of the best golf course in Lima. Lush verdant driveways, beautiful tended greens, all set within carefully and tastefully arranged evergreen trees. What a contrast to the stark browns and greys of the coastline I'd so recently over-flown. Along the right flank the course was held in check by Avenida Pezet, twenty-storey apartment blocks interspersed with luxurious villas. Along the left, bounded by Avenida Quesada, were similar structures but they were hotels, schools and municipal buildings.

Straight ahead where the mist closed with the horizon I could see the sharply rising foothills which reminded me how close Lima is to the Andes. The view in the summer must have been superb. Stretching my head out of the window and trying to peer round the corner I could sense rather than see what would have been an equally wonderful view out onto the Pacific Ocean. In the mist I could just pick out the Monumento Soldado Desconocido thrusting upwards from the sprawl of Chorrillos.

Like many Spanish homes the room was stocked to the point of clutter with ornaments and objets d'art, much of it pre-Columbian as far as I could tell. Silver was in great abundance; crudely but somehow beautifully sculpted Inca masks and figurines, some traditional pieces verging on what would be classed as obscene in Europe. Ornate plates, candelabra and huge goblets were scattered around the place in a manner belying their value.

There were some technically brilliant photographs of the Inca ruins of Cusco, Peru's dramatic coastline and the high Andes; I wondered if the artist was a member of the family. They were unsigned and block mounted behind non-reflective glass which took none of the colour away.

Alpaca scatter rugs were everywhere, on the floor, the chairs and some very good ones hung from the walls. In the corner was a magnificent Spanish chest which had been criminally mutilated by having a huge section cut out of the front in order to install glass shelves which carried an abundant assortment of liquor. Out of idle interest I noted that there was a predominance of scotch and bourbon with precious little by way of local delights such as Pisco or the famous Huaral liqueurs. Even the wines in the adjoining rack were essentially Californian. What a pity when there are such good South American vineyards.

I returned to the window. Lima was beginning to twinkle attractively as daylight conceded to neon. I was suddenly aware that I wasn't alone.

'Good evening, Mr March. Welcome to Lima and not for the first time, eh?' The handshake had masonic pressures which were not returned.

'Good evening, Don Arenas. Thank you. Yes I've been here before, though not for some time and not during the "neblina".'

'Never mind, we shall be leaving it behind shortly. Thank you for coming; it's not an easy journey from London is it?'

'Not if you're in a hurry. The flight itself isn't too bad; English fare on British Airways, Spanish on Avianca and Dutch on KLM – at least it's a variation of plastics, monoglutamates and soya.' He laughed at the eternal traveller's complaint.

He was about five feet nine inches tall, stocky and running to fat around the waist and jowls. His prematurely white hair was bushy at the sideburns stretching round his head on a level with the tops of ears which supported brown horn-rimmed spectacles with tinted lenses. The tan did little to hide the purpling veins on his nose and stretching from under the sideburns which bespoke his alcohol intake. He was smartly dressed in a conservative dark grey suit which could have matched the handshake, his striped tie was vaguely familiar. He saw me looking.

116

'Yes, Eton. I was an Oppidan, couldn't quite make King's Scholar. Happy days though.'

Well it certainly explained the impeccable English. He was very tense though he carried himself with confidence. The anguish was there but he was hiding it well. He continued talking.

'I am in fact Chilean. I left my country in 1970 when Allende came into power and I joined my brother in his business here. By training I am a psychologist and still practise occasionally, privately you understand. Here in Lima there are many who have adopted the American tradition of a private shrink and it keeps me in contact with a society which I'd normally be too lazy to mix with.' He grinned somewhat weakly. 'Don't worry, I'm not about to apply my training to this case.'

I wondered when he was going to get down to brass tacks. Maybe he was waiting for me.

'Shall we talk about the problem?'

'No. We are going to my villa in Santa Maria del Mar if you have no objection, we'll discuss it there. I'd like you to stay with us for a few days. Will it cause you problems if we call by the hotel and collect your luggage? Retain the room in case you need it. They are used to such things in the Condado.'

'I know where Santa Maria is but I've never been. No problem. I shall have to leave a message for Arturo to contact me when he returns on Friday. Perhaps your office number rather than the villa?'

We headed south out of Lima on the great Pan American Highway along the edges of Herradura cove with the brown tendrils of grasses eking out subsistence on the crumbling cliffs. How this had come to be called the Costa Verde I wasn't sure. It was a good, fast road and from the scenery we could have been driving along the coast of Oman. Brown, barren, dry and dusty, the ground rose sharply on our left and occasionally I caught glimpses of the navigation lights of fishing boats to the right.

About fifty kilometres later we cut off sharply towards the coast and wove on good roads between the low sand and gravel dunes, through a small village and onto a narrow isthmus connecting the mainland to a rocky outcrop of indeterminate size when viewed in the dark. Rounding a bend, Arenas stopped the car and I was faced with an incredible sight. In front of us was the rocky feature, maybe 150 feet high and 300 feet wide. It seemed to be an island.

On each side of it were other high features stretching up to maybe 250 feet. Half-way up the feature in front, set into the side, was a white building the like of which I'd never seen before.

To the left and an integral part of the structure was a rotunda reminiscent of a scaled down British lighthouse with small lighted windows which must, from their diagonally ascending positions, have been tracing the course of an internal spiral staircase winding its way up to the top which was surrounded by an open walkway or balcony. At the base of this was a circular sun house with a red-tiled roof, part of which backed onto the main building which was traditionally Spanish at first sight. As my eyes got used to the lighting, however, it was possible to see the different levels and aspect laid to a mathematical if not artistic template.

I could see now that narrow channels of water to each side of the 'rock' separated it from the other features. Waves about fifteen feet high pounded through these, exhausting themselves against the sea wall in front of the car. To the right was a small white stucco building with camera lenses glinting behind the grilled window.

Arenas hooted and we got out of the car. He took my bag and gestured with his thumb at the small house.

'Security. They'll take care of the car.' Taking my arm he led me to the left. 'Watch your step, the footpath is quite slippery when the tide is in.'

We passed through a heavy metal gate which opened automatically at our approach; along a narrow path hacked into the solid rock, past another white house seemingly built into the side of the cliff. We crossed the channel by a narrow bridge with sturdy clutch rails; I understood the reason for these as we narrowly avoided a sudden inrush of waves. The path ended at the foot of the tower and we went through the sun lounge and turned sharply onto a flight of downward stairs. Walking along the subtly lit marble corridor I was struck by the silence and suddenly realised that we were underground. At the T-junction of corridors we turned and I was led through a majestic oak door of traditional Spanish design into a large bedroom.

It was magnificent. We'd actually walked right through the island! The frontage, facing out to sea, was a long double-glazed patio door opening onto a spacious lounging area. The spray was hitting the windows and it was difficult to see through the salty rivulets of water. In one corner of the room was a working area with a great oak desk equipped with telephone and telex. Another was taken up by two sumptuous leather reclining armchairs accompanied by a television and hi-fi music centre. Concealed wardrobes covered most of the length of one wall before terminating in a door which led through a dressing room into the bathroom.

Not just a bathroom – a sauna, jacuzzi and high pressure shower turned it into an experience rather than just a luxury. The bed, centrally placed, was huge, a family affair if I ever saw one. The decor was expensively simple, finely textured walls painted with a subtle cornflower wash interrupted by more of the magnificent photographs I'd noted in the apartment in Lima.

'Your home for a few days, James. I hope you like it. Feel free to use the communications, they are private to the room, no house exchange here. I recommend breakfast on the patio as the sun rises; you'll never get a view like that in London. I'll have some coffee sent down. Why don't you freshen up and Luisa will collect you at eight for drinks before dinner when you'll meet my family. Here in the villa, away from the city we are casual. Wear whatever you wish. No,' he forestalled my question. 'I'd rather discuss the business over dinner if you don't mind. It won't be long.' Patting my shoulder in an almost avuncular fashion he left me to enjoy my surroundings.

So, I'd been wrong. It wasn't Luisa who'd let me into the flat in Lima. Not that it was important as far as I could judge. Why the hell didn't he want to talk about the case? His eleven-year-old daughter kidnapped, himself tense and strained and he hadn't made a single reference to it yet. He was going to have to get down to it very soon. Tomorrow would be the seventh day and as far as I was aware the family wasn't even prepared for a contact phone call. I was going to force the pace. I'd certainly take my briefcase in to dinner.

I played safe and dressed army casual, wearing a light jacket and tie. I needn't have bothered. Fernando was wearing a track suit which made him look even plumper. His glasses had been replaced by contact lenses and I could now see the brown eyes. Standing alongside him was a tall, slim, erect man in sweater and well-cut slacks. His hair was grey with odd silver highlights which looked quite artificial. The thin, long-nosed face was Conquistadorean in its haughtiness and his piercing blue eyes were steady as he reached out and walked over to me.

'Mr March. I am Andres Salazar. Welcome to our country. I know of you and I look forward to hearing what you have to say. I have seen this business from the other side; it was not pleasant and my wife did not benefit from professional advice. I was imprisoned for six months, not so good at my age but all ended well. I am here only to comfort my good friends, not to interfere with your instructions.' I took an instant liking to this proud old man and wondered why Arturo had made the 'knows it all' comment. Perhaps they'd clashed as personalities.

His English was as good as Fernando's if a little more formal, the handshake firm and dry, again with the questioning pressures. I hadn't realised the influence spread so far.

'Thank you, Don Salazar. I too look forward to comparing notes with you. Experience such as yours is invaluable at times like this. I remember your case but didn't it take place in Cali, in Columbia?'

'It did. About a year after my release my wife died and I decided to move down to Peru where I have many friends. Despite my age, I escape into work. It stops the memories of Margarita dominating my life.'

'Andres is an international tax lawyer and a very astute one. He is in great demand here in Peru.' Fernando threw an affectionate arm around him. 'Come, meet my son, Acevedo.'

He was twenty-one, I knew that from the notes, but he looked far younger. He was plump and untidy. The over-generous lips, the limp handshake and petulant expression failed to show me why Fernando should dote on him as he so obviously did. He merely shook hands, he didn't speak and though Fernando's lips pursed in disapproval there was no rebuke in public and I suspected there wouldn't be one in private either.

'James, we should cease this formality. "Don" this and "Don" that; it's Fernando, Andres and Acevedo and my wife is Isabel. This is an informal household, treat it as your own. Now, a drink?'

I took a dry white wine, noticing that they were already on pretty healthy whiskies. Acevedo was drinking some strange rainbow-hued concoction of his own construction and ignored everyone.

'Isabel will join us shortly. I thought over dinner I would tell you about the case and afterwards we can discuss it in whatever manner you wish.'

I explained to Fernando that I would like to start the session with a brief on myself and some general facts on kidnapping. Prior to that they should take some immediate actions to ensure they were prepared if the gang should call. I asked if the kidnappers were likely to know the villa telephone number and was told that one of the lines to Fernando's office was listed publicly. I drafted a holding script for them which consisted of asking for proof that Teresa was alive. I advised them not to get directly involved in discussions about money. Initially at least Fernando had decided to take the call.

I asked him to consider someone else handling the calls, Andres perhaps, as this meant he could always buy time by purporting to have to refer everything to a higher authority. Andres agreed promptly. There was no argument from Fernando.

Fernando asked for the subject to be dropped completely until Isabel could join us. The reason for her absence was that she'd been busy discreetly collecting money from various places. Safety deposit boxes, friends, different bank accounts and the like. Andres had persuaded the Arenas to do this; it was a good idea as Uribe knew of the kidnap; far better to amass some money now before they were put under surveillance. This implied that they were not inclined to co-operate with the authorities.

Isabel Arenas was dressed as casually as the others when she came into the ante-room, wearing tight-fitting, plum-coloured trousers tucked into the tops of knee-length brown leather boots. She had lost herself inside a loose white fisherman's knit sweater. She was about half an inch taller than her husband, slim, with the same classically erect posture as Andres. Dark brown hair, pulled to the back of her head and held in a white ribbon so it hung down her back, accentuated her slender face with its high, smooth cheek-bones. Light blue, worried eyes were slightly swollen from crying though she smiled bravely as we were introduced. Her grip was light and fleeting but the hostess in her was first to emerge as she enquired after my comfort and well-being.

'I wish the circumstances of our meeting were more fitted to your welcome,' her voice was almost accentless, low, with the vibrant power of a trained singer.

'Are we going to talk about it, Fernando? I have collected, I think, about half a million dollars. I simply told them we wished to move some currency. No-one will suspect, we have been discussing it often enough of late.' She looked at me. 'If Belaunde's reorganisation of the economy goes the way we think it might, we, like many others, have to get some hard currency established outside the country. Dollars are the easiest to obtain.'

It was Isabel who rang the bell for dinner to be served, but before the servants began their work I asked if we were to talk in front of them.

'Only Luisa will be serving', said Fernando. 'I will tell you more about her later but feel free to say anything, she is absolutely trustworthy.'

After we were seated, Fernando told Isabel that I was to lead off with my brief. Pointing to my briefcase by the fireplace I told them that much of what I would be saying could be demonstrated to them later and I set about giving my background, analogising kidnaps to Fernando's business, explaining the importance of a properly constructed team and generally getting into the all-important educational phase. I explained the system of threats and how we could treat them and the probable psychology behind the current silence. All the different forms of communication we might be using were covered and Fernando was warned of the need for a secure telephone line. Aware of their feelings, I gave the brief in a leisurely chatty fashion, trying to relax them. Periodically Andres would grunt or nod in agreement and I sensed that he was going to be very useful. The most delicate part was getting them to understand that the process of negotiation and apparent haggling over money was in the interests of their daughter and not for financial savings.

Acevedo's only comments during the dinner were self-centred; he mentioned a coming cinema attraction that he wished to see, a new model of car about to hit the market and so on. He was jealous of the attention being focused on his sister. I don't say he didn't care, it's most likely that he hadn't even thought about her predicament too much. I could see that Fernando was annoyed (not sufficiently to shut him up) and Isabel was hurt. Unfeeling little bastard. I had the distinct impression that the lad might soon feel the weight of a tongue-lashing from Andres.

Isabel and Acevedo excused themselves for a short time and I seized advantage of this to ask: 'Fernando, do you really see the need for Acevedo to be on the team? He is young and we don't want to disturb his emotions unnecessarily.'

'You mean he's a spoiled brat. Yes he is, but Teresa is his sister and he has a right to hear what is going on.'

'I think James is right.' Andres stood. 'Acevedo is young and what is more he likes to impress. He is quite likely to discuss the business freely in the office and we can do without that. You know this is the sensible thing, Fernando.'

'How do I tell him?' he pleaded. 'How do I say: "This is none of your business"?'

'Leave it to me', growled Andres. 'I'll tell him.' He left. Fernando looked anxiously after him as he went through the door to find the boy. I don't know what Andres told Acevedo but when he came back he reported that the matter was settled. I explained to them after Isabel rejoined us, that even though there were only three of them it was important for them to appoint a chairman. Fernando straight away assumed the mantle, saying: 'But there are four of us, James. What about yourself?'

'I only advise. I'll outline courses of action but I don't vote for or against tactics. That must be your decision at all times.'

Once we settled down at the table again I was able to demonstrate some of my tapes and show them the letters and logs from other cases. This didn't take long. It was just a polishing-up of what I'd said over dinner but it helped as usual. It took away the feeling of isolation. I asked Andres if he knew any of the families of the other cases where children had been involved. He knew two of them and promised to visit them the next day to see if he could glean anything useful from them. He then asked my opinion on co-operating with the police.

I'd been expecting this question. It's one I never like but it can't be shirked.

'Essentially that is a team decision. Let me say that there are pros and cons to police co-operation and these are directly related to the efficiency and security of the local forces. There are some countries where it's positively dangerous to co-operate with the police and others where it's foolish not to. Take the FBI in America as an example. In return for total co-operation they will undertake not to interfere in the drop-off of ransom money. They will observe instead and take their chances on picking up the gang afterwards. That is the safest possible way of doing things from the victim's standpoint. No danger of being killed by the gang as the police attack goes in, no chance of being mistaken for a member of the gang or being shot by a stray bullet from the security forces.

'In Bogotá, the DAS Unit is well trained and equipped and it has a lot of experience and I'd probably advise my clients to co-operate fully. In Guatemala, that same advice could be foolhardy. Here in Peru I don't know the police force so well, therefore it's you who must assess their efficiency. There are other more personal factors which come into the equation. Are they likely to question you on where you obtained the dollars – I don't for a moment suggest anything illegal in your actions but they could cause you embarrassment? I'm told that Captain Uribe is aware of the kidnap. He hasn't yet been to see you but I assume that he may have tapped your telephone. Do any of you know him personally?'

'I know him well. He is a good man basically but his organisation is poorly paid and badly motivated. Fernando is a man of considerable standing here in Lima and Uribe is probably awaiting an invitation to come and discuss the matter. His department's equipment is pathetic and we certainly couldn't allow them to know all of what is going on.

'It is my suggestion that we appear to keep Uribe informed but perhaps we could delay each move by a few days. As for tapping the telephone, their equipment is crude and we would know but in any case they will have no knowledge of the line we intend to use here. It was secretly installed. Money can buy anything here, James.' It was the longest speech Andres had made and it was sensible advice. Fernando agreed to it and said he would personally handle Uribe.

'Why don't they say something? Why don't they ask us for money?' Isabel was plaintive.

The question led me into telling them about silence as a tactic calculated to make the family lose its nerve. A deliberate ploy to confuse and frighten. I was able to go through many cases and let them see from my files how long some of them had been. In one notable Italian case, the family had endured a silent period of six weeks. I discussed with them how we might consider breaking the silence if it continued for too long. I wasn't aware of one lasting more than ten or twelve days in Peru. The kidnappers didn't have the experience or the patience of the Italian professionals. Not surprising; there was more immediacy about the requirement for money in this country.

We talked long into the night covering a lot of ground, more than I would normally have stretched to on the first night but both Fernando and Isabel were soaking it up and it was calming them down. Constant referrals to the business aspects were effective on Fernando while Isabel reacted to case comparisons which somehow lessened her loneliness. Andres interjected occasionally with comments comparing what I had said to his own experience as a victim. He was particularly helpful when I was describing how the gang usually scripted their tapes – it had happened to him.

Even though Fernando conducted a lot of his business from the villa, I advised him to try to instil a time discipline into the gang. Psychologically it's all part of getting them to react to the team apart from the fact that it tended to give us a predictable amount of time in which to debate the next move. We set a crude budget, more because I wanted them mentally prepared for bargaining than it being a necessity at that stage. I think we said our first good night of the case at about two in the morning.

My body alarm is pretty good but I overslept. Whether it was the peculiar silence of the underground chamber or the tiring flight from UK I don't know but it was Luisa who called me to breakfast on the patio. Fernando hadn't exaggerated. It was stunning. Above and behind me the short but precipitous black cliff and to the front the Pacific Ocean. Gone was the 'neblina'. The sun shone benignly over the fishing boats bobbing exuberantly in the low swell and the gentle breeze was soporific even after a good night's sleep. Andres joined me, still in his dressing gown.

'An old man's privilege,' he said, sweeping his hands downwards, indicating his attire. 'I can see you slept well. You were very interesting last night, James, I hadn't realised how much ground you'd covered in this business. How many cases have you advised on?'

I think it was fifty or so then and he whistled.

'Whew. Don't you get confused? Mix up Italian tactics with Sardinians and South Americans?'

'It's not possible. Every case has some unique quality about it. The common factor is that somewhere out there is a frightened victim dependent on the team's ability properly to appreciate the situation and work towards the fastest possible return.'

'You avoided the question about the police last night.'

'I didn't. I stated certain facts and you made the decision yourselves. That's how it should be. At the end of the day I would have given a recommendation if I'd been pressed. I believe if you take fees in this job you must have the courage of your convictions and be prepared to positively recommend if the team cannot reach its own decision.'

'That in itself is a more positive statement than some insurance consultants have made according to my information.' Andres got up and quietly slid the patio window together.

'I have already spoken to the Gonzalez and Leichner families. This morning I have an appointment with the Jaramillos. They are the ones who lost their children. I want to complete this next meeting before I give you my notes. That way you can study all three together. If I had said this last night, Fernando would have insisted on seeing them and it would have been stupid to bring up the deaths again in front of Isabel. I think she got a little sleep for the first time this week.

I agreed with him although I'd have liked to have had his notebook right then. I asked him how he'd found Arturo. He laughed.

'He doesn't like me, does he? I had heard on the grapevine that he acted for the Englishman and I was the one who contacted him for details. He was overselling you to the Arenas, James. He was telling them that you've never failed. This may be true but there is always a first time and it was wrong the way he was assuring Isabel that her problems were over. I was glad to hear last night that you did not disguise the dangers.'

He was a good friend, this one, he was serving the Arenas well.

125

He left for his appointment and I made up my files with my observations to date. It was by no means certain that Teresa was in the same hands as the other children. I decided to leave my section of the gang until Andres's return. I decided also to have a word with Arturo when he returned from Bolivia. He could have lost us this case through over-zealousness.

Fernando and Acevedo were in Lima, presumably at the company headquarters, and I sought out Isabel who was on the other side of the island in the sun lounge looking at photographs of Teresa. She'd been crying but she forced a smile as I asked if I could join her. To get her mind onto other things, I inquired as to the degree of trust they placed in Luisa and for details of her claims of surveillance.

Luisa had come with them from Santiago. Fernando had found her on the streets when she was about four years old, abandoned as so many children are in South American cities if they become too much of a drain on the slender resources of the parents. She'd been brought up by Elena, their cook, and been with them ever since. There was no questioning her loyalty, Isabel said. She worshipped Fernando. As to her stories that she'd been followed, there was no way of knowing the truth. Luisa was not a fanciful girl but she did know about the kidnap and with the drama of this in her mind she could have imagined something. On balance, Isabel told me, she thought the girl was telling the truth, real or imagined.

She asked me if I'd ever dealt with a case involving a youngster before and how the child had come out of it. I told her I had and that children were remarkably resilient, often more so than adults. There would be a need for careful handling at first, but she should be all right.

'I am aware that we may not see her again. You do not have to choose your words so carefully.'

I asked her about the villa.

'It's quite something, isn't it? I feel secure here, in another world almost. It was built about fifty years ago by a very wealthy man who was later assassinated. It's rumoured that he was a Nazi, hunted down by Simon Wiesenthal. When extradition attempts failed, the killer squads were put onto him. It may be true, but most of that type tended to head for Brazil rather than Peru. In a city with little entertainment the dinner table breeds all sorts of rumours. When we bought the villa it was in the hands of the bank.

'We looked around the place, Fernando at first found it oppressive. I can't imagine why. Teresa was on the way then so it didn't take much to persuade him. It is so peaceful. At the weekends this part of the coast is a playground for the rich but we don't hear them and we don't have to see them. I like it best at the other side, when the seas are angry and pounding away at the patio walls. It's like defying the gods. Sometimes I just stand there and shout "Do your worst". Come, James, the pelicans should be feeding now.'

She led me through the ante-room adjoining the dining area and out onto the patio which was angled away from the one in front of my bedroom, carefully designed for privacy. There were jagged rocks reaching out from the water and the pelicans were all over the place. Great clumsy birds as they took off, lumbering like under-powered Boeing 747s, but once airborne they were very graceful. Luisa was at the water's edge throwing fish into the air. The birds swooped, scooping the fish into the big lower jaw pouches. Every so often they'd perch on the rocks, toss the fish into the air again and catch them, always head down so that the scales and fins didn't obstruct the passage into the gullet.

Isabel told me it was common to find them with yards of fishing line wrapped around them. Apparently they were so voracious that they'd swoop on the fish being pulled from the water by local fishermen and take them, hooks and all, snapping off the lines which eventually became entangled round them. We had a light lunch in the sun. It was a pleasant diversion and we were still sitting there when Andres returned.

'Join us, Andres,' Isabel invited.

'No thank you, time for an old man's siesta.' Over her shoulder he winked at me and jerked his head in the direction of my room. I stayed for another ten minutes or so and then excused myself, saying that I wanted to study my notes before the evening meeting. I joined Andres. He closed the patio window and bedroom door. He handed me three slim sets of papers.

'My notes. I've made my own conclusions. Read them while I take some refreshment and then I'll answer any questions if I can.'

He opened a cupboard which I'd not noticed before and took a bottle of Glenfiddich malt whisky from the well-stocked interior. I shook my head at his silent offer and began to read. He was an orderly man, as befitted a tax expert, I thought. All the notes were in the same neat format. Very similar to the style Arturo had used but with much more detail.

I read the notes three times. The second and third time told me nothing I hadn't noticed at the first scan. I walked round the room a few times and thought it through. I noticed Andres was sitting on the edge of his chair and I sensed he wanted to speak. I sat down and helped myself to a glass of wine.

'Interesting, isn't it?' I volunteered.

'Ah. So you've noticed similarities? Yes? Let me tell you what I've picked up.' He wanted to – so why not?

'First and obvious, all the victims were killed after the ransom was paid. Secondly, they were all snatched as they went to or from school. Thirdly, they were all mutilated, and fourthly the first contact in each case was a tape of the victim crying and an identifying name for the gang's negotiator. It was the same gang in each case. If our first message is a tape we are dealing with the same gang.' His expression was a comic mixture of pride at his observations and sorrow at his foreboding of Teresa's fate.

'I agree with most of what you've said, Andres, but there's more. In each case the mutilation came with the first threat but was not carried out until the second demand needed reinforcing. The speed of events was the same within two or three days – about three weeks to reach a pay-off agreement. In none of the cases was proof of the victim still being alive produced before the money was dropped off. Therefore how do we know when the children were killed? Also, and I believe this is important, in every case the police were informed of every move.

'Similar enough to support your conclusion that they were all kidnapped by the same gang, but not conclusive even if the first communication turns out to be a tape. There are copy-cat kidnaps, though I grant you it's odds on that the gang is the same if a similar pattern is followed. The rule is – no certainties unless proof positive exists.'

'James, I'm going to stick to tax manoeuvring. I thought I'd picked everything out.'

'I've been at this a long time and the secret is to isolate inconsistencies rather than look for similarities. There are so many similarities in cases that you can get mesmerised by mentally listing them. The inconsistencies tend to stick out and the process becomes easier. While looking for these, the similarities seem somehow to gel automatically.' I know I explained this badly to him but that's how it worked for me. It wasn't important anyway. What we'd discovered, though I didn't comment at the time, was a route forward if the gang turned out to be the same.

'Andres, can you get hold of Fernando before he speaks to Uribe? We must discuss this first. I think you can see why.' He left immediately and when he returned he said that Fernando was on his way back. He'd told Uribe to have dinner with us in the villa that night.

'Don't worry, James, he did listen to you last night. He hasn't said a word about your presence. Uribe will be very conscious of the company he is keeping and he will leave promptly after the meal. You will have an equally good dinner, albeit in your own company. We will have a couple of hours before dinner and as long as we need after.'

'Is there a chance that Luisa can serve my dinner tonight? I'd like to talk to her, to hear what she has to say about being followed. I'd like to do it without her being inhibited by the presence of Fernando or Isabel.' Andres promised to fix it, adding that he would let Luisa know she could trust me. He then left, claiming that he really did need his siesta.

Before dinner I went through the holding script again with Fernando. We discussed the information Andres had brought back and I reiterated to them that we'd have to wait and see what we were up against before we read too much into it. They'd decided to be honest with Uribe insofar as they would give him the facts, give him the telephone number (not the one they intended to switch to) and an assurance that they'd keep him informed. I suggested they should also ask for his advice but not overdo this and make him suspicious. If he asked who was to be the person who collected messages, if this were to become necessary, I suggested they nominate Luisa.

As Uribe arrived at the security lodge Andres took me up into the 'lighthouse' where I had a good view of him. He was small and dapper, his uniform smart and well cared-for though it showed signs of wear. Fernando greeted him personally, under the arc light so I got a decent view. His deference to Fernando verged on the obsequious but he remained confident. His dark face (no Indian blood) pencil moustache, flickering brown eyes and still, expressionless face told me little about him. I'd like to have heard him speak. He was brought into the building and passed out of my vision. We waited a while and Andres dropped me at my room as he went to join them.

Luisa served me dinner on the low coffee table. She resisted my attempts at conversation and I was beginning to think Andres had forgotten to brief her but as she brought in the coffee she pulled up a chair and sat down facing me. She was stiff and upright as though facing a Gestapo officer.

'Luisa, relax. I want to talk to you because I'm trying to help Don Fernando and Doña Isabel to get little Teresa back safely. I think you may know something which could assist. Do you want to help them?'

'I owe my life to Don Fernando. But how can I help?' She was genuinely puzzled.

I told her I was interested in the people who had been following her. When had it started, where was she followed and what sort of people were they?

It appeared that Luisa did a daily shopping trip for fresh vegetables and fish. This happened whether the family were in Lima or Santa Maria; she usually went at the same time each day. The day after Teresa was snatched, Luisa noticed a man following her. She only spotted him because she was so upset by the kidnapping that she kept forgetting things. Twice she'd had to turn round and go back to the shop she'd just left and she became aware of the same face ducking behind the stalls as she turned.

From that day she'd deliberately taken routes where she could check if she was followed. She was certain of it. Sometimes it was a man and sometimes a woman. Always the same man and woman. The woman was vaguely familiar but not a friend of the family or anything like that, she just thought she'd seen the face before. She thought it could have been a policewoman she'd noticed on traffic duty but she wasn't certain. It was a ten-minute walk from the villa into the village. Did she think she was followed all the way from and to the house? She hadn't seen anyone near the house but she felt them watching.

I was satisfied that Luisa was under surveillance. If it was the gang then they were being very slap-happy; it was more likely to be the police in the light of her comments about the woman. If this was the case we should assume that others were being watched. It could, of course, be a situation where both the gang and the police were watching. I let Luisa go back to her duties and went through Andres's notes once more. I noted the names Diego, Pablo and Felipe from each case as being the persons who had actually carried the money to the drops. I'd have to ask Andres about them

Captain Uribe left about nine o'clock and we all settled in the ante-room. Fernando told me the dinner seemed to have gone well. Uribe had asked to be kept informed about every move as it happened and promised that when the drop was arranged he would have his best squad available to follow the kidnappers to their lair and make his arrests. He had asked apparently about the 'Englishman', whether he had tried to contact the Arenas, whether they knew Arturo. They disclaimed all such knowledge and promised to inform Uribe if either of these two persons made contact. It was unlikely that I'd been followed from the airport and equally unlikely that I'd been seen arriving here in the dark. If Uribe really wanted to he'd be able to track my presence down through immigration but it was such a chaotic airport it would take some time. I wasn't worried about it but I decided to confine myself to the seaward side of the villa just in case.

'Andres – Diego, Pablo and Felipe. They were the ransom carriers in the other cases. Who were they? Friends, lawyers or members of the family?'

'Neither, James, they were all domestics. This was at the insistence of the gang. Hah! Another commonality. Is it important?'

'It could be. I've spoken to Luisa and I believe she was followed. It could be the gang; if they stipulate that Luisa should carry the money then that will probably confirm it. On the other hand it could be the police. Luisa is the only servant who makes the daily trips from the villa or apartment and they'll be aware that in each of the other cases a domestic has been used. Whether it's the gang or the police, I think we may be able to use this to our advantage later.'

I spent a couple of hours going through different aspects of kidnapping and making sure Andres was prepared for the call when and if it came. He was to try his best to urge the spokesman to use the new number at seven o'clock at night. Whatever was said on the phone, he was to keep repeating this.

I was instinctively sure that we were dealing with the same gang but there was nothing conclusive. If we were, then a new approach had to be worked out to avoid Teresa suffering the same fate as the others. I had some ideas but I couldn't consolidate them until we had a contact.

Contact was made early next morning, on the ninth day. It was short and brutal. Fernando took the call thinking it was from his office. Throughout it he kept stuttering the new number and the time. He was very shaken. This was reported to me by Andres. The team assembled. Fortunately Acevedo was still in bed and unaware of events. We listened to the tape:

> Arenas. Listen. I am Alberto. (There followed an unearthly wailing and a young girl screamed) 'Mummy, Daddy, get me out of ...'. Arenas. Five million dollars. Be sure to collect your own mail at the office today.

Superimposed on this was Fernando's plea: '763 0981, 763 0981. Eight o'clock. Eight o'clock. 763 0981, eight o'clock.' He'd done his best and I could only hope the gang had noted it.

Great gasps of anguish shook Isabel's shoulders violently as she

crouched on the edge of the chair. 'My God, My God,' over and
over. Andres was shaken too, but it was he who put his arm around
Isabel and tried to comfort her. Fernando had gone to pieces. Sitting
on the floor he was crying uncontrollably. Shivering with emotion,
tears streaming down his shirt front, he was incapable of speech.

I knew and understood what they were going through but it was
a fact that Fernando was not going to be able to handle any future
calls and it confirmed my advice to let Andres act as negotiator.
Andres was a tower of strength. He spoke sharply to Fernando. Still
comforting Isabel, he got them quietened down.

'Listen, Fernando, you have to collect the mail. Call the office and
tell them you will do this on your way in. You must look and act
normally. If Uribe is having anyone followed we can't afford to
arouse his suspicions. Come on, snap out of it!'

When Fernando left he looked far from normal. He was glassy-
eyed and moving like a man entranced. I hoped he would pull himself
together by the time he reached the office. At the last minute Andres
decided to go with him. After they'd gone, I asked Isabella to send
Luisa about her duties normally, advising her not to tell the girl
about the call so she couldn't inadvertently give anything away.

I don't know how Andres managed to keep Fernando at the office
until his normal departure time for lunch, but he did it. When they
got back they had an envelope addressed simply 'Personal – Don
Fernando Arenas'. Fernando hadn't even opened it. He kept staring
at it, mesmerised. What a remarkable change in the man. He was
totally incapable of making decisions now and I could only hope that
Andres would step into the breach to lead team discussions. I looked
at him and gestured at the envelope. He gently removed it from
Fernando's clutch and opened it.

He read silently first and then out loud:

> Arenas Family.
> The price for your little daughter is US$5,000,000. You will
> have this money in three days time. If it is not ready, you
> will begin to get your daughter back – piece by piece. You
> will be called at the same time three days from now.

The note was signed 'Alberto'.

I examined the note. There was nothing to be gained from it other
than the bald demand statement. It was cheap, common paper, badly
typed. The envelope could have been slipped into Fernando's box
unnoticed by anyone. The three of them were looking at me. The
tears had subsided. Fernando and Isabel held each other now, both

terribly vulnerable. Andres was pale but alert. I made a summary of my mental appreciation.

'It seems probable that we're dealing with the same gang. At least the method of operating is much the same so far.' Isabel gasped but I carried on. 'This is no bad thing as we at least know something about them. Look at it this way. If, in the other cases, the police have been aware of every move and followed the courier to the ransom drop-off point, I'm pretty sure the gang would have spotted them. They usually force the courier along a specified route – a route on which they've set up their own surveillance operation to check for "tails". If they'd spotted the police it's my guess that they'd have taken the money, gone back to their rendezvous as fast as possible making sure they lost the badly trained policemen on the way, killed the victim and got the hell out of the area before a police cordon and search was put into operation.

'What we have to do is something different. Something which takes away this threat of police action. To do this, we have to fool the police and force the gang to communicate with us. Fooling the police is not difficult in the short term but it may cause you problems with Uribe in the long run.' I could see that Andres wanted to speak.

'James, we can take care of that.' He rubbed forefinger and thumb together in the international gesture for money. 'The concern is only for Teresa.'

'Let's start with the demand, five million dollars. This is ludicrous, we know it and the gang knows it. They'll have an expectancy of about a quarter of a million, somewhere around the established going rate. I believe you should make an offer which shows you are being serious but which falls well short of their expectancy. The other families I note made first offers around the $200,000 mark, probably on police advice. I think if we go in at about $180,000 we can achieve two things. It's about the sort of money you could reasonably get together at short notice. This will establish credibility and secondly, it give us the chance to mention the police. You see I think we should say at the earliest oppotunity that the police are following the staff. We should tell the gang that we want nothing to do with the police, that we're even prepared to deliberately fool them. This implies our honest desire to help the gang to help us. If we go in at $200,000 we're too close to the other families. Remember, the gang may also be looking for similarities in our response. We don't want them to think we are taking the same police advice as the other families.

'If you agree, we have to get this message across to them and also get proof of Teresa's life at the same time. You'll be tested, of that

I'm certain. They'll threaten in order to establish your strength. You must be prepared for this. Remember we've already acted differently to the other families in that we've tried to press a secure phone number on them. We may not have to wait three days for a contact. We should be prepared from now.'

Neither Fernando or Isabel seemed to want to comment. I dreaded to think what their reaction was going to be when they were really put to the test. Andres, however, was doing their thinking for them.

'Isn't this a dangerous course? Offering such a low amount and mentioning the police?'

'It is dangerous but I think it's safer than conforming to the set pattern. I honestly believe the statement about the police could be a swinging factor provided that I'm correct in my assumptions with regard to the deaths of the other victims. It's your decision of course, and let me say again that your strength will be put to the test by the gang.'

'I think you can safely say that we agree.' A wry glance at the parents. 'I will talk to them alone, James.' I was happy to leave him with them. He was 'on side' and he had the best chance of getting the Arenas' to agree.

He came to see me later. He said that Fernando was virtually useless. Sitting there, staring into space, he was no comfort to Isabel.

'She's stronger than you think, James. She's convinced that it's the correct thing to do. To try to be different and reassure the gang that we will not co-operate with the police. I have a feeling, I can't explain why, that we will hear from them tonight. If we do, it would be foolish after your explanations to offer more than we could reasonably expect to get hold of at short notice.'

We talked over the ways in which he might get our message across to the gang and how it was vital that we got proof that Teresa was alive. I suggested that he mentioned the police first. This was the statement most likely to keep the gang on the phone long enough for him to get the rest of the information across.

They did call that night and on the new number. Andres was very good. Inadvertently the gang helped. Their first instruction was to 'select a trusted member of the staff', to which Andres quickly reacted by saying he couldn't as they were being followed by the police. He got across the willingness to fool the police and the demand for some proof that Teresa was OK. He said they'd go $180,000 and that to get more would be very difficult without the police knowing. The reaction from the spokesman was violent.

'This is Albert. I don't mess around. Get all the money. Check your mail tomorrow. I mean business.' He ended the call.

It was a good sign in one respect. The conversation had taken about five minutes, longer than most kidnappers would have spent on a call. Alberto had listened quite calmly until his final outburst. A good indication that he was acting. Isabel listened to the recording intently but Fernando seemed not to absorb anything. It was difficult to reconcile this man with the confident old Etonian who'd greeted me in the apartment a few days ago. There was no point trying to make him part of the discussion. In the modern idiom, he'd dropped out.

At lunchtime on day ten, Andres returned with the package. Seated at the head of the table in Fernando's old place, he unwrapped the greasy brown paper. Under the first layer was a polaroid photograph and I saw his face suddenly blanch as he stared at it. He tried to slip it under the package but Isabel grabbed it. She screamed when she saw the image. High-pitched, piercing and full of pure agony. It was Teresa, small, defenceless and very dirty. The left side of her face was smeared with blood, her eyes were full of pure agony as she faced the camera full on. On her lap was a copy of *El Tiempo*, the national newspaper with the day's date clearly visible.

Isabel was sobbing hysterically and I moved behind her and took her shoulders. Fernando stared at the photograph with an impassive face. He wasn't even seeing it. Andres continued to unwrap the remainder of the package. A small blood-stained cardboard box came into view. He opened it with trembling hands and suddenly turned his head and vomited. He sat there half-turned, retching involuntarily. I pressed on Isabel's shoulders, forcing her to remain seated. Andres, however, knocked over the box and a small, pink ear covered in blood fell out.

I caught Isabel as she fainted and laid her on the chaise-longue. Fernando gave a great roar and started to bang his head against the table. Feeling sick, I reached out to cover up the filthy object and then noticed something. It was probably animal blood.[1] Shaking Andres, I thrust the plasticine 'ear' in front of his face.

'It isn't real. Look, it isn't real.' He responded immediately, turning it over and over in his hands. I took the photograph from Fernando's hands. It was blood-spattered. He'd made his nose bleed against the table. Looking closely it was possible to see that little Teresa's ear was perfectly intact under the 'blood'.

Andres was reviving Isabel. She was slow to accept the news but when she did, she quickly became alert again. She began to comfort

[1] This is a fairly common trick. I would usually have the blood analysed very quickly to confirm this to the family.

Fernando. It wasn't clear whether he understood or not but at least he sat still again.

'Andres, is there anything else in the package?' He searched through the pieces of rubbish and found a short note.

'Tonight at eight o'clock. Be at the telephone. Alberto'.

'We must raise our offer. Next time it may be a real ear.' Isabel had recovered remarkably well.

'Yes. We can raise the offer but we have to be realistic about it. By the time the call comes you'll have had just a day to raise extra money. Remember you've had to do it quietly, no police knowledge. I don't suppose under those circumstances you'd have been able to collect more than $10,000 would you?'

'That's probably a very realistic figure, James, but will it be enough to stop them harming Teresa?'

'It's a risk but we have to stay with our story. You have to get across to them that you are trying to protect them from Uribe. Tell them you're trying to raise more money. You don't think you'll get a lot but you need time. Tell them that it's Fernando and Isabel who are trying to get the cash. They were devastated by this morning's package. If anything else happens to Teresa you think they'll collapse completely. Be as convincing as you can. Try to end the call with a reminder about the police.'

He was good on the telephone, very good. We were given a further day and instructions to raise a million dollars. Alberto would call the next evening.

Andres went to see Uribe and said that they'd had a demand for five million. Uribe suggested they offer a quarter of a million and asked to be kept informed. Andres, knowing he was probably being followed by one of Uribe's men, went to three or four banks. Inside he would stuff his bag with more and more leaflets. To the observer he was collecting money, or at least that's the impression we were trying to create. If the gang was watching and not the police they'd assume the same thing.

That night Andres offered $192,000. Alberto was abusive. Andres got all his message across though. He said they were still trying to get more but it was getting very difficult. 'One million or else ... was Alberto's parting shot.

The next night the offer was increased by only $4,000. Andres requested further proof that Teresa was all right. He was told to shut up and concentrate on the money. In the mail at the office the next day there was another photograph of Teresa. Dirty, dishevelled and very unhappy. There were small bruises on her face but no ketchup.

'You will have her for $200,000. No arguments. Collect a letter from the usual place tomorrow.' Alberto was emphatic. He wouldn't listen to Andres at all. He delivered his message and put the phone down.

The letter gave detailed instructions for the drop. It stated that Andres should take the money. When he had the money he was to call a designated public phone booth on the hour at any hour between six a.m. and seven p.m. He was to let the phone ring six times and then start out exactly thirty minutes later.

The briefing to Uribe was that the gang had accepted the sum of $350,000, and that Luisa was to make the delivery driven by one of the security men. Uribe was given the start time thirty minutes before Andres intended to move. A scruffily typed set of instructions was concocted, photocopied and given to Uribe. They were planned around streets at the opposite end of Lima.

The money was packaged as instructed and Andres made his call. As soon as this was done Luisa was sent on her way. It was made very obvious that she had a heavy, bulky bag as she got into the car. Exactly thirty minutes later Andres departed to 'good lucks' from Isabel and myself.

'She is dead. She is dead,' was Fernando's only contribution from the private world into which he had retreated.

Two hours after Andres returned the phone rang.

'The entrance to the Church of Santa Rosa south of the bridge.'

Andres was away like a shot, Isabel could hardly keep up with him. It must have been a record breaking drive to Lima for they were back within two hours. They had found her. Hair tangled and matted with dirt and grease; thin white legs marked by angry bruises, Teresa had been cowering in the cold damp corner of the huge arched doorway to the church.

Shivering as the ancient stones, cooled by countless 'neblinas', stole the body heat through her thin, torn dress she whimpered pitifully. As Andres had run towards her she had moaned aloud, desperately trying to make herself invisible in the shadows. Her eyes showed only fear as she shrank away from him. It was not until she had heard her mother's anguished cry that recognition had come to her. Trembling and unsteady she had held out her arms and locked them around Isabel's neck as she stooped to lift her. Mother and daughter sobbed in unison as they clutched each other with an intensity made savage by the relief of the moment.

Now, safe at home and huddled to her mother's bosom, she was sleeping peacefully as she was carried in. Even so her arms were still round Isabel's neck, the whitened knuckles showing the strength of her grip. Andres and I left them together. This was a private moment.

Fernando dramatically reverted to his old self the next day. He behaved as though he'd never been otherwise. Neither Andres or I commented. I didn't see Isabel before I left. I wanted to be away quickly before Uribe started investigating. I called the El Condado but Arturo still hadn't returned. I left a message saying that I'd call him as soon as I could. I said I was taking a trip up country, along the tourist trail to Cuzco. It might help to delay the police if they checked the hotel. Andres made my booking and drove me to the airport.

As I walked across the tarmac at the end of the line of Miami-bound passengers, I became aware of the two men closing in on me from the sides. I didn't pay too much attention, late arrivals probably. As I got to the bottom of the steps each of my arms was seized. I struggled free and turned to face my assailants. One of them pulled his jacket aside and showed me the gun holstered at his waist, the other patted a bulge under his arm. I looked up the steps and saw a third man looking at me as he descended. His hand was in his pocket and thrust outwards towards me. Would they shoot if I simply pushed them aside and raced up the steps? This was Peru – they probably would! I shrugged, turned with them and started back to the airport.

They were short and we must have looked an incongruous quartet as we walked back. Me, head and shoulders above them, one on each side virtually hugging me and one so close behind that I could feel his body heat. Stupid way to move. I could have broken away at any time but the airport wasn't the place to do it. There was nowhere to hide there. It's a fairly basic layout. I was steered through the crew and officials' door into the terminal block. This section is screened from the public. They stopped me. One of them went to the front entrance, another to the telephone on the wall; the third tried to look as though he wasn't with me. What peculiar behaviour.

A pretty Avianca stewardess walked towards me. With a smile on my face I asked her: 'Did you hear about the Arenas kidnap on the news this morning?' I kept the smile on my face and pulled out a packet of cigarettes. I extracted one and bent forward as though I'd asked her for a light. She caught on quickly, nodded and took out some matches.

'I helped the family to get the girl out. I think I've been arrested. Please contact them.' She smiled and lit a match.

'Of course, señor. Keep the matches.'

'Thank you. Please, have an English cigarette. Ah. There's only one left. Keep the packet.' I emphasised the 'keep' and pushed the almost-full packet on her. My guard was getting twitchy but he didn't really know what to do.

'Thank you, señor, I like English cigarettes.' She smiled again and walked on unhurriedly.

The guard at the entrance signalled to my escort who took my arm and eased me forward. We were joined by the third man and went outside to where a battered car was waiting. No one had spoken yet and my demands to know where we were going were met with silence. In truth I don't think they spoke English anyway; I didn't want to admit to speaking Spanish. I might overhear information useful to my escape attempt. We bucketed around old Lima on failing shock absorbers until we reached what appeared to be a police barracks. Inside I was led along dirty corridors, smelling of urine and faeces and deposited in a small cell.

It was filthy. It stank. The sole furniture was a plank bed with no mattress or other coverings. It was damp and cold. I sat on it, watching the cockroaches foraging on the floor. I thought out my options.

I was pretty certain the stewardess would contact Arenas but I was by no means certain what he could achieve. I didn't even know what his mental condition was! If she looked inside the cigarette packet, and I thought she would, she would find my note. I carry a note everywhere. I don't smoke but a cigarette is such an innocuous object that I reckoned it to be the easiest thing to pass on if the opportunity arose. This was the first time it'd been put to the test. The note gave my name, passport number, Arturo's telephone number and Maria's London number. It simply told the reader that I was in trouble and asked that they contact those telephone numbers and the British Embassy telling each of the circumstances in which they'd last seen me. It wasn't much but I knew it was possible to be locked away in a cell in South America for considerable periods without anyone being the wiser.

It had to be Uribe's doing; probably annoyed because he'd been fooled by the Arenas. What could he do to me? I'd done nothing illegal. There were certainly no legitimate charges they could bring against me even if they could prove my involvement in the case. I'm not so naive to suppose that they were incapable of concocting evidence if they wished. They'd never get through a court of justice but they could hold me for weeks, months even. It wasn't a pleasant thought.

The other option was to escape. They hadn't yet taken anything other than my bag. I had my passport, money in my pockets and more sewn into the lining of my trousers waist-band. I'd a fair idea of the geography of the city and I had friends I could contact. I looked at the lock. No problems there. No windows. I thought back to our route through the corridors. We hadn't passed anyone on guard. A few prisoners in similar cells, that's all. The barracks wasn't busy, if I got out I could probably bluff my way onto the streets by walking confidently and purposefully through the gates.

It occurred to me that they might want me to escape just so they could shoot me. No, that was too extreme even for Peru. Or was it? I decided that just after dusk was probably the best time. I'd have some cover if I needed it and it was the time when the greatest number of people would be eating their evening meal. I settled back to wait forcing myself to mentally walk the route into the cells over and over again. There must be no hesitancy when I made my move.

I eventually dozed off. I was rudely awakened by being rolled off the bed. I was grabbed, there were four of them. I was hauled off down the corridor. Rule number one; never offer violence. Accept what comes, don't give the bastards an excuse to beat you. It serves no purpose and only saps your strength and lowers the awareness. Unresisting, I went along. I tried to memorise as much as I could.

I was pushed through a door and immediately blinded by powerful lights aimed at my face. I was moved to the centre of what seemed to be a stage and told to stand up straight. I complied. As my eyes got used to the light I could vaguely see rows of people sitting in front of the stage. They all appeared to be hooded. What the hell was going on? Periodically one of the hooded men would get to his feet, come up onto the stage and walk around me; eyes would peer at mine through the slits in the hood. I tried to look relaxed. Not to the point of smiling or speaking – that could have been asking for trouble.

I heard the occasional voice. I was supposed to.

Questions like: 'Is this him?'

'Is that the Englishman?

Statements such as: 'Ah. He is the one who knows who the kidnappers are.' There were never any answers, just the questions none of them directed at me. It was surreal. As though I was standing outside myself watching some strange charade. There was no doubt

I had to escape. I'd go that night as planned, assuming I went back to the same cell of course.

I suppose I stood there for at least an hour. I was longing to look at my watch but equally, I was determined to give them no excuse, no matter how small, to beat me. The watchers got up one by one, came onto the stage and did another circuit of me before leaving the room individually and in silence. I was taken back to my cell, again in absolute silence and pushed roughly inside. This time, watch, passport, wallet and trouser belt (I hadn't planned to hang myself) were taken.

I had the lock open when I heard them returning.

'Shit,' I jumped back on the bed and pretended to be asleep. Maybe they'd think they'd forgotten to lock it. Small chance.

There was only one man this time. He made no comment on the unlocked door. He beckoned me to follow him. I was taken along the same route, through the cinema which was lit normally this time, up the aisle and into an office at the back. Behind the desk sat Captain Uribe. He didn't speak to me, merely indicated that I should sit. I was offered a cigarette which I declined to his obvious surprise. He was flicking through a copy of Eliot's poems which has been with me since my university days. The margins are covered with neat student's notes. He obviously thought this was a code of some kind. He continued to stare at me. He picked up the shrilling telephone.

'The tenth? No, it must be the fifteenth. The tenth is no good I tell you.' He was staring at me the whole time.

'No. We will try the fourteenth. No, that's not possible. Very well, the twelfth. Confirm this tonight.' He put the phone down. He still held my gaze, devoid of any readable expression. Suddenly, without a word he stood up, put on his uniform cap and left without a backward glance.

I was left alone and after five minutes I decided I'd never get a better chance. I'd noticed my bag on the floor beside the desk so I picked it up, put passport and wallet in my pocket, noted the fact that my watch was missing and opened the door. I was going. I turned right and bumped straight into Andres. He laughed at my expression.

'Come on, James, it's Miami for you.' He put his finger to his lips to forestall any questions. As we left the barracks he stopped at the public telephone kiosk. I could only hear his side of the conversation.

'Yes. I've got him. Twelve thousand dollars. I agreed he could have it tonight. Yes, I'll do that.'

Once in the car Andres breathed a sigh of relief.

'Clever of you with the stewardess, James. If you ever see her again you must thank her properly. Fernando has given her a memorable tip. Here, she gave me this. I didn't call Arturo or your wife.' He handed me the packet of Benson and Hedges. 'I told you money would buy anything in Lima, James. Captain Uribe settled for $12,000. He tried for fifteen but we didn't want to risk a mutilation or a double payment.' He roared with laughter at his own joke.

So that's what the conversation about the dates had been. Haggling over my release fee. I wish every case was ended as quickly as that.

CHAPTER
7

Author's note

In most cases of kidnap negotiation a team of some description will be the focus point for decision making. The team may consist of myself plus one other or it may be a group of four or more committed parties. However large or small the team is, there is a necessary and essential element of trust. When that trust breaks down a cancer begins to grow. Decisions cease to be based on reality, information is withheld or misinterpreted and the negotiations begin to flounder. The person to suffer is the innocent party – the victim. In the case which follows, legal niceties, an agreement with the client and a personal desire not to cause harm to the reputation of a fine family dictate that identities be disguised.

I HADN'T expected to get involved with the Vencato affair; I'd read about it, it was headline news for a couple of days immediately after the kidnap. The grapevine message was that it was being handled by Michael Barton.

Donato Vencato was an exceedingly wealthy man even by Milan standards. He had something of a chequered background. He was a major figure in the construction industry and had been the subject of controversy more than once over suspect deals. One newspaper article I remember stated that he'd spent time in jail on one occasion.

He'd been taken using an increasingly popular American technique known as the 'walk out'. The kidnappers had gone to his office and under the threat of a gun he'd been forced to walk out with them. A couple of years before, his daughter, Gabriela, had been seized on the streets but she put up such a noisy and spirited resistance it resulted in her attackers running away, one clutching a set of very painful testicles.

I'd read the newspaper articles about the Vencato snatch with great interest at the time. It had happened about three weeks earlier and the press had a field day, dragging up his questionable past and the attempt to kidnap Gabriela. I seemed to remember there was something about a pending divorce as well. On hearing that Michael was involved I'd assumed it was an insured case. Within a couple of days of the news breaking the press had lost interest. They wouldn't bother with it again until he was released or injured.

It was Rodrigo Arenas who'd called me at the Lord Byron and told me Michael had been pulled off the case on the instructions of his company. He knew one of the lawyers involved with the family, Pietro Santini; did I want him to follow up and offer my services? I knew why he'd asked rather than going straight ahead. I was in Rome on holiday with Maria and I'd promised that we wouldn't be diverted by work.

The other aspect was that if Michael Barton had been taken off the job, there was something wrong. Maybe the actual kidnap circumstances were questionable. It wouldn't be the first time someone had faked his own kidnap to make a false insurance claim; indeed I'd once been obliquely approached by an underwriter to do just that! Maybe the family wouldn't co-operate with the police. Certainly Michael's company made this a condition before they committed a consultant. I asked Rodrigo to give me half an hour to discuss it with Maria and call me back.

We'd already used up two very pleasant weeks of the planned month's break so I didn't feel too guilty. If the Vencatos wanted me it would mean a move to Milan but that was certainly no hardship. It's the fashion centre of Italy, which would appeal to Maria, and the city is full of museums and ancient monuments which appeal to me! The northerners are far less gregarious than the Romans and life tends to be much more leisurely. It could be just the place to round off our holiday; there was no reason why Maria couldn't stay on with me. She agreed and I told Rodrigo to go ahead and make contact.

I'd have to meet the family before they made the decision to use me and we'd planned that I should go to Milan alone leaving Maria at the Byron until the job was confirmed. Janice, in the London office, had the hotel number as the contact point and there was no need to change that until it became necessary. At that time my Italian was limited to say the least and when Gianna Vencato called that evening, we had to change the plan.

She spoke no English at all. Very slowly, with lots of repeats, we managed to agree that I would catch the next morning's flight to Milan. Maria was going to have to come with me to interpret. We'd worked together on cases before, and apart from her fluency in Italian Maria's a very useful sounding board for appreciations and tactics. She knew the Latin mind well (having one herself!) and she was often able to give me interesting psychological angles.

We didn't bother Janice, just told the hotel that we'd return that evening. It's a short flight to Milan but en route you see some of the most beautiful countryside in the world. The city sits up well into the headwaters of the Po valley, and stretching down to the south east is lush green pasture land which summons to mind a few lines by Shelley:

> Beneath is spread like a green sea
> The waveless plain of Lombardy.
> Bounded by the vaporous air,
> Islanded by cities fair.

Stretching the full length of the northern horizon are the mighty snow-capped Dolomites, providing some of the finest climbing and skiing in the world. Banking to turn into the airport there's a perfect view of the Duomo, the spiritual centre of the city. It's a huge Gothic structure, the third largest church in Europe; its one hundred and thirty or so pinnacles inspired D. H. Lawrence to call it 'an imitation hedgehog of a cathedral'. At the top of the highest pinnacle is the gorgeous, gilded Madonna.

To me it's one of the great wonders of Italy. It took over five hundred years from the time Duke Gian Galeazzo Visconti authorised it to be built, to the finishing touches being administered in 1813. The world-famous statue of Saint Bartholomew carrying his own skin after being flayed is in one of the transepts, just one of about two and a half thousand statues from all periods. Milan is a great mixture of ancient and modern in both architecture and culture. As well as being the true business centre of Italy it also houses da Vinci's *Last Supper* and is home to La Scala, the world's premier opera house.

Knowing that Maria would be making a bee-line for La Scala if we stayed I made a mental note to try to get into the Marino alla Scala, a small, friendly hotel next to the opera house in Piazza della Scala. There was a car waiting for us and we were taken straight to the apartment in town.

If Gianna Vencato was surprised to see Maria, she made no comment and came straight to the point.

'The other man has left because I refused to co-operate fully with the police. Why should I? I tell them only what I want to tell them. It is stupid. They talk in the bars and chatter to their women. I do not want my affairs to be the gossip of Milan.' A rural accent, working class.

'I do not speak English. None of us do. Why should we? Our business is in Italy. It doesn't matter. If you work with us, Pietro Santini will translate. He didn't want another consultant but if my husband plans a new building, he first employs an expert architect. I'm not a kidnapper therefore I want an expert. Will you assist and how expensive are you?'

Maria translated with a straight face but her twinkling eyes said: 'Get out of that one'.

'I'll help but first you should know what you're buying. Let me tell you a little about myself.' Through Maria I gave her my background brief. She listened intently without interruption and when I concluded with my daily fees, she simply nodded acceptance. I asked her for all the details she had on the case; in particular I wanted to be sure she had a holding script ready in the event of a contact. She had. The kidnappers, she said, were very punctual with their calls. The next contact would be made some time after she placed the next advertisement in *Il Tempo*. She was using the telephone of one of her husband's employees. This was at the instruction of the gang's spokesman who used the code name Mussolini to identify himself.

The file she handed over to me was Michael's.

'He didn't want to give it to me. In my opinion I'd already paid for it.' I laughed. Poor old Michael would catch it when he got back. It was good news for me. It meant I could study the notes during the return flight to Rome and get a feel for the case before the first meeting. We managed to get a room in the Marino alla Scala and I left Maria there, going back alone to Rome to collect our luggage and settle up at the Lord Byron.

From the hotel that night, I called Janice and gave her the address of the Marino in Milan. I told her we were on a case and asked her to send my briefcase and the Rossetti file to Milan by the fastest means. I then read through Michael's notes again. They were too disjointed to be used in their current format so I re-organised the sections I wanted and set about creating my own case folder. After a while I reviewed what I had to date:

THE KIDNAP

Took place 22 days ago. About 8.30 p.m., from the office. Seen to leave building with 2 other persons. Got into small Fiat. Vencato sat in back with 1 man, other drove. Family not too concerned until about 11.00 p.m., thought he was working late. Did not, inform police.

THE VICTIM

Male. Married. Money from wife's father gave him head start in construction business. Hit headlines in press when all his buildings were sequestered under instructions from communist judge. Decision overthrown after High Court appeal.

Lost 4/5 miliardi when ordered to pull down illegally erected building.

Said to be shy, introverted but very, very clever. No political interests, resolute and will probably stand up well to ordeal.

THE FAMILY

Family wealth began in 1957, money from Gianna's father.

4 children, 1 daughter, 3 sons (latter at school).

Attempted kidnap on daughter 3 years ago.

Gianna reluctant to talk to the police as believes this may attract attention of fiscal authorities.

THE NEGOTIATING TEAM

1. *Full time*

   Gianna Vencato (Wife – chairperson)

   Giuseppe Antonioli (Family solicitor)

   Pietro Santini (Solicitor – translates)

   James March (Consultant)

2. *Occasional*

   Gabriela Vencato (Daughter)

   Guido Santarelli (Lawyer – friend – police contacts)

THE KIDNAPPERS

Known to be at least 2 men (from snatch)

Known to have Fiat.

Known to use codeword 'Mussolini'

Known to have used same man on phone so far

Thought to be criminal

Seem to be following predictable pattern

Could be same gang as Rossetti case

Comment. Gang appear to be using force of argument rather than threats at this stage. This was so in Rossetti case as well. If same gang, they may not resort to threats.

THE LAW ENFORCEMENT AGENCIES

Carabinieri first informed 14 days after kidnap.

Took Gianna to police station and 'buggered her about'

Carabinieri have confidentially notified some friends that they will make a real effort to intercept the drop.

May be a grudge factor against victim. Many brushes with the local law but they've never convicted him.

Gianna has put a lot of effort into keeping contact and updating a specific policeman. Never given them true events. Sent presents of whisky.

Guido Santarelli appointed as official liaison person.

OBSERVATIONS WHICH MAY HAVE RELEVANCE

1. Santini said to have stated Donato wealthier than all his clients put together.
2. Vencato reported in newspaper as having told a journalist he could pay his tax bill out of the 1 miliardi he kept in his back pocket. (This was outside a court room).
3. Family live very high profile life style and flaunt wealth. (May have raised gang's level of expectations above going rate.)

COMMUNICATIONS

Gang have made following phone calls to date:

1. Day 2. 'Well done not calling the police. We have him and he is OK. We'll phone later. On Monday.'
2. Day 5. 'There is instruction in a garbage can outside the hospital.'

   Note. Gabriela collected it. Found Vencato's ID card and message saying: 'Well done not telling magistrates. We want 10 miliardi. When ready, put ad in *Il Tempo*: "An Australian parakeet has been lost and whoever finds him gets a reward". As a sign use your phone number with last digit wrong.'

   Comment. Similar ad used in Rossetti case.
3. Day 7.   Advert placed as instructed.
4. Day 7.   Gang called. Didn't let G. speak. Told her to go to same place for message.
5. Day 7.   Message said: 'Go to house of Santos (employee of husband) on Thursday at 8.00 p.m. How much do you have?'
   G. Not given chance to reply.
6. Day 8.   Phone call at above house: 'How much do you have?'
   G: 'All I have is my own money. I'm getting separated from my husband, all I can offer you is 283 millions which is clean money. Police know nothing so let's move fast.'
   Mussolini: 'We want 10 miliardi and when you have this money put the same ad in the paper.'

7. Day 12. G. puts ad in paper.
8. Day 12.   Gang phones:
    Mussolini: 'What have you got?'
    G: 'I can add the bail that my lawyer would get back from the time my husband was in jail.'
    M: Became insulting. Didn't ask how much the bail money was. Said: 'We want 10 miliardi.' Hung up.
9. Day 15.   Gang called house.
    Mussolini: 'Go to get message at gas station (close to house). It's on top of the pump.'
10. Day 15.   Message was from Vencato in own handwriting:
    'I have agreed to pay 5 miliardi.' He gave some names saying: 'Go to them for these amounts.' Quoted some small figures.
    In same package was letter from gang:
    'We have agreed with your husband to pay a figure – do not discuss this or start crying.'
    Note. This letter has been destroyed.
11. Day 16.   G. placed same ad in paper.
12 Day 19.   Call from gang:
    M: 'How much?'
    G: '600 millions.'
    M: 'What is this?' Angry. 'This is what your husband has in his current account! We go back to demand 10 miliardi.' Hung up. No threats.

Comments. Calls approximately 2–3 minutes duration.
Mussolini seems to be mature from voice, 30–40 years. Roman accent. So far same voice each time. (Negotiator, Piccolo, in Rossetti case had Roman accent.)

FINANCIAL (TO DATE)

Case Day	Demand	Offer
Day 5	10 miliardi	
Day 8		283 millions
Day 15	5 miliardi	
Day 19		600 millions
Day 19	10 miliardi	

Comment. Same initial demand as in Rossetti case.

RELEVANT TO APPRECIATION
1. Vencato had agreed with his wife that if he was ever kidnapped, he would pretend they were separating. This would give her an excuse to claim difficulties in getting money.
2. Why had the letter delivered on Day 15 been destroyed?

3. Was G. afraid of police co-operation purely on fiscal grounds?
4. Would high life style affect gang's level of expectancy?
5. Had G. and V. ever discussed an 'inside deal' with gang in the event of kidnap?
6. How much money could G. genuinely raise? Had they ever discussed a ransom figure in the past?
7. Get brief from G. on CMT members.
8. Any Mafia connections?

The last note was relevant. During the late 1940s and early 1950s, many of the most famous Mafia bosses were deported from the USA following Senator Kefauver's investigations into organised crime and illegal immigration. This 'new Mafia' moved into Sicily and Italy with a different type of sophisticated crime. Apart from the racketeering, smuggling cigarettes and drugs, they entered with enthusiasm into construction site speculation during the building boom of the 1950s. This was the time Vencato had started. There could be a connection. I hoped not!

Case day 21
There had been no movement by either side when I returned to Milan the next day. The CMT was due to meet that evening and I was able to get a couple of hours with Gianna to go through my notes, verify some of Michael's statements and ask my personal questions. As Maria translated, I studied Gianna Vencato.

She had photographed well; I'd have identified her from the news clippings without any problems. About forty-five years old, she was beginning to round out in that very Italian way, the spaghetti and pastas relentlessly attacking waist, bosom and buttocks. Her hair still maintained its colour without the assistance of the tinting bottle and she wore it quite short. She was round-faced, her cheeks just starting to flesh out; rather coarse features, peasant-like, open-pored from the ravages of teenage acne. She held herself well but it seemed forced, it wasn't natural. Yet she hadn't come from peasant stock, her parents had been very wealthy. Her make-up wasn't as carefully applied as would have been expected – perhaps she didn't particularly care. From the nervous scurrying of the servants she seemed to rule the household firmly; at the slightest tinkle of the small silver bell she kept to hand the maid would be instantly present.

I asked her about the separation mentioned in the telephone conversation with Mussolini. Was it a fact? She told me it was a ploy they'd worked out a long time ago. If he was kidnapped she would claim they were to separate. He would support this and in this way they may be able to lower the gang's expectations if she could be shown to be dependent on her own money. In answer to my query about the letter which had been destroyed, she was evasive, just brushing it off as an accident. I didn't believe this woman had such accidents. Still, I couldn't make an issue of it. But I did point out the importance of having all the facts in order to make a balanced appreciation. She said it wouldn't happen again.

I asked if her fear of the police was just as she'd stated earlier or whether she was more concerned about the fiscal authorities?

'It is as I said in the beginning, but there is more. They don't like my husband. He is not a criminal but he moves too fast for them. He plans quickly, makes up his mind instantly and goes into action. This has caused many of his rivals in the construction industry to complain on ethical grounds. Poof. They're just too slow. It's led the police to investigate deals from time to time but they've never got a real conviction. Of course we don't want involvement with the tax lawyers. No wealthy person in this country does. We have money put away against the possibility of kidnap and if this were discovered we would have embarrassing questions to answer.' She expressed these views quite openly.

Yes, they lived a high life style and why not? Her husband had come from a poor family and he was now very, very wealthy. He had worked hard for his money and taken risks. Why shouldn't he enjoy it?

I asked about him as a character. She bore out the notes Michael had made. I asked if she thought Donato was the sort of person who may try to deal from the inside; to make a bargain with the gang?

'It's quite possible. We never discussed it but he is an instinctive businessman. He can't resist a deal. He's not a gambler in the accepted sense but if he can pit his wits against someone he doesn't like, then no matter what sort of business it is, he'll have a go. And he'll win.' She answered proudly. 'He's been known to make deals in the restaurant on the back of a packet of cigarettes, deals worth millions of lire with never a question from those who know him. His word is his bond.' She was sitting upright, shoulders back, proud now and as pert as a sparrow.

When I asked the question about the Mafia, I thought she was going to explode. Her face flamed and she burst into a torrent of gutter Italian causing Maria to blush. She didn't even try to translate, simply said. 'You can take that as meaning "no connection".' I still wondered though; this was an uncharacteristic outburst from what I'd seen so far.

Would she tell me about the members of the negotiating team?

'I take the decisions. It is my husband's life at stake and therefore my responsibility. I listen to advice, of course I do; I'm not a kidnap expert as I told you, that's why you're here Giuseppe Antonioli is our family solicitor and has been ever since we started in business. He is more than that, he is a good friend to both Donato and myself.

'Pietro Santini is better known to my husband than to me. He is also a solicitor. He has handled some of Donato's deals in the provinces. He is competent and his English is good which helps Donato sometimes. He has been close to other families who have suffered kidnaps and he offered to help us. I warn you, he was not happy having you join us, but, as I said in this matter I make the decisions.

'Occasionally we are joined by my daughter Gabriela. There was once an attempt on her as you know. The fools, she is a firebrand and no mistake. She has little to say at the meetings but she collects the letters and it is only right that she should know how her father's case progresses. My sons, they are too young and excitable.

'Sometimes we are joined by Lorenzo Cutolo. I do not know him at all well. Giuseppe has met him before. He joins us when we are deciding what to tell the police and he is the one who relays it to the Captain downtown.'

So, I had them in perspective. A good mix of friends and clinical support. We made our excuses and went back to the hotel to freshen up before the meeting. I asked Maria what she'd made of Gianna.

'She's a strange one. She's dominant and very strong. Probably the best person to head the team. Knowing her background I'd say she learned her more basic Italian from her husband. She may have adopted his accent in his defence, a sort of inverted snobbery. She can put her emotions behind her and look at things objectively but I do think she's hiding something. It's not necessarily a Mafia connection. I believe she used that as a convenient excuse to blow her top as a result of your question about destroying the letter. She was a bit off guard when you asked about it. That made her angry with herself, not you, that's why she exploded.'

It was an interesting observation. I might be able to raise it with Gianna later, when the team had gelled together more.

'It's time to go, Maria.'

'Ah. I'm not coming. Gianna told me quite positively that Santini was to be the translator at the meetings. She doesn't want to upset him any more. She's quite happy for you to discuss the case with me and she's quite happy for me to translate when we meet her alone. You're on your own. I'm going to La Scala. As it's your first meeting and you'll probably be late back, I'll book a table for supper.'

She was in fine spirits and it wasn't just La Scala; it was probably because we were working together again and it looked like being an interesting job. In many ways it was a good thing that Maria wasn't going to translate. We didn't know when she'd be needed back in the UK.

I was thrown straight into it that night; it's the best way. I was introduced quickly and then Gianna asked me to repeat the background brief I'd given her. Once this was over, she summarised events with excellent brevity.

'They asked for ten miliardi, we offered 283 millions. They said they'd done a deal with Donato for five miliardi, we offered 600 millions. They reverted to ten miliardi. We have to make a counter-offer. I want to discuss how much and when. James, you first please.'

'If we accept the going rate of about 800 millions or so as being what the kidnappers probably have in their minds, I would suggest a modest raise of somewhere in the region of 50 or 60 million. Where we have the problem is the area of doubt concerning whether Donato has made an inside deal. If he has, the gang's level of expectancy will be considerably higher than the going rate, though perhaps not as high as the five miliardi they mentioned.

'I think when the gang went back to the ten miliardi demand, it was purely because their negotiator was angry and wanted to scare Gianna. We have to test the water. It will fit with you having had some success in collecting a little money from those persons your husband named in his letter. It's an increase sufficient to show willingness but not so large that it makes life difficult for us if we want to slow down the progression and aim for the going rate.'

'Giuseppe?'

'That makes sense. We mustn't forget what Signor March said at the start about tempting double payments by escalating too quickly. I would vote for that. Place the advertisement and offer 650.'

'Pietro?'

Now, after translating for me, it was his own turn. His Italian was much more rapid this time as he spoke for four or five minutes then turned to question me.

'Have you handled cases with a demand as large as this before. Do you keep records in London?'

'Yes, ten miliardi is not an unusual amount at all, there were at least three such demands in Rome last year. I have all the records I need here.'

I patted my folders. It had seemed a particularly pointless question. I didn't know whether it came from him or one of the others. Pietro Santini was one of those characters I always associate with the term 'lounge lizard'. He was dapper, immaculately dressed from his Pierre Cardin tie down to his white Gucci shoes. Thin-faced, black pencil moustache, very carefully tended thick black hair which shone with some patent, highly scented concoction. His eyes were shrewd, never still, he looked at a person as he spoke and then his glance flickered away again, returning from time to time for the briefest instant. He spoke very rapidly, using his hands almost violently to emphasise points.

'Are you sure about the 650 millions?' Our eyes met for a second before his flickered over my shoulder to the wall beyond.

'It seems the most logical course to me. We shall have to prepare a script to go along with it. A list of topics for Gianna to work from. Of course I was sure. What was he playing at?

There was another burst of animated conversation with Gianna conributing more this time. He translated.

'It has been decided that the offer will be 712 millions.'

'I think you ought to consider it again, you're getting well up towards the going rate. That's an increase of 112 millions. It will be difficult to slow it down.'

What on earth made them pluck that figure from the sky? It was dangerously high.

Pietro was gesticulating wildly as he hammered his point home. Was he arguing my case? If so he was trying very hard. Giuseppe at the other side of the table had a frown on his fat, normally genial face. He interjected a couple of times and I picked up the word London. Looking across at me, he smiled almost apologetically, he was sweating profusely but I put this down to his weight more then the argument.

'The decision is made. 712 millions. We place the advertisement tonight.' Pietro looked sadly at me. 'She is a strong woman.'

Well, the job of the team is to make decisions, I had argued my case and they had chosen to disagree. We put together a script for Gianna.

Case day 56

It took the gang some time to respond to the advertisement. Gianna had been placing it on a daily basis and getting depressed at the lack

f communication. At the meeting on case day 46, I'd suggested yet
gain that they stop it.

'The gang know you're not going to offer the full amount. So long
s you're communicating with them it's most unlikely that they'll
ontact you. The critical information at any stage of a negotiation
omes from the family. The gang's getting a steady flow and you're
etting down in the dumps about their silence. I suggest you stop it
omorrow, place it again the day after then stop it completely if the
ang haven't resumed contact.'

This tactic worked and on case day 49 the gang called. There were
aily contacts up to case day 52. The gang slowly came back down
o five miliardi against Gianna's constant pleadings of poverty. She
layed the separation factor to the hilt. She told Mussolini that the
ajority of her husband's business was based on credit and if he
asn't released soon all his properties would be sequestered and
en where would they all be?

There was another letter from her husband on case day 56. It gave
nother list of names. By each name was the amount Giana had to
sk for. She wasn't happy for anyone on the team to see the letter
nd it was during a private conversation with us in her apartment
e told Maria.

'These men. I think they are criminals. It doesn't change things.
Iy husband is not a criminal himself but he has friends who are.
n the construction industry you have to mix with all sorts of people.
have all the money we will need to get Donato out. I don't want
o go near these people and I don't know why he's asking me to.'

'We can discuss it at the meeting. He could be saying one of a few
nings. He could be offering you a means of raising the money.
emember he will be supporting you in the separation story and he
ay feel that this sort of letter gives you a way of raising extra money
ver a period of time as you go round the names to collect.

'It may be some sort of code. Do these persons exist? Can you see
ny hidden message in there? If they do exist, some of them may be
nder surveillance by the gang, just to see whether you are trying
o get the cash from them.'

'Oh, they exist all right. I've met some of them and heard of the
thers.'

'One possibility is that he is signifying that he's done an inside
eal. Have you noticed these figures add up to 1.5 miliardi. Add that
o your offer and we have a rough total of two miliardi. He may have
one a deal for that amount. If he has, why not say it openly? It
ould of course be that he thinks the gang may settle for that amount.'

At the meeting we discussed the letter much as I'd gone throu
it with Gianna. It was decided to use it in future scripts where
Gianna could claim limited success with some of the names a
claim that others didn't want to know. This time the team accept
a slowing down operation and went for a sum only a little high
than I recommended. It was decided to raise the offer by forty-fo
millions to 756. The advert was placed the next day.

Each of the next few days brought a telephone contact with t
gang remaining coldly adamant; they would accept nothing less th
five miliardi. Gianna stayed calm and said she was getting arou
the names in Donato's letter but she had to be cautious in case t
police followed her. None of them had given her cash but there h
been a few promises. It was decided that the offer could now
increased a little. Once more the team went above the figure
suggested. A raise of fourteen millions brought the total up to 7
millions.

Case day 61

The 770 millions was at first treated with contempt by the gar
However, in the days following they reduced their demand to ?
miliardi. This led to an excited meeting of the CMT.

Gianna reviewed and asked opinions about a large increase on o
part. Would this bring a speedy conclusion? For my part I remind
her of the obvious dangers: the double payment and a lengt
extension to the case. If the gang had been prepared to come do
to 1.5 miliardi, the chances were that they were beginning to belie
her story. A sudden large increase would give the lie to this.
couldn't recommend it.

Santini was prominent in the discussion. As translator his que
tions kept flying back to me. 'Was I sure?' 'Surely it made sense
try to conclude quickly?' 'A big increase would meet them half wa'
It seemed to me that Gianna was arguing very forcefully for h
increase. It was surprising as she'd seemed so logical up to the
Giuseppe didn't contribute much to the conversation, the odd ques
tion here and there. London was mentioned on a few occasio
Lord knows why. They came to a very depressing decision. Th
were going to offer 945 millions, an increase of 175 million lire! M
heart sank. They were asking for trouble.

I tried my best through Santini to get them to change their min
but he told me they were adamant. I felt like walking off the case.

Case day 64

The gang accepted. Instructions were issued to change to a ne ean telephone. A letter was collected from a garbage can only three undred metres from the house giving the drop details.

ase day 67
he drop takes place.

ase day 68
Message from Mussolini: 'Money received. Will call 20.00 hours omorrow.

ase day 69
0.00 hours. From Mussolini: 'Go collect a message from the res-urant. In the litter can.'
0.20 hours. The message informs Gianna that the demand is for other five miliardi.

She was too distraught to hold the team meeting. I didn't press er; I sensed there was plenty of time now.

I reviewed the whole thing with Maria that evening. From start finish we analysed the case, the team meetings, everything I'd id and as far as I could glean from my notes everything the team ad said. It's difficult to be exact when a translator is being used. Maria remarked a couple of times about the fact that I'd been oodling. Shapes which revolved around the blocked out letters of London'. I mentioned that it was one of the few words I'd picked t at the meetings. 'Why London?' she'd quietly mused.

'Look, James, I'm going round to see Gianna. I may be of some omfort to her. No. You stay here. This is for two women to talk out.'

I used the couple of hours of Maria's absence to lay the foundations a new strategy. I'd never been in such an odd situation. No, not ld – unsatisfying. I was used to long persuasive sessions at meetings t here was something I just couldn't put my finger on. On every ccasion the team had decided against me. Santini arguing enthusi-tically for me, Gianna seeming to accept all I had to say in private onversations and then – everything changed at the meeting. How as it happening? Why was it happening?

It wasn't the influence of Giuseppe. He said very little. He gave e odd looks from time to time but then I'd never had the chance sit and talk to him. Perhaps he'd have dinner with Maria and me. might help. We could do the same with Santini although he was side. Hang on. If it wasn't Giuseppe Antonioli, it wasn't Pietro

Santini – it had to be Gianna Vencato. Had there been some sort
coded message in Donato's letter after all? I couldn't spot it but
wife could even if she'd denied it. I'd have to get Maria to try h
feminine wiles.

It still didn't make sense. Rich she was, but she spent wisely; sl
wouldn't continue to pay my fees if she'd worked out some secr
strategy with her husband. Why should she? I looked down. I w
doodling again. London. Yes, why was it that London kept comin
up? All three of them mentioned it at some time or another. I look
through my files to see how often I'd noted it down. It appeared c
the pages for case days 21, 56, 59 and 61. The only common fact
was that these were the days when offer decisions had been mad
There were no doodles against any of the tactical or scriptin
sessions. That was in part logical as the offer meetings were f
lengthier than the others. More going on, more long Italian speech
and hence more time to doodle I suppose. I wasn't much furth
forward.

Maria was looking quite grim when she came back. The first thin
she did was pour a brandy for herself. That wasn't normal. I kne
her so I let her pace around a bit. When she sat down by me I cou
see she was angry.

'Had some more gutter Italian, darling? She's under a lot
pressure you know.'

'You don't know the half of it. Tonight we got onto discussin
the tactics. She said she thought your advice hadn't been at all goo

I flared up instantly. 'Good God, the woman hasn't taken a blir
scrap of notice of anything I've damned well said. That last off
was the most ludicrous thing I've ever seen. Come on. We're goir
to see her.'

'No we're not, James. I think someone's playing silly bugger
She also told me that she got better advice from Santini and h
wasn't based on London computers.'

'What the hell is she talking about. London computers. You knc
my feelings on those bloody mechanical monsters.'

'She also said Santini may be on a percentage – but he's cheape
She dropped her bombshell neatly. Right on target.

I took her arm and led her over to the table.

'Look. The doodles you pointed out. They only appear on t
records of those meetings where we discussed offers. What do y
make of that?' I think I already knew.

'You hardly speak any Italian. Put you in a room full of peop
speaking not only quickly but with heavy accents as well and y

ouldn't possibly hope to understand more than the odd word, ondon, for instance. What's to stop Santini saying whatever he ants?'

The little shark was a ringer. He was advising her for some sort ransom percentage. Worse, he could even be informing to the ang and taking a cut there. I'm not sure what his deal would be but it was in his interests to make the ransom as big as possible then e could quite easily pervert everything I'd said.

He'd simply say that I'd advised a very big increase but he was commending a lower figure. He made a good pretence of arguing ith me. It also accounted for those odd irrelevant questions he ccasionally threw at me and his perpetual avoidance of my eyes. od. The slimy, immoral toad. He'd used my reputation to force p the ransom. I've rarely been so angry. Why the hell hadn't Gianna id anything before? When we'd talked in her apartment I'd stressed he safety of relatively low increases for the time being, then at the eeting table I was supposed to be advocating high payments. She ust have thought something was odd. Worst of all, he'd put the ctim's life at risk! The longer the gang held him the less secure ey became and the greater the chances of police action with all the herent dangers.

What did we do next? This situation couldn't be tolerated. They'd ave to change translators. I'd have to try to get Maria in with me. aria disagreed.

'It may look as though we're trying to set something up ourselves. emember she knows Santini but she doesn't know us. Let me go ack and tell her about the discussion we've just had. I'll just give er the facts. Nothing more. We'll leave it to her.'

Maria told me later that Gianna had listened in virtual silence en thanked her very formally. She'd be in touch the next day.

Gianna called me in the middle of the afternoon and said there as to be a meeting at four o'clock. Would I please attend. There as another man there. He was introduced as Lorenzo Cutolo, I membered he was the man who liaised with the police. Gianna's ce was deadpan as she reviewed the situation and then asked for y opinion. She looked hard at me; was there a message? I wasn't re so I carried on as normal.

'This is not the time or place for recriminations but you moved r too quickly to 945 millions. It went too easily to the gang. They now now that you were bluffing in a lot of what you said to them rlier. You could now be in for a long wait. The only chance you ave is to try to get an early indication of the amount they really expect, not the five miliardi they've demanded. If you can get measure of this then there's a chance that you can work out a strateg to meet that and avoid the possibility of a third or even fourt payment.'

I sat down. I'd deliberately switched from 'we' to 'you' an wondered if Santini would put the subtlety across. Not that I'd kno anyway. I was finding it very hard to stay calm as he 'translated'. H constantly referred back to me in his usual style, 'Are you sure?' an sometimes quite irrelevant demands: 'Have you had many doub and treble payments?' I kept my answers short; at least I'd mal him work for his pieces of eight. The meeting lasted for about a hour. We didn't discuss the next offer which I thought was odd, b then the whole set-up was odd. As we all stood up, Gianna sai something to Santini and nodded at me.

'Gianna says would you be so kind as to wait in the lounge ne: door. She wishes to discuss something privately with us. She wi have some coffee sent in.' Charmingly translated, butter wouldn melt in his mouth.

There had been a note in front of Gianna which she hadn't opene at least not in front of me. I knew it was from the gang. I recognise the same grubby envelope, still slightly curled from its journey insic the inevitable Coca-Cola can, dark patches, stains from the residu of the drink. I called Maria.

'I think I'll be back shortly, darling. I don't know what's goin on. They're probably working out the kindest way of giving me th chop. To tell the truth I don't much care in one sense but I hate t think of Donato sitting in a bloody cupboard somewhere bein ripped off by his friends. Book a table for some afternoon tea wi you, I'm ravenous. Ciao.'

The door to the meeting room opened suddenly and Santini cam out. He gave me a venomous stare, held my eyes for the first tim made a very crude but very Italian gesture and left. The next perso out was Lorenzo.

'I'm sorry about the charade, James.' Surprise, surprise, h English was perfect! 'It was necessary to allow Santini to han himself. We gave him enough rope and he did exactly that. He wa reversing your figures and his own, as your wife suspected. He wa then dissuading himself from his own advice by bowing to the fa that in between each meeting you were able to refer to your con puter-controlled data bank in London. Who was he to argue with computer? Role reversal at its most skilful. Don't worry, from no on I'll be doing the translating.'

'What happens to Santini?'

'He's been paid off. Gianna insisted. Her husband's reputation is f one who pays his debts and she was determined to maintain it.'

'Do you think there's any chance that he's been talking to the dnappers?'

'We think there's every possibility. He would never admit it and e could never prove it but we have to consider it. At the end of is case, I want to take you and your wife to dinner. Not just to ractise my English but because I have a message for you which will ve you from embarrassment in the future. Be patient.'

There was no need for him to practise his English at all. I was ly mildly curious about his 'message', there was work enough to here and now.

We had a real brainstorming session with the rejuvenated team. he hardest fact to put across was that they had to prepare them-lves for a very long haul.

In seventy days the gang had achieved 945 million lire, almost one iliardi. They'd taken it without resorting to threats or appreciably ng silences. In simple mathematical terms they could equate every venty days to one miliardi and from my experience, once a double ayment situation is entered into, this sort of scale can be chron-logically if not financially accurate. In their minds there'd be a rtainty that silences and threats would stimulate more cash.

There were some important unknowns. Had Donato made an side deal? If he had it would be pretty hard, if not impossible, to ake the gang from this. Inside dealing is dangerous for this very ason; it clouds the issues to those on the outside trying to accurately sess the situation and often gives the lie to perfectly sound tactics hich would otherwise have been convincing.

Had Santini been dealing with the gang? If so, they would know vo important things: the extent of the wealth and the ease with hich it could be gained, and the fact that the family were taking rofessional advice. Both these factors weakened many tactics we ould normally have had at our fingertips.

Our task now was to get the gang back into communication with and try to establish what they really expected to get. Gianna leaded tiredness and asked if we could resume the meeting the next y. Everyone agreed but I asked that first we spend a couple of inutes sorting out a holding script for her in case she was called.

The principal action had to be to establish that Donato was still ive. Double payments had occurred in the past after the victim had en killed. Gianna devised a suitable question to satisfy that aspect

and I suggested that at this point she make no offers at all. Sh
should verge on the distraught and hysterical, demand the proof an
also demand that the gang accept a new phone. She should accus
them of reneging on the deal – this was something her husband ha
never done. She must portray a clever mixture of outrage, fear an
hysteria, she must have proof before she could consider money.
would be appropriate to ask for a letter from her husband – if h
was inside dealing he may be able to get a clue out to us.

I didn't expect a call from the gang that evening but I wanted
try to establish the normal disciplines in the team now that we wer
all on the same side. I was late back for my afternoon tea with Mari
I got to our room to find her packing.

'That's a bit extreme, darling, just because I'm late for tea.'

I could imagine what had happened. A case had come up in Sout
America and we needed Maria in the London office. She would b
the filter to me if Carson had problems. Nine times out of ten she'
answer the queries herself and it was comforting to know that
wasn't going to be disturbed with petty problems. We discussed th
Vencato case. I updated her and we decided if it looked like being
long drawn-out affair, I would offer to return to the UK and advis
them by telephone to reduce their fees. In any event I'd drop to a
hourly 'on the job' rate rather than a flat daily fee. If they decide
they wanted me full time, I was morally obliged to see it throug
especially after such a disastrous start.

It was sad to say farewell to Maria. It'd been splendid workin
together again – we were getting far too much separation and
suppose we'd both begun to mentally question whether it was a
worth it.

Case day 81

The last ten days had been quiet. No communications either way.
was glad. This period gave me plenty of time to get down to the rea
education on kidnap and ransom negotiation which had prove
impossible with Santini at the table. Gianna was standing up to th
stress very well. I noticed that her figure was returning as th
effects of stress beat back the pasta attack. She'd noticed it too.
occasionally caught her examining her reflection in the mirror.

We decided to place an advert in *Il Tempo*; if the gang responde
there was to be no offer. Gianna would stick to the unused scrip
we'd devised on Case Day 70. It was in the evening newspaper an
the gang reacted quickly, about two hours after the papers hit th
streets.

The call didn't last long. Gianna was listened to and then got a brusque query.

'The money. Five miliardi. Where is it?'

Again she went into her act. Proof. Proof.

'You'll get a letter tomorrow. You'll get your proof. That's it then until the money is ready. Don't waste our fucking time again.'

So it was to be the hard line. It had to happen.

ase day 84

They waited three days before they made contact. Again, a brief call. First they answered the proof question.

'Mussolini here. The name of the friend is Roberto. You'll find a package taped under the tow bar of a trailer in your street. Get it now.'

When Gianna tried to interrupt, she got short shrift.

'I've told you. Don't piss us about. Don't want to hear from you until you have the money. Five miliardi, is that fucking clear?' The phone went dead.

Gabriela collected the package. There was a tape, photograph, a letter from Donato and a short note from Mussolini. The tape had only one sentence on it from Donato. His voice seemed steady if a little weak. All he'd been allowed to say was: 'Hello. Please start collecting the money from those names.'

His letter gave a further list of names and amounts of money. They totalled two miliardi.

The note from the gang was curt. 'We have your measure. It's now a matter of principle. Pay up or lose him forever. In August we're taking a holiday.'

The photograph showed Donato reclining on a bare mattress. He was dirty and unkempt. He'd not been allowed to shave since his kidnap and he'd lost weight but he didn't look too bad. He was clutching a copy of the previous day's newspaper with the date clearly visible. The headlines for that day had been 'Two Killed in Riots in Rome'. Was his forefinger against the figure 'two' by accident or design?

We were still on the horns of the 'inside deal' dilemma. Once again, Donato had come up with the total of two miliardi in his letters. There was the indication on the photograph. None of these were in any way conclusive yet Gianna's early remarks about her husband's trading instincts kept coming back to me.

The gang had made their first threat. However, it was a very mild one. There was no deadline and no specific detail. They'd followed

it up by saying they were going on 'holiday in August'. It almos
robbed a potential silence of its sting.

'It's a matter of principle'. Any hidden meaning there? I thougl
not. They were stating they had as much time as they wanted. The
had some money and could afford to wait for the full five miliardi.

It was my opinion that the only real test of their expectatior
would be a substantial offer, something in the region of 400 to 50
millions. If there was no inside deal; if they were aiming at the goin
rate and treating the first payment as gratuitous; if there was n
collusion with Santini, then after the next round of abuse, silenc
and maybe more severe threats, a further very small offer could t
expected to make them reduce the demand. If they didn't reduc
then I for one would be fairly sure that Donato had done a dea
Therein lay the other dangers which we'd face when the time cam

It was important to get the timing right. Ideally I thought w
should leave it for about three weeks before making the offer. Th
would leave us credible with that amount inasmuch as if we wer
speaking the truth, it was a reasonable time in which Gianna coul
have collected the sum. It would give credence to the fact that w
could get no more. 'We knew it wasn't what the gang was asking fc
but it was all there was'. If there was no inside deal it should wor
If there was a deal or collusion then the threats would come bi
we'd have a clearer idea of the gang's true expectancy.

Sod's Law strikes unexpectedly. Coincidental to our discussior
the press did a series of articles on kidnapping and one of the lea
journalists had based his piece on the fact 'that most families face
with double payments eventually pay the full amount'. We cou
have done without it. It caused Gianna to ask me whether it wouldr
be better just to offer the five miliardi and get it over with – the
could afford it after all.

I was firmly convinced that if we took such a course we wer
inviting a third demand. We were committing Donato to an eve
longer imprisonment than he faced now and increasing the chanc
of him being killed. It was going to be very difficult for Gianna
accept three weeks of inactivity but I reckoned it to be the best b
if we were to get any positive indication of what they'd set the
sights on. To get that across to a distressed wife after her husbar
has been locked away for three months you not only have to l
convincing – you have to be convinced.

It was accepted, however, and the decision was made to place t
advert three weeks later unless there was a prior contact. Gianna
script allowed her to offer varying amounts depending on when t

ontact came. The offer which we'd agreed should be 450 million
ire would grow proportionately to the elapsed time; if Gianna had
been called during the first week, she'd have offered roughly a third
nd so on.

Case day 105

The advert was placed implying we had a solution. No contact.

Case day 109

A call from Mussolini:

M: 'Hello this is Mussolini. How much do you have?'

G: 'This is Gianna. How is my husband?'

M: 'How much do you fucking well have?'

G: 'Please, how is he?'

M: 'Tell me what you have or I go away.'

G: 'I must know about him. For the money, I've tried everywhere.
Exhausted all possibilities...'

M: 'Your husband's right. You're a cow. You don't care what
fucking happens to him. You know what we want. I'm going
now. That's it. No more....'

G: 'He said that? Stop. Don't go. I've got 450 millions more. I've
been ... everywhere. There's no more ... I'll try ... Tell him
I'm trying. How is he? Is he alive? Can he answer a ques....'

M: 'Piss off, cow. Five miliardi or he dies.'

The call upset Gianna; not the language, I'd heard her use far
worse, but the cold, impassive hardness of Mussolini. What next?

I told her to bear in mind that Mussolini was the gang's negotiator,
ot the boss. It was highly unlikely that the leader would expose
imself to the dangers of the telephone. Mussolini would be report-
ng back and they would have their own 'CMT' meeting. We had
o give them a few days to respond.

Case day 113

Gianna got a terse call to collect a package from behind the fender
f a car parked nearby. Once again it was Gabriela who picked it up.
The contents were similar to the previous parcel. Letter, note,
hotograph and tape.

The letter from Donato: 'What are you doing? Don't you care?
ve told you where to go twice now. Two letters and you still haven't
ot the money. I'm getting desperate; for God's sake get a move on.
ou can travel at will to collect money, I am a prisoner. Gabriela
n take some time off work and so can Juan, only the two boys at

school can't help. What's the reason for the delay?'

The tape: 'How long have I been here? Two months, three months no, two months. It's enough, I can't take much. . . .

He sounded weaker, confused, his voice rasped and he panted.

The photograph: It showed Donato in the same posture as befor but this photograph was in colour. His hair and beard were streake with grey, his face was ashen between the purple blotches of th bruises. He was a sorry sight.

The note: 'It's five miliardi. You know where to get it. Do it c he dies. You have fourteen days. We call at seven o'clock tonight Mussolini.

Gianna was hit hard by the photograph.

'Think, Gianna, think about what I've said to you regarding tape and photographs. They're almost certainly faked. How easy woul it be to use talcum powder to create the grey streaks and pal face? How easy, with make-up to paint on those bruises? Take th microphone away from Donato's face while he's recording, mak him do some push-ups and you have a weak, panting voice. Did yo notice that though he was breathing heavily, the words were perfectl clear. Don't worry too much about the visual and sound effect they're very easily accounted for.'

She calmed down.

What had we got this time? In Donato's letter and tape the figur 'two' or 'twice' had been referred to on five occasions. It could n longer be coincidence, I was certain he'd done a deal. It was si thirty, time for Gianna to go off to the other apartment and take th call.

M: 'It's Mussolini, did you get the package?'

G: 'Yes, but I want to know if Donato is alive.'

M: 'Shut up. I know your mother has two miliardi in her accoun Get it. If it leaves you 1, 1.5 or so short place the ad and we talk.'

G: 'But I want to know about Donato. If he is alive. Ask him. . . .'

M: 'Shut your fucking mouth. Get the money and place the fuckir ad. You're running out of fucking time.'

We could now consider a major offer (possibly bring the total u to 3.2 miliardi) and try for the release. I reviewed the notes whic had brought me to this conclusion before presenting Gianna wi the options. My notes read:

Position of Kidnappers (Demands and Offers)

DAY	DEMAND	OFFER
Day 5	10 miliardi	
Day 8		283 millions
Day 15	5 miliardi	
Day 19		600 mill (+317 mill)
Day 19	10 miliardi	
Day 21		712 mill (+112 mill)
Day 52	5 miliardi	
Day 56		756 mill (+ 44 mill)
Day 59		770 mill (+ 14 mill)
Day 60	1.5 miliardi	
Day 61		945 mill (+175 mill)
Day 64	Accepted	
Day 69	5 miliardi	
Day 105		1395 mill (+450 mill)
Day 113	5 miliardi	

The Gang's Level of Expectation is probably around 2 to 2.5 miliardi. This is based on:

A. The tapes, references to figure 'two'
B. Victim's letters, references to 'two/twice'
C. Gang's last call stating family should have 2 miliardi from mother but saying call if 1, 1.5, short i.e. subtract from total of 5 plus what's on offer, roughly 2.5 with room to negotiate.
D. Victim has probably made deal with gang for around 2.

E. Victim wrote correct names and totals on letters. This means 1 of 2 things:
   1. Gang are very amateur to allow such letters
   2. Gang trust victim is telling truth and they want him to convince family to pay (most likely)
F. Gang now taking hard line and insisting on full amount every time.

Conclusions

A. Gang's tactics have proved successful – no need for them to change for some time.
B. Offer of 3.2 miliardi will initially be seen as just another offer.
C. 3.2 is probably in excess of an amount they were hoping for in beginning. However, their present hopes could have risen to 5 miliardi
D. Gang are now likely to use time as their greatest weapon (holiday in August etc.)
E. Offer of 3.2 miliardi will provide both initial incentive to remain 'high and hard' in terms of demand and negotiating style but as time goes by i.e. after 14 days or so there will be big temptation to accept this amount is all family can collect; it's a substantial figure to turn down.
F. If gang collect 3.2, may be tempted to go for third demand for full amount

Position of Family

A. It will be difficult for Gianna to withstand further long period of silence
B. Family want victim back in shortest possible time
C. G. prepared to use all weapons at her disposal to emphasise strength of position
D. Number of newspaper articles have appeared saying families eventually pay full amount in 'double' situations

Conclusions

A. G. To place an appeal indicating important contact. If gang call – give them strong line – offer 3.2. Place in about 7 days
B. G. should be prepared to remain in that position for 3/4 weeks and then consider reaching agreement (with guarantees) at 5 miliardi

Much of the strength of reasoning behind this major increase revolved around Gianna's rapidly fading strength. In order for it to work the gang had to be convinced that there was no more in the pot. If they were talking to Santini, he had to be convinced as well. He would know that Gianna's morale was getting very low; she'd shown some of the signs before the showdown with him. Therefore the best way to achieve it would be for her to be unmoving. She'd made a last desperate attempt and there was just 'no more'.

If she could stand the tension and accept a wait which could still be in excess of two months there was a fighting chance that it would work. To capitulate too early and reach the full amount would almost certainly lead to a long difficult negotiation over a third demand. This was accepted and an aide-memoire rather than a script was worked out for Gianna. It was a list of the topics she could keep playing on:

- The separation factor
- Mother would give no more (she hadn't had 2 miliardi anyway)
- The police were now 'sniffing around'
- The judiciary were going to sequester property against debts unpaid since Donato's kidnap. Hadn't she told them he worked on credit?
- Only a few of Donato's friends had paid up
- She'd sold everything she reasonably could without police interest becoming too heavy (if they searched the house they'd find the cash and seize it)

In case of surveillance by the gang Gianna had to make frequent trips to her mother and speak at least once to all the men named in Donato's letters. At every contact she had to demand proof that her husband was still alive.

Everyone accepted the tactic. Gianna was warned that it may not work and she could still end up paying the five miliardi; having been exposed to a double payment already, she was happy to take the route which lessened the risk of a third.

Case day 119

The advert was placed; within the text the full amount of 3.2 miliardi was stipulated.

Case days 120 – 144

During this period, the advert was placed on five or six occasions. There was no reply from the gang. Gianna and the team took comfort from the fact that at least they hadn't called to say the offer wa ridiculous. We had to hope that the figure of 3.2 was tempting th gang; hope that they would be arguing about it. It was a lot of money If we were right and Donato had made a deal, I was sure they' crumble. If we were wrong then at least Gianna was prepared fo the full consequences.

I didn't see the sons at all during this long period of silence bu it was pitiful to watch Gianna and Gabriela fading fast like unwatere plants in a greenhouse. They paled, lost more weight and wilte visibly. Every day showed up another stress line, a deepening i colour of the blue circles round their eyes. They took to movin everywhere together, drawing physical and mental comfort fron each other. These are the times when a consultant begins to question his own advice. Not because he thinks it's wrong but because th temptation to take a chance becomes so strong; take a chance an try for a closure, it may just work and their suffering will be over Common sense has to prevail. The equation of suffering now for hopefully limited period versus the near certainty of a later pro longation interrupted by the tensions of a drop which may or ma not result in the victim's release; the scales have to come down o the side of patience.

The relationship between these two women, mother and daughter was going to be stronger than ever after Donato came home. Thi shared agony would never leave their memories. If Giuseppe an Lorenzo were good friends at the beginning, they would be bonde by something much stronger at the end. Something good comes ou of most tragedies but it's of little consolation during the time o waiting. Minutes become hours, days are weeks and a week is a shor lifetime. Silence will sap the strength of Samsons and Amazons.

Every day we met and I went through old cases, tapes, letters an recordings of telephone conversations. It all helped to reinforce th convictions that this was the correct tactic and offered them th speediest return of Donato. He was a businessman, I kept reassurin Gianna and Gabriela, he'd understand the negotiating process; o course he'd be uncomfortable but he'd understand. It was all bein endured in his interest. I told them to fix their minds on that singl issue.

When the first contact comes after a significant period of silence it is almost unwelcome. It isn't known whether the call is going t be an acceptance, a demand, a threat or worse. There's a reluctanc to even accept it. Fear is the dominant emotion. You can feel it. Yo can smell it. It won't go away. Not until the call is made.

Case day 145
Mussolini accepted.

Case days 146 – 152
There was a bustle of activity as clean telephones were arranged, used and changed again in a desperate attempt to make sure the police couldn't make a tap. Every time Gianna or Gabriela went outside the house I had to remind them:

'Nothing's changed. You haven't heard from the gang. Stop looking so cheerful, so hopeful. It's a clear indication to the police that something's about to happen. Things can go wrong. OK, let yourself feel good inside but out there on the streets of Milan you must round your shoulders in depression. Don't give us away.'

We had to have guarantees that Donato would be released. We tried to arrange for a direct exchange of victim for money. It was refused. We kept up the pressure for proof. Questions and photographs. Gianna had to maintain the facade that this was really it. There was no more. She had to relax a bit on the hysteria; if she appeared too unreliable, they may call it off. Lorenzo volunteered to make the drop with Gabriela. All the time I kept up my warnings that something could go wrong. I wasn't being a depressant for the sheer hell of it. If there was a cock-up, if something did go wrong and we didn't get Donato back this time, I didn't want Gianna's final reserves of strength to dissolve. Gabriela, despite her youth, was a tower of strength to her mother. She constantly brought her down from the 'high', back to the reality of the situation.

Case day 152
The proof questions were answered and a photograph of Donato was sent. He was still very pale and unkempt. He looked desperately thin and his eyes were red-rimmed. He was unrecognisable against the press photographs printed some five months ago but there was a bonus, a reason for hope. The white streaks had gone from his beard. This proved to Gianna that make-up had been used on the last picture we'd seen. It was unlikely the gang would overlook that point. It was an indication, a small one granted, but it seemed as though the threats may be over. I didn't mention this to the team, no point in raising hopes unnecessarily.

Case day 153
The drop went off without a hitch. The gang had said that Donato would be released the same night but I'd warned the team that it

was unlikely. They'd count the money first. It was my guess there'd then be a long, heated debate as to whether it was worth going fo a third payment. This could take a few days. When and if they decided to release Donato, they'd probably get out of the area and pay some minor hireling a small sum to free him. We didn't know where he was being held. He was probably in a rural area; it would have been difficult for them to maintain their own security in a bustling city. If Donato wasn't given money, it could take him a while to persuade someone to bring him home. He was unlikely to head for the police. All these and a host of other factors could cause a delay. Above it all hung the possibility of a third payment.

Case day 157

I spent a lot of time preparing Gianna and Gabriela for Donato's release. I demonstrated from the debriefs of other cases how they would need to be delicate and diplomatic with him regarding the negotiations. If he'd done an inside deal, and we were pretty sure he had, he could be embittered because they'd taken so long to respond. After he'd relaxed for a few days he'd be in a better state of mind to accept the team's decisions and the factors on which they'd been based.

I suggested that Gianna make preparations to get him out of the city fast before the police moved in. Let him get everything straight in his own mind before he faced their interrogation. They were going to be annoyed anyway so a wait of a few days wouldn't make the situation much worse. Get him away to the villa, away to the clear fresh smells of the countryside.

We were lucky. Donato was released. Apart from the loss of weight and the lice-infested hair, he was in relatively good health. In the middle of the night of case day 156, his cell door had been unlocked. It was some hours before he gently tested it, tottered out and made his way through the surrounding woods to a village. He'd persuaded a family with a car to drive him home with the promise of a suitable reward if they kept quiet.

I was taken to my dinner by Lorenzo but he waited until we were sipping our coffee and, for me at least, a rare liqueur before getting it off his chest.

'James, in this country there is an amazing number of solicitors and lawyers. The legal structure is so complex with so many departments that it can be an attractive profession. However, because there are so many competitors, the route to the top is open only to the very best.

'So, we have good ones and not so good ones. The not so good ones tend to be able to scratch a living from the less wealthy, the good ones do very well among the rich but, even so, only the selected few move through into the higher ranks of the judiciary.

'Most of us accept this, after all we make a good living. There is a strata, though, which doesn't like it. They become jealous of their client's wealth, bitter when they finally see that they are not going to become high fliers. It is within this strata that the Santinis of Italy ply their trade. The scavengers without morals. There are a surprising number of them, you know.'

He paused to relight his cigar and I began to wonder what his point was. I was aware of the breed he was talking about though Santini was the first I'd met. It was interesting though and I waited for him to continue.

'Even though they are the carrion of our profession (his, not mine), they should be treated with circumspection by outsiders like yourself. You are out of the country, you don't know to whom they speak or what they say about you. You for instance are dependent on an 'in-country' agent to offer your services when kidnaps occur. You need someone who will do this honestly, someone who has seen you at work and understands how you operate. You can't afford the taint of a Santini.'

He paused reflectively.

'I think you've found the person you need, James. Yes, I think you've found him.'

'I agree, Rodrigo's been pretty effective. I have a proper business relationship with him. He gets a percentage of my fees, it's acceptable, legal and morally permissible. He's done well for me.'

I was feeling relaxed. It'd been a pleasant evening. Lorenzo suddenly laughed, a great roar, all the way from his belly.

'Ah, James, in time you'll speak our language very well indeed. You've learned a lot on this case but really to understand us, understand us up here,' tapping his forehead, 'you're going to have to talk to that beautiful wife of yours, Maria. You see, James, Santini was not alone. He was also paying off Rodrigo Arenas!'

To say I was thunderstruck would have been an understatement. I was immediately angry. Lorenzo saw this.

'Calm down, James, it is a fact of life. Rodrigo has had many such arrangements. He pays some of your fees out on occasions and when he has the opportunity he takes a little extra from the other side. It's not generally known yet. Santini told us while he was still trying to shift the blame back to you. Now don't go all English on me and scream down the autostrada in search of Rodrigo. If you want to terminate the arrangement, do it the Italian way. Pay Rodrigo the normal fees for this case. Let him know, politely you understand, that you have become aware of his little game. You do not tell him how you found out. He will probably blame Santini. Simply thank him for his past excellent services and tell him that the business partnership is over. He will not argue or complain.'

Lorenzo was so relaxed, so at ease with this, for him, perfectly normal situation. My anger dissipated quickly. The case had ended well anyway, why should I get uptight and ruin my digestion? I threw my own head back and laughed as loudly as Lorenzo.

'So what's your proposal, Lorenzo?'

'I am from Rome. Rodrigo is a Neapolitan. Let me tell you a story, James.

'There was once a frog sitting by the banks of the River Tiber. As he contemplated the muddy waters, his thoughts were interrupted by the arrival of a scorpion.

'"Hey," said the scorpion, "would you let me sit on your back while you ferry me across this river, frog?"

'"No," replied the frog. "I'm not stupid. You'd sting me and I'd die."

'"Don't be silly, if I did that I'd drown in the river."

'The frog saw the logic of this and agreed to ferry the scorpion across the Tiber. Half-way across, the scorpion plunged his sting into the frog's neck.

'"Why did you do that?" asked the frog as it started to lose consciousness. "Now you'll die as well."

'"Ah," said the scorpion, "it's because I'm a Neapolitan!"

'Do you get my message, James?'

Chapter

8

Author's note

Conflicting personalities in the negotiating team can be a real problem.
When that conflict verges on hatred between two characters central to
decision-making the situation becomes very tense. As often happens in a
kidnap case, sensitive personal secrets can emerge; private facts often not
suspected by the nearest and dearest. This can weaken their resolve and
cause them to question even their desires to retrieve the victim. Disclosure
of the identity of the client in this case could cause great embarrassment to
a respected ex-member of Italy's judiciary.

'HE IS my son! You will sit down, shut up and bloody well do as
you are told!'

Enrico Soussi was angry. He was not used to argument. Dis-
obedience was unknown in his family. His flushed cheeks were
puffed with an awful intensity of emotion; the redness slowly spread
up over his brows, colouring the crown of his balding head. His
hands gripped the edges of the table so fiercely that his arms shook.
Any more provocation and his eyeballs threatened to pop out of their
sockets, so potent was his rage. He must have been a fearsome
sight to the slender woman. Well over six feet tall, broad, powerful
shoulders tensioned against the anguished seams of his jacket, he
was almost out of control.

'We will do this thing my way! Do you understand? In this matter
you are nothing! Look after the kitchen, run the house and leave this
to men.' I said sit down, woman!' He was screaming. Any more and
he was going to literally burst.

She was not impressed. She was not frightened. She slowly and

175

deliberately walked up to the man, thrust her face into his and held his choleric stare.

'Fuck you. All his life you've unmanned him. You'll not take away my spirit. He's my husband; do you understand that? My husband He's no longer tied to your shirt tails. I will be heard in this matter of his life.'

While he was clumsy, trembling and uncontrolled in his anger she was cold, icy and precise. It was the sabre against the epee; the claymore against the rapier; the one hacking and slashing, the other riposting, then darting in with deadly accuracy.

He wasn't beaten, not by a long way. But he had the sense to go back to his corner, take a break and recover his strength. Sensing a round to her, Giulia Soussi also retired. No wound-licking for her just the glacier-like control and a fierce pride holding her together.

'Coffee. We resume in fifteen minutes.'

Not an order in the way it was delivered, but certainly a command by intent. He straightened, took a deep breath, held it for a while and turned round. He had to work very hard at the slow, dignified walk to the door.

'One day you'll push him just too far, Giulia.'

The young man got up to follow his father out, pausing only to look briefly in her direction.

'Oh, shut up Alberto. You'll have to get off the fence sometime you know. The sooner the better. You can't let him rule your life forever.'

He made no reply but did the hint of a blush indicate his shame as he left? He had not been able to meet her eyes. At the other end of the table, Guglielmo Rossini was unmoved by the flare-up. He calmly lit another cigarette, looked at me and shrugged.

'I would like to be able to tell you not to worry, that underneath all this they love each other. Alas, I cannot. Under the surface and on the surface they hate each other like poison. She has robbed him of something, you see. He has lost the son he was moulding in his own image to a vixen who is turning the boy against him.

'We shall have a lot of this I dare say. For Edoardo, I shall try to persuade them to fight before the meetings if they must; fight after the meetings if they have to, but for the sake of tranquillity, sanity and sensible progress they must not fight during the meetings. I have no great expectation of success.'

Guglielmo's presence was a public admission by Enrico Soussi that there was a need for an elder statesman on the negotiating team. They both respected this calm old man but it did not stop the utbursts. There was a quiet authority about him but he had the ense to stay out of the fights. I knew he would speak to them both. What he would say would be out of my earshot but it would stop he gladiators for a few days maybe.

He was over eighty years of age and he looked it sitting down in he old basketwork chair which he favoured over the delicately moulded seats we occupied. The chair was a mark of esteem, I suppose. I could not see why they should have tolerated it in the ouse otherwise. It was stained, creaky and insecure, as seemingly fragile as Guglielmo until he sat down and then you didn't notice it. The wrinkled nut-brown features of the old man were what held you hen. Shrewd old eyes, paling with the years, dominated everyone. Humour, sorrow and compassion were reflected alongside wisdom and patience. He was a good listener and had been sparing with words during the meeting. He made up his mind quickly and cast his vote positively.

He had been one of Rome's finest and most respected judges until he had grown tired of the endless promenade of man's wickedness in front of his bench. The growth of terrorism and the drugs trafficking had disgusted him and he no longer trusted himself to be impartial in his sentencing. For a judge he had a tolerant outlook on the crime of kidnapping. Not that he had any patience with the perpetrators, far from it, but he had seen enough of the human misery they caused. He advocated co-operation with the police but he never remonstrated with families who resorted to lies if they genuinely thought police actions would place the lives of victims in jeopardy.

He smoked incessantly. I had seen him use up a full packet, lighting one cigarette after another from the previous stub. He had been a friend of Enrico since the war. I wondered how the friendship had survived. They were so opposite. The one calm and patient like a tawny owl, the other emotional, intolerant and as unpredictable as an Atlantic typhoon. When he stood up he shed his age like an unwanted mantle. He was upright and sprightly. I had walked with him around the villa gardens and been surprised at the pace he set himself. Despite the cigarettes his breathing remained regular and deep. He put it down to yoga, he said. Self contemplation and total relaxation for at least an hour every day drove all manner of ills away. It was to him I had first been introduced by Lorenzo and it was he who took it upon himself to brief me on the case.

He had related it to me as we walked around the gardens. Edoardo Soussi had been kidnapped two weeks previously. Falling into the trap of predictability and complacency, he had been seized as he went to his office car park early in the morning. He was usually the first to arrive, when the underground park was practically deserted. The one eye-witness who had sensibly taken cover testified to the fact that four men had taken Edoardo, two of them equipped with sub-machine guns. He had noticed my raised eyebrows at that statement.

'Yes, sub-machine guns. We may have a "political".'

It was unusual for the criminal fraternity to be armed with such weapons. They were pretty tightly controlled in Italy even then and the most common arms were shotguns and handguns. It was only an indication, however, not a fact and he dealt in facts, he observed. It had taken the kidnappers nine days to make contact. Of course the police knew about it, the eye-witness had reported it to them before he had told the family. Captain Carrera was in charge of the matter. I knew him – a good man.

It was an unusual demand in that the gang had asked for payment in American dollars, two million of them. That amount would be difficult for any family to get in dollars and it could be a pointer to two things. It could be an early if inadvertent expression that the gang did not seriously expect to achieve that figure, or it could be another indication of a 'political', dollars being of more use than lire on the international weapons market. Again, not facts, not even assumptions; at this stage merely hints.

The gang had made the demand of Enrico, not Giulia; that was not too surprising as Enrico's wealth was well known. The only threat had been in the statement: 'We have all the time in the world. This is political.' This time, to my mind, an indication that it was not political. It was not uncommon for a criminal gang to use the expression 'political' because they knew it struck fear into the hearts of the family. A kidnap by the Red Brigades was quite likely to end in the death of the victim whether the ransom was paid or not. A political kidnap for cash could signify the funding of an operation and equally that could mean the terrorists were in a hurry. It would be very unusual for them to declare that they had plenty of time.

So far the telephone call, five days ago, had been the only communication. I asked what measures the family had taken to prepare for the next call.

'Ah. Signore March, very little has been done. All they have achieved is an agreement to disagree about everything. I should tell you something about the characters you are involved with in this household. Let's go and sit in the sun over there.' He pointed to the bench alongside the rose garden.

There was little space for women in Enrico Soussi's life apart from the solace of the flesh on those infrequent occasions when he felt the need. His late wife, Francesca, a terrified mouse of a woman, had served her purpose in breeding and rearing two sons. This done she was retired into obscurity to a country villa until her early death some ten years ago. Enrico quenched his periodic sexual thirst on a variety of mistresses, all of a very temporary nature. He made no attempt to hide the facts. Women had no other duty than to father sons and comfort men when required.

He dominated his two sons totally. After the best education he could provide he began to indoctrinate them into life and business according to Soussi. Edoardo, the eldest, was a natural businessman and quickly became the favourite. He was being schooled to take over the company when he committed the unforgivable sin. He fell in love!

Enrico tried everything to stop the marriage but Edoardo was completely under the spell of Giulia. What was worse, the wretched woman was clever. She also had the fighting spirit of a terrier; she would not be cowed by the old man. She was a person, not a breeding machine. She would have sons (or daughters) when she chose and not at his whim.

Enrico's time with his heir apparent became more limited as Giulia showed the young man the pleasures of skiing, dancing and dining out. They actually took holidays! In short they were enjoying the happy married life of a wealthy couple very much in love. The first flush inevitably wore off and Edoardo spent more time with the business. Not enough to disrupt his marriage but not enough to fully satisfy his father either. However, an uneasy truce prevailed.

Enrico would occasionally flare up and demand to know why they had no children after six years of marriage. At those times Edoardo would merely state that they had plenty of time. Giulia, though, was quite likely to fly off the handle and demand to know what business it was of the old man's. Sometimes this would lead to a bitter argument which could rage for days. Giulia had discovered that Enrico was driven into a real rage when he heard a woman swear; he had no qualms about using this as a weapon.

Alberto steered a middle course along life's path. He had never been known to contradict his father, indeed it was rare to hear him pass an opinion in front of him. The effect of this was that Enrico virtually ignored him. This suited Alberto; the path of non-conflict was easy. He was careful to perform consistently at the office, never giving his father a reason to notice him. Giulia despised him for what she saw as weakness but also recognised that he was happy in his non-aggressive limbo world.

Guglielmo was a regular visitor to the house of his war-time friend. His calm logic and gentle philosophy had a calming effect on Enrico and he was probably the only person with whom he was prepared to relax. Consequently, when the kidnap happened he was naturally involved. He was very fond of Giulia, it was reciprocated and he had some influence over her when her temper reached flash point.

He told me that the first battle had been after the gang made contact and Enrico decided dictator-fashion that he would make any and all decisions. Giulia would be informed of events as he saw fit. This was resolved by Guglielmo in a tactful fashion when he suggested that as he had spent so many years on the bench it would be sensible if he took the role of chairman at the meetings. He could listen to both parties' points of view, meditate on them and suggest a course of action. It was accepted and the first advice he gave them was to retain a specialist consultant. He had further advised that Alberto sit on the CMT.

'Mainly in his own interests, James, that boy has to start learning about life and decision-making otherwise he will vacillate for ever.' He asked me how I liked to operate and whether I wanted to meet Captain Carrera.

I told him I did not particularly want to meet Carrera but if he Carrera wished it, then I would. We decided to leave the asking to him. I outlined my normal methods *à propos* of the initial briefing and educational phase and he appeared relieved at my statement that I only advised and did not push my opinions onto the client. He had secretly feared that the war of personalities would take on a third dimension.

The flare-up at the first team meeting boded ill for the case. I had given my background brief and started in on the process of likening the kidnap negotiation to a business when Giulia had stopped me and asked her first question.

'Signor March, my husband and I have always thought that in the event of a kidnap, it would be a good plan if we were to say that we were getting legally separated. We had been considering it anyway. Purely for fiscal reasons, you understand. This would give us an ability to negotiate from firmer ground. What do you think?'

I could see Enrico starting to bristle so I answered quickly.

'It's a tactic which has been used very successfully. However, you

180

just accept that it's known to some of the gangs now. We can consider it of course. If we are to use it, it should be brought in at an early stage; if it's to be credible, your husband in captivity has to support it.'

'There will be no talk of separation. It will not be said that my son has no control over his wife, that he cannot keep her in her place. He is my son. The ransom has been asked of me, not her.'

His voice was getting progressively louder and he stood up, leaning over the table, gripping it hard, glaring at Giulia, no-one else. Giula rose as if to speak but was verbally slapped down by the irate Enrico.

'He is my son. You will sit down, shut up and bloody well do as you are told!'

Guglielmo and I did not join the others for coffee. He sat, content with his cigarettes, and I did some quick calculations, converting dollars to lire. I arrived at figures which gave me a rough going rate of about US\$6–800,000 against the wildly fluctuating lire; the demand had not been that much over twice the rate. This was probably due either to the known difficulty of getting clean dollars in that quantity or, if it was political, based on the cost of a planned operation. I tinkered with the figures and various options for setting a negotiating budget. I made notes on the topics I wanted to cover when the meeting resumed:

- Script
- Clean telephone with alternatives
- Police brief
- Negotiating budget
- Team meeting times/frequency/location (business as normal)
- Security
- Gang's possible communications methods
- Tactical options/reasons
- Compilation of proof questions
- Brief on Edoardo's character (from G.R. ??)
- Contact with me: How/When/Why
- Questions from the team

A collision course between Enrico and Giulia was avoided somehow although there were near misses when we discussed the budget and tactical options. I advised that if Edoardo and Giula had already planned to use the separation ploy then it should be initiated in case the victim had already mentioned it. The potential eruption regarding the budget was not so much caused by how much they should be prepared to pay as to who should do the paying. Obviously through Giulia's eyes there was potentially another hold on Edoardo if Enrico was allowed to pay.

Guglielmo skilfully avoided the first clash by making a business analogy which appealed to Enrico. If there was a possible negotiating edge on the deal we should use it. Had Enrico not often said: 'There is no prize in the market arena for the fool who does not use every tool in his box?' I managed the second by simply saying that we were a long way yet from having to pay. It could be argued later.

I added that while this was the subject under discussion, they should start to consider how they were going to put the sum together and perhaps even kick the ball into motion. It was Guglielmo who added that this was wise advice as if they started now they could do it without alerting Carrera.

Guglielmo was to stay in the house and the same invitation was extended to me. I declined for the time being but agreed to move in if events began to progress quickly. I did not want to be in a position where either party could get to me independently of the other. I could see a situation arising where accusations of biased advice could arise. I opted for the Lord Byron instead. The police knew I was on the case and it was pointless to behave like a guilty schoolboy and change my habits. I accepted the invitation to a fairly frigid dinner and vowed not to do so again until they had started to pull together. I had every reason to think they would as the case progressed, after all they both wanted Edoardo back.

My mind was not on the case that night as I took a lonely drink in the bar of the hotel. There were tensions between Maria and me. We both knew the cause. I was spending far too much time away. A marriage cannot work properly with so much separation no matter how strong the love. Problems, even the small domestic variety, cannot be properly talked out on the telephone; to resolve anything you need to see each other, touch each other, relax, flare up momentarily and maybe curse each other – so long as you are in the same room the problem will be resolved.

We had tried to train other consultants to operate with us. We had offered very good deals but we just did not seem to be able to get the right quality. The one kindred spirit we did get could not give a long-term commitment to the company and even though he was immensely useful and became a good friend, it was not sufficient. I still ended up going off for long periods.

We had been let down badly on two occasions just before I joined he Soussi case and it had damaged the business temporarily. Carson had been a disaster on a South American case; he could not be used again. In this business news travels quickly. Reputations are lost overnight. It would not be regarded as 'let down by one of March's men' but 'let down by March'. As President Truman said: 'The buck stops here.' Unjust at times but so is life.

We had two consultants under training in London at that time but I knew in my heart of hearts that they were not going to make the grade. I trusted Maria's assessments completely and she was far from happy with them. It was depressing. Maria was having a hard time and it was not easy to keep my concentration on the case. It was becoming increasingly obvious that if we were to recoup our happiness, some big decision-making would have to take place.

As the 'education' process continued, I was relieved to see that Enrico and Giulia were warring less. They seemed prepared to tolerate each other at least and I suppose that is the best that could be hoped for under the circumstances. I cannot remember Alberto asking a single question in those early days. He had the lowest profile of any person I ever met. He would be sitting in full view of everyone and by his singular lack of presence he could, to all intents and purposes, disappear. He would have made a superb spy – the original grey man.

When the call came, it was Giulia who answered.

'This is Angelo. It will always be Angelo or you don't talk. Who are you?'

'I am Giulia. What do you want? Who are you?' She was puzzled. Not mentally prepared for a call from the gang.

'Stupid cow. You are the wife. We have him. From now you will take all calls. There is a letter in a magazine in the litter bin outside Giorgio's Pizzeria. Go, get it now.' The phone was put down.

She was furious at being caught short. Not so furious as Enrico though. He ranted and raved about her inefficiency. He would take the next call. He would give the bastards what for. This was man's business.

'Stupid cow they called you, heh? Even on the telephone they can tell. Go and get the letter and do not screw this up.'

Amazingly she kept quiet and went out. He immediately ran after her; he had suddenly realised that if she collected the letter she would read it first and that was not in the correct order of things. Guglielmo sighed, drew on his cigarette and spoke quietly.

'It will settle, James. When the realities hit home, when the threats begin, they will eventually find comfort in each other, you will see.'

The letter when it got back to us had been torn in half as the two antagonists had fought over it. It was pretty standard.

> The Soussi family.
> It will always be Angelo from us. It will always be Giuli from you. You have the demand. You will not tell the polic or it will be dangerous for him. When you have the money you will place an advert in *Il Tempo*. It will say:
> 'Wanted English car. Good price paid in cash.'
> Do not waste our time with low offers. The price is fixed Angelo will call at eight o'clock or maybe tomorrow. Pic the phone up at the first ring. He will say: 'Angelo.' You wil only give the new number. Nothing more.

There was no signature or date.

It was a good letter from my point of view. It was along the line which I had predicted and it also gave me the opportunity to g through part of the analytical process with them. I was tempted t ask for their individual observations first but I suspected that Giuli would have scored over Enrico which would not have improved th atmosphere.

'Let's read the letter and see what it tells us about the gang.' made the first point gently; they should try to keep all letters and other deliveries intact. They may at some stage be of forensic import ance to Captain Carrera. I explained that for our part we had t analyse every communication from the gang whether it was a letter note, tape or photograph. This was the only communication s far and now we had to begin the process of getting to know ou opponents.

I went through the note sentence by sentence.

'Firstly, the delivery means was normal. You'll invariably find that notes are left quite close to your house. The main reasons fo this are so that you can react quickly and get to the dead letter bo before someone accidentally removes the message. It also allows yo to move quickly, before the police have time to get round and set u surveillance (assuming that they have heard the instructions via thei telephone tap). On occasions, especially early in the case, they ma even watch you collect the letter. Always assume that this is the cas and do not act suspiciously, do not behave as though you know you're being watched; this could be misinterpreted in that they ma think you are co-operating with the police.' No questions so far. continued.

'The first two sentences are well phrased. The gang is dictating o you. They are in control. "It will always be Angelo. It will always e Giulia." They're stating at an early stage that you dance to their une. The demand was made to Enrico in the first place but the etter is addressed to the "Soussi Family"; there was no insistence o speak to Enrico and this may give us the opportunity to change egotiators at this end if we want to.' There was a growl of assent rom Enrico and an exasperated 'Tut' from Giulia. I did not look at ither of them. I carried on quickly, not allowing them to intervene.

'The instruction not to tell the police is of course a standard varning that you would find in any letter as I've shown you in my les. The warning is quite gentle: "it will be dangerous for him", ot: "we will kill him".'

'The advert is straightforward though I've never had an English ar stipulated before. I wouldn't have thought there was much call or them in the land of the Ferrari and Alfa. It may stand out in the ewspaper columns. If it does we could ask them to change the style. ou'll notice that there's no time limit imposed – not even an nstruction to hurry. They could already be trying to implant in our minds that they have plenty of time; that they feel secure.

'"Don't waste our time with low offers" is interesting. Note the se of "low" as opposed to "lower". It implies a willingness to argain, it suggests that their price is not fixed despite the next entence.

'There's a deliberate vagueness about the timing of the next elephone contact from Angelo, "eight o'clock tonight or maybe omorrow". Again the implication that there's no hurry but it's also alculated to keep you, Giulia, at the telephone for a long period of me. Sitting right by it, have you not been instructed to pick it up t the first ring?

'"You will only give the new number". An obvious precaution. f the police have tapped this line there's a good chance that if you ick up the phone quickly, state the new number and the connection broken, the police will not pick it up.' A long speech, but I wanted o get across the business of analysing everything. They had to pull ogether as a team.

'Now, have any of you noticed anything which I may have missed? Vhat does it tell us about the kidnappers?'

It was Guglielmo who answered first.

'It would indicate to me, James, that the business of the gang eing "political" is highly unlikely. From this letter alone we seem o be dealing with a professional organisation. They have made an mmediate attempt to exercise control. They are calm, well-balanced

and they have covered the essential ingredients of discipline an
security. I question whether a political organisation would be
thorough.'

'You could be right but remember that there's nothing to stop
political or terrorist organisation hiring the services of a profession
gang to actually conduct the kidnap in a surrogate fashion. That
not at all uncommon. Better all round for their security. I'd prefe
to wait until we have more to go on before making my mind up.'

'They are fools. What man in his right mind would choose
negotiate with a woman?' Enrico scornfully added his contributio
Before Giulia could launch her broadside, I moved in.

'In many cases a gang will prefer to deal with the wife or moth
of a victim. Generally speaking, present company excepted of cours
women are more easily frightened by verbal abuse and threats. It
not uncommon for a gang to insist on changing negotiators fr
quently in order to exert the pressure of fear on a greater numbe
of individuals.'

His 'humph' was non-committal. He thought they were fools an
nothing was going to change his mind.

'It seems to me that we've no decisions to make at this stage. W
must wait for the next call and react to that.' Giulia was a little glun

'No. We must never be in a position where we're just reactin
There are some things in this letter which we cannot accept. W
must set about imposing our own will on the kidnappers. The
cannot have it all their own way.'

I went on to suggest we should consider what we wanted. I aske
them to think about it for ten minutes before we pooled idea
Between them they got most of the essentials. This time I did as
Enrico to lead off.

'Two things have to be sorted out quickly. One, that Giulia wi
not be the negotiator on behalf of the Soussi family. Two, that th
amount of money is ridiculous. Not in terms of Edoardo's life yo
understand but we would be setting a precedent in a market
thieves. How we achieve these things is a matter for your advice.'

'Giulia, what do you think?'

'The negotiator is fine. The gang want me and I want to do i
There can be no argument there surely. I agree about the mone
and one method we can use is to get the separation factor across t
the gang right from the beginning. Uppermost in my mind at th
moment is the answer to the question: "Is Edoardo still alive?"'

Well, she had put her finger on the burning issue. We had to fin
that out pretty early. So at least one of them had been listening t

ny lectures. It was Guglielmo's turn.

'I have made similar notes to Enrico and Giulia. We can talk about the negotiator later of course. I would like to suggest that we work out a budget and that we should be prepared to have at least one more clean telephone available to us. Carrera knows what is going on and it will not take him long to discover just by simple surveillance which phone we use next.'

'Good. Together you've covered most of it. There's one more important aspect. Your lives have to carry on as normal, not just for the psychological reasons I mentioned last night but also in the interests of your own security. If you spend hours waiting in a particular building where the clean phone is, or even make regular visits to it, it will not be long before Carrera is on to it.

'To achieve this we have to get across to Angelo that our negotiator will only be at the telephone between set times. We can make this a period of an hour, say, to give the gang a little flexibility. But having stated this fact we must stick to it. We simply cannot afford to have a person sitting day after day just waiting for a call. It would be quite soul-destroying. You'll find that the gang will accept this; it's in the interest of their security also.'

That wise old bird knew why I asked him to lead off on the question of the negotiator. He resolved the problem in exactly the manner I had hoped he would.

'If we are to take the advice of James here, and that is why we have retained him, it seems to me that whoever negotiates on behalf of the Soussi family will need to exert certain disciplines over him or herself. There will be particular messages to put across to the gang; there will be borders of conversation and statement which cannot be transgressed. I believe this sort of discipline is beyond both you, Enrico, and you, Giulia. Apart from the fact that you both have the courage of Spartans and the tempers of wildcats which could lead you to say things we would all regret, particularly Edoardo, you would be forever trying to score points off one another. You would carry your personal campaign onto a battlefield where it does not belong.' He was not a man to mince his words.

'We have been told how important it is to adopt the "business as normal" attitude. Both of you work full time and there may be occasions when calls clash with these hours. It may be an abnormal situation, especially as you have elected me as chairman to this team, but I think the best option is for me to act as your negotiator. What do you think, James?'

I waited a good few seconds before answering. If either of th
others wanted to get anything off their chests, now was the time to
do it. Amazingly they both accepted without demur, Giulia with
light, expressive laugh and Enrico with a wry smile.

'I think it's an excellent idea. We have to convince the gang bu
I don't think that will be a problem. We can tell a few lies abou
our weak, hysterical lady here and a few more about Edoardo'
unpredictable bad-tempered father with the weak heart.'

So Guglielmo was chairman and negotiator. Unusual but no
unique. He was the best equipped for both roles anyway and th
others knew it. It was agreed that Giulia should respond to the firs
call to prevent the gang's negotiator instinctively putting the phon
down at the sound of a man's voice. It was unlikely that she woul
be asked anything other than the phone number but she was briefe
to act a little hysterically and demand to know if Edoardo was aliv
It was almost certain that the phone would be put down but th
hysteria would be noted and it would make Guglielmo's task easie
at the next call. I warned them not to be too depressed if it took th
gang a few days or even more to make the first call: it would fit i
with the implication in the letter that they were not concerned abou
time.

'This is Angelo.'
'This is Giulia. For God's sake how is my husb. ...'
'Shut up. The number. Only the number.'
'789 6564. How is ...'
Connection severed.

They had not given a time. I explained that this could be eith
deliberate – no time problem from their point of view – or it coul
have been an error on the part of Angelo. It was likely that if the
were going to call, the first contact at least would probably be arour
the same time as the last call. Eight o'clock. they were using th
phone in an apartment they had purchased some time ago. It ha
been bought as an investment, for resale, so there was no well-know
link to the Soussis. Guglielmo was to attend the apartment betwee
eight o'clock and nine o'clock each night.

He was very good. In that first call he got across most of what v
wanted.

'Angelo here.'
'This is Guglielmo. ...'
'Where is Giulia. I said only Giulia.'

'She is hysterical. It is this thing on top of the separation, you now. She is going to pieces. From now it has to be me if you want to talk sense. I can be here each night between eight and nine o'clock. We must know....'

'Shut up. Have you the money?'

'We do not even know if he is alive. You ask him: "What was the name of his first dog". When we know we can talk about money.'

'Fool. Of course he's alive.'

'We do not know this. Ask the question.'

'Two days from now.'

There was no request for a repeat of the question. Either Angelo had been expecting it, in which case it was another pointer towards professionalism, or it had been ignored. Time would tell.

Guglielmo had to be ready for the next call in two days. If the proof question was not mentioned he would continue to insist on an answer and be evasive about money. If the question was answered correctly, he was authorised to proclaim how difficult it was going to be to get anywhere near that amount in dollars. The father's dollar resources were limited and the wife, under a separation order had only her own small reserves. They had calculated that they could acquire about US$350,000 and did not see how they could raise more.

US$350,000 was about one third of the demand and about one half of the going rate. This should be high enough to stop the gang becoming too unpleasant but not so high that it would take the boussis too quickly into the zone of acceptability.

The only note of discontent in the team was from Enrico. He took mention of the separation as an insult to the family honour. He was reminded by Guglielmo of his earlier words, 'every tool in the box'. He reluctantly accepted. They were at ease with the logic of the budget, there had been a lot of publicity about the payment of double and triple demands and they were prepared to accept the business-like approach. They had started getting the dollars together. I did not question how this was being done, it was no concern of mine. I wondered how this must be setting on Guglielmo's shoulders. An ex-judge condoning and co-operating in a ransom payment. I thought about Captain Carrera; he had not yet appeared on the scene. Guglielmo himself was keeping him 'informed'; I did not ask for details but it was a point I covered every time we discussed security.

During the next contact the proof question was answered. Guglielmo went into his act and put across the money angle. There wa no sign of anger from Angelo. He coldly refused the offer.

'I told you the price. No less will suffice. Place the advert whe you have it.'

At the meeting we went through the possibilities. On balance thought there would be no further communication from the gan; until we placed the advert. It was pointless publishing this until w were ready to make a slight adjustment to the ransom offer. Th timing of the publication should be in keeping with how long i could reasonably take us to produce the increase. It was decided tha a week would be reasonable, in the Soussi's circumstances, if w were to make an increase of US$110,000. This would raise the tot to US$460,000.

We planned a meeting each day of the week to chat through th tactics which might be encountered. Enrico was mellowing as h became absorbed in the business but the flash point between hir and Giulia remained low. Provided that I showed no apparent bias I was treated respectfully and politely. All the questions they aske me were intelligent and searching; it was a pleasure to work wit them in those early days. I continued to resist the invitations t move into the house. I wanted privacy for a number of reasons. had my own problems to sort out.

This had the earmarks of being a medium-length case; it is neve possible to predict when things are going to break but I reckone that it was a three to four month job at least. I did not see ho I could move either Carson or Wilson out here. They were no temperamentally suited to working alongside characters like Enric and Giulia. I had even discussed this with Guglielmo. He firml advised against an exchange.

'I know some companies do that, James, and the pretext is that allows a number of different minds to be brought to bear on th case. That may be a valid point on occasions but both you and know that the trust element is vital in holding the team togeth when the hard times begin. Both those two in there trust you; it your decision of course, but I would say stay. They would view as desertion.'

That night in the Byron I was working on some details of a U business venture Maria and I were launching when there was a ta on my door. I went across and was surprised to see Giulia throug the spy hole. My first thoughts were that something had happene and as I let her in I went across to the wardrobe and took out m jacket. She put a hand up and sat down on the only chair.

'No. I've come to talk. Not about the kidnap, at least not all about the kidnap. Have you the time? Perhaps we should go to the restaurant, though I'd prefer to talk here. Do you have a drink, please?' She was tense.

I did not have a drink, I rarely touch it but I got her some Bacardi and Coca-Cola from room service and mixed it for her. I sat on the bed. She stayed silent, got up and walked around the room for a while. She was composing her words.

If I had been asked, before I met her, I would have said she was Scandinavian. She was a natural golden blonde with the rounded fresh features that spoke of Nordic mountains and fjords, not the avenues and plazas of Rome. There was a whipcord toughness about her but I question whether I would have noticed that before witnessing her confrontation with Enrico. The bright, piercing blue eyes were direct; I had seen how cold they could be but there was a capacity for softness too; it showed when she laughed, that quiet bubbling mirth which had burst out when Guglielmo had elected himself to be the negotiator.

Something was disturbing her. I waited for her to find her own way to tell me. She continued her pacing. She was tall, long-limbed with the walk of an athlete. She swung her legs from the hips, positively, no high-heeled mincing or chicken-stepping from within the confines of tight, hobbling skirts. If she gave a mute expression of anything it was freedom. 'I am what I am – take me, leave me, I don't give a damn.' She must have seen the father-fettered figure of Edoardo as a challenge. One she had successfully risen to, according to Guglielmo. I looked forward to meeting Edoardo; she must be quite a challenge herself. There was an excitement about her, a magnetism, she was her own statement: 'I'm an equal – I'm daring you.' I suddenly became aware that our eyes were fixed on each other, that she had said something.

'I'm sorry. I was thinking about something. What did you say?'

'I have not said anything yet but I was about to.' She was still hesitating.

'You are married? Yes, of course, Maria. Guglielmo told me. It makes it easier, perhaps you'll understand why I cannot yet talk to the others. This is in confidence. Yes?'

'If it affects the case, we really should talk as a team you know.'

'It may affect the case,' grimly, 'we shall wait and see.' She indicated the Bacardi and I poured her another drink.

'Every Tuesday and Friday Edoardo spends the night in Milan. He goes to visit the manufacturing plant the family owns. It's possible that he will soon be appointed president and then I suppose we should go there to live. At first I went with him but he worked late he would come home very tired and go straight to bed. He suggested about six months ago that perhaps I would prefer to stay here in Rome, he could then work as late as he wished and who knows, he may be able to reduce the visit to one night each week.

I had a foreboding. I knew what was coming.

'It seemed reasonable enough to me. He did not manage to reduce the visits but as I knew the factory was taking on much more work this was not unexpected.' She took a deep breath.

'I now believe that Edoardo had, has, a mistress in Milan. I know he has. There have been calls from his secretary in the factory with little messages. "Rosa called", "Please contact Rosa". For the first time since we were married, I've searched his clothes, desk and briefcases. I've found these.' She threw two or three letters on the table.

'Read them.'

I declined.

'Giulia. I don't wish to read them. That's a personal matter between you and Edoardo. I'm here to advise on the case. I'm sorry you must be shocked and hurt but we must not let it affect the negotiations. There may be a simple explanation when he returns.'

'Pah! Men! The explanation is very simple indeed if you read those letters. I'm very angry about this "Rosa" person.' She spat the name out with pure contempt.

'I am more angry that the spineless bastard I married did not have the courage to tell me that the separation process we were about to go through, for "fiscal" reasons,' she sneered, 'was for the sake of his "puttana" in Milan. Once we were legally separated, the bastard was going to throw me out. Throw me out! He would have hidden while he had the bailiffs do it for him! He must be crapping himself in his prison right now. Sitting there wondering if I'm going to find out his miserable secret. They can keep the bastard!'

She stood up violently, threw the glass against the wall, folded her arms tightly; eyes screwed shut, teeth clenched she ground out what I suspect was the nub of it all.

'What hurts the most, what really makes me want to vomit is that when that dictatorial, egoistic old bastard finds out, do you know what he'll do? He'll laugh! He'll laugh so hard it will hurt him. "My son is not so bad after all," he'll proclaim. He'll delight in telling his friends. He will try to make me the laughing stock of Rome. Fuck Edoardo. He can rot in his cell or cave or wherever he is.'

She threw herself on the bed behind me. At the same time I stood p, trying to look as though I was lost in thought. Great sobs racked er as she lay face down. Sobs of rage, not sorrow or self-pity. God, e was lovely to look at as the loose silk skirt settled and moulded self to that athletic, well-formed body. She was suddenly quiet. lowly, sensuously she rolled onto her back, legs ever so slightly arted. She drew up one knee exposing a tanned thigh. Eyes still osed, her face softened, the slightest of smiles appeared.

'I have been told that the English can be good lovers. Is asking ur Maria the only way I'll find that out?

Dry-mouthed, I tried to sound calm.

'Revenge is no motive for an affair, Giulia.'

She laughed and came off the bed in a smooth leaping motion, rew her arms round me and kissed me full on the mouth. A fleeting ss but a kiss with a promise.

'You're right. Take me to dinner. I want to talk to someone tonight ho is not Italian.'

A safe and sensible solution. My thoughts alone had been enough prick my conscience!

Relaxing over coffee, I raised the subject again.

'You know we could use your discovery to attempt an early release. we were to convey to the gang that you have no real interest in ur cheating husband, it may just give us an edge. To make it work, doardo would have to be convinced that you know the truth but at wouldn't be difficult. It could be done in such a way that Enrico inks it's all a pretence. The truth wouldn't come out until after doardo's release and you could make sure you have him to yourself r the first few days.'

It had an almost comic attractiveness to me. It was the first and ly time I ever suggested a private plot to an individual member a negotiating team but in this case I do not think Giulia would go ead with anything which gave Enrico a chance to deride her. This ay she could have the last laugh. If she decided to go ahead with I privately vowed to let Guglielmo into the secret.

I explained how a similar tactic had been used in the Romero case ith good success. Her only query was how to let Edoardo know.

'It's easy if you really have discovered who his mistress is. Ask a roof question: "What is the surname of Rosa from Milan?" He'll ow all right. Do you know the name by the way?'

'Yes. It's Santorini. She's just been fired, on my instructions. She ft without a reference. Perhaps my question should be: "What is e surname of jobless Rosa in Milan?"'

The idea had appeal but she wanted to think it through. Would I propose the idea using the Romero case as my example? This would sit well with Enrico. I told her that I would. My interest was in getting her husband out.

'I suppose it's time to say goodnight, James?' The spoken question was backed up by the very open invitation in her eyes. I pretended not to notice either but I do not think I was very convincing.

I went with her to the car park. She smiled 'goodnight' as she lowered herself into the little sports car, taking full advantage of its awkwardness to manufacture temptation again with glimpses of thigh and bosom.

The advert was placed on schedule. The gang responded to it quickly but Guglielmo was given very little time to complain about the difficulties of raising the money. 'The price is the same' was the message, there was to be no more time wasting. During the meeting that night I caught Giulia looking speculatively at me on a number of occasions. She did not mention our chat; I would have been surprised if she had. When we broke up I invited Guglielmo to have dinner with me. I know Giulia guessed my intention; she smiled faintly and nodded.

Over the meal I mentioned Giulia's revelations (not the invitations); I put the concept to him. He laughed at the idea.

'It has great appeal, James. What I like about it is that Edoardo and Giulia get to sort out their own problems without that cantankerous Enrico getting involved. Tell me more about the Romero case. Did it really shorten the captivity.'

'It's difficult to say "yes" with any certainty. I felt at the time that it did get things moving forward fairly briskly. There's always the chance that the kidnappers will suspect a ploy, that's why Edoardo has to be convinced. It should give him time to get his excuses together so there is a bonus from his angle.'

I suggested it at the next meeting. The committee had decided on a smaller raise to be offered in seven or eight days time. They were going for US$49,500 bringing the total up to $510,500. They were rushing a bit, I thought, but not to an alarming degree. Guglielmo asked a question.

'James, is there anything we can do to make the separation factor a little bit more important to the gang. They do not seem to be at all concerned about it.'

'There is something which may work to our advantage. It would require some lies to be told and if it gets to the ears of Edoardo, it may cause him some stress.

Enrico was interested. Guglielmo considered me carefully through the perpetual blue haze of smoke. Giulia's mouth was compressed in a good imitation of a disapproving wife; a closer inspection would have revealed the humour in her eyes. Fortunately Enrico was not that perceptive.

'If the gang were to be convinced that Giulia's interest in Edoardo was waning, say for instance she'd discovered that he had further mistresses. Of course I'm assuming that a fictitious mistress was the cause of the fake separation in the first place? If this fact had also greatly angered Enrico, because he is so fond of his daughter-in-law; that he too was not very concerned how long his son was imprisoned, then it might just make things move a little faster. It'll probably cost you the same amount of money at the end of the day but it just may speed things up. There's an increased danger of Enrico taking a beating and the gang will certainly begin to threaten you to test your convictions. I think it's something you should think about together. You and Giulia.' To Giulia's disgust I addressed the final words to Enrico.

'No need for me to discuss it; it may sow some proper ideas in his head. A man should have a mistress, at least one. If it could help Edoardo without increasing the danger significantly, I would vote for it.'

'I of course am worried about the effect it may have on poor Edoardo.' Said so sweetly it was painful.

Unknown to Enrico, the next proof question was to be about Rosa in Milan. Of course Guglielmo would have to forget to switch on the tape recorder to hide the fact. They had first thought to pass off Rosa quite openly, as being a mutual friend of theirs in Milan but it was Guglielmo who cautioned Giulia by telling her that it was always possible that Enrico knew about the mistress. In which case he would be having a quiet laugh at Giulia's expense.

'But, not the last laugh. That is for me.' I believe she was looking forward to it. I wondered how she spent her evenings when Edoardo was in Milan. It was an interesting thought.

I had not expected her to appear at the Byron that night but somehow when the tap came at the door, I knew it was her. I flashed across the room, put my jacket on, and as I opened the door I took her by the elbow and steered her straight to be lift and down to the restaurant.

Edoardo was not mentioned over the meal. I cannot really remember all the conversation but I was very conscious of her. At one point she was facing me, chin cupped in her hands, elbows on the table, just looking. With the candlelight flickering across her face, casting elusive shadows over her warmly liquid eyes, she was as desirable at that moment as any woman has been to me. I cannot remember my will power ever being put to greater test. I got the thoughts out of my mind by playing the old mental game of 'comparisons'; Kipling's original idea, I think. 'She was Italian: I was not.' 'She was wealthy: I was not.' 'She was beautiful: I was not.' 'She was available: I was not.' 'She was lonely: I was not.' The last comparison struck a jarring note!

I was rescued from further thoughts by a 'hrrumph'.

'Captain Carrera. How good to see you. What are you doing here?'

'I thought I may find Signor March in his usual hotel. I thought it was time we met again.'

I stood up to shake his hand.

'Captain Carrera, it's good to see you again.'

It was good to see him again. I never looked him up when I was in Rome; it could have been embarrassing for both of us. If he wanted to see me, he made the contact.

'Please, sit down. Join us for a drink. Signora Soussi will be leaving shortly.'

Will power had saved me the first time, fate the second. I would have to make sure there was no third testing of human frailty. Indeed Giulia did leave shortly afterwards. She was not in the least upset by my comment to Carrera; I think she read me well enough.

Carrera and I reminisced about some of the cases we had both been involved in. He only spoke about the Soussi case once.

'He is a good man, Guglielmo, a great loss to the judiciary. He holds you in some regard, James. He tells me everything that is happening.'

I knew this was an invitation to comment. I did not follow his lead and he would have been surprised if I had. Carrera was a man who would be unnoticed in a crowd. His face was that of everyman. There was simply nothing to attract attention. He was not ugly, he was not handsome. He had an ordinary voice and he wore ordinary clothes. He drove an ordinary car in an ordinary way. He did have an extraordinary job, however. A job he was very good at; a job helped by his natural anonymity. He was head of Rome's anti-kidnap squad and he had had some outstanding successes. I had, and have a high regard for Captain Carrera. He did not stay long. I suppose he was letting me know that he knew I was 'on the job' and perhaps hoping I may have contributed something to his knowledge about the case.

The day after the advert was placed Guglielmo took a call.

A: 'This is Angelo. I hope you're not wasting my time.'

G: 'We have managed to get a little more money. It is getting very difficult. Perhaps you would take some in lire.'

A: 'How much more?'

G: 'We must know that Edoardo is still OK. Ask him the last name of Rosa in Milan. I also have problems with the family.'

A: 'Problems. What problems?'

G: 'Giulia is angry. She is spitting blood. She has discovered even more mistresses. She says: "Let him rot in hell." The father is on her side. My job is getting very difficult. They do not seem to care any more.'

A: 'Balls. Ask her, ask him if they care enough to receive one of his fucking fingers. Now, how much do you have?'

G: 'With great effort we have managed to collect another $49,500. That is $510,500 altogether.'

A: 'I can count, idiot. We want at least one and half million. No more fucking time wasting. If it happens again you get a finger to help you remember him by.'

G: 'Look, when will you call? With the answer. You must help me to help you. They are so difficult. I tell you they do not care. They said he is not worth any more. When will you call? They will do nothing until they know he is alive. That way I can try to persuade them to borrow something, to find a little more.'

A: 'When you have the fucking money. That's when I'll call.'

Guglielmo did produce the tape. He had recorded a chair scraping over the floor at the point when he asked the proof question. Enrico was none the wiser.

So, the gang had reduced their demand by about half a million. That was surprisingly quick and a fairly hefty drop. There was always a chance that they had seen me with Giulia and then watched Carrera join us. It was highly unlikely though – there would have been a mention of staying away from the police in the phone call.

The team was excited about the sudden decrease and wanted to place another advert and raise the offer straight away. They were soon talked out of it. If anything our adverts should get further and further apart with the increases correspondingly smaller. I went along with the placing of the advert but suggested that there was no raise at this point. Guglielmo should use the resultant call to lay it on about the disinterest of Enrico and Giulia. He must insist on proof as an aid to his own bargaining power with the other two. He was after all trying to help the gang as well. They had to help him. Psychologically he was joining their team.

'Santorini' was indeed given as the answer to the proof question. In private, Giulia told me of her glee.

'Edoardo, dear, Edoardo, how you must be sweating now. Let me tell you, James, that little bitch Santorini had just lost her third job. She will never hold a job down in Milan.' She told me she was having the girl followed. Every time she got a job, Giulia hired someone to make sure she was just as quickly sacked. 'Hell hath no fury' took on a whole new meaning.

When I called Maria that night I realised how strained our relationship was becoming. She was engrossed with setting up the new company in London and I wanted to discuss the case. We were becoming remote from each other. I felt unsatisfied after the call. Things were happening in the UK and I was not involved. It was irritating and frustrating. This was a dangerous state of mind; a consultant needs to be able to devote full and absolute attention to the case in hand. We had to do something. I made a decision and called Maria again.

'Send Charles Cox out. I'm going to see if I can get away for a few days.' Charles was one of the team. He had advised on a number of short cases in South America which made him my most experienced consultant at that time. Cox was very sharp on the appreciations and he had grasped the tactics quickly. Maria was not at ease with him, though. There was something she could not put her finger on.

I told the Soussis that Charles was coming and the object was to give him further on-the-spot training. Once I had assured them that he was bound by the company rules of confidentiality, there was no problem. It was three days before Cox got to Rome. I decided not to introduce him to the family until he had had a chance to thoroughly read himself into the case and ask me all the questions he wanted.

It did not take him long. As Maria had told me, he had a quick mind and was at home with the technicalities. The day after his arrival, I took him to a team meeting. He took a back seat; at this stage he was there to listen and get a feel for the Soussis and how they ran their meetings. Enrico had placed the advert that morning and a call was expected later. When Guglielmo went off to the other apartment to await the contact, I took Charles into the garden to chat over the meeting, the family and the tactics we were using.

'Well, what do you think, Charles?'

'Considering the tactics being used, they seem to be standing up to it rather well. I get the feeling that Giulia is the least worried of them all. Why's that?'

That was pretty perceptive. He had only had her facial expressions to work on. If he was to take over from me, he had to know the full facts and so I told him the background to it.

'Good God. Do they always get internally complicated like this?'

'There are always internal complications. We, as consultants, try to stay out of the family squabbles. This is something of a unique case where I was told about the discovery of the mistress and saw a way to take advantage of it. If Enrico were to find out before Edoardo is released I dare say his anger at being fooled would blind him to the realities of the situation. Afterwards, I think he'd be OK, probably appreciate it in fact. For the time being, neither you nor I know anything about Rosa.'

Guglielmo had taken the call and we were summoned back to the meeting. I looked at my watch. He had been away over two hours; they had made him wait this time.

Guglielmo reported that the call had been abusive when he had said that he had no more to offer. However, Angelo had answered the proof question. He had then been instructed to collect a package. He brought the package out of his pocket and grimly dropped it on the table. It landed with a dull thud. It was about four inches long, wrapped in a dirty reddened piece of rag and tied with some grubby twine. It rolled once and left a red patch on the surface of the table. I looked at the others. Guglielmo, slightly paler under his tan; Enrico looking quite sick; Giulia's face was a strange mixture of revulsion and shock; the 'invisible man' Alberto stared, horrified, and with a retching sound left hurriedly. Charles Cox was fascinated. He had seen enough gore in Northern Ireland not to be sickened; in fact I think he came to the same conclusion as I did and almost as quickly.

If that package was a finger, and it was obvious that everyone except Charles and I thought that was the case, it would have to have been severed in the very recent past; blood does not stay as liquid as whatever substance was on those rags for very long. Hoping I was right, I reached out for the package. I unrolled the material and sure enough, inside was a tube of paper and a rolled up Polaroid type photograph. A few pebbles wrapped in tissue paper had been put down the middle of the tube to give it some weight.

The photograph was of a very dirty Edoardo, sitting facing the camera with his eyes partly closed against the flash. He looked reasonably well, pale, thin and dishevelled but unmarked. He was holding a copy of the previous day's newspaper. The letter was signed by him.

> Cara Giulia,
> With all my heart I beg you to end this torment. Get the money as quickly as you can. I know it is not easy but we have friends, for God's sake. I am in misery here. I am chained to a bed, I cannot wash and I feel so ill I think I will die if I do not go home soon. We will talk about our problem. I love you, Giulia. Now they say they have to cut off my fingers to persuade you. Speak to my father. Tell him I am desperate.
> Edoardo

On the reverse of Edoardo's letter was a message from Angelo:

> Soussis:
> You have 7 days to get some more money. After that it is 1 finger for every day you delay.
> Angelo

This part of the communication had been typed.

Even though the initial shock had now been replaced by sheepish grins and a general relaxation, the 'blood-stained' package had lent a reality to the threat. They believed it could happen. I talked to them about the contents.

'Remember what I've been telling you about letters. They don't come from the victim. They're messages from Angelo. Sure, Edoardo wrote the letter but he was told what to put. Read it. Is that Edoardo talking? No, of course it's not. The trick they used with the ink or ketchup, it was very effective. It has thrown you off-balance, weakened your sense of resolve. This is exactly what it was supposed to do.'

I was walking round the table, looking at them all in turn, animated and excited. This is what the job was all about. Taking away the fear and demonstrating the true meaning of the crude threats.

'You've been set a deadline. Seven days to produce "some more money". Note that, please: "some more money". Not, as you may expect, "the rest of the money", but "some more money". It robs the threat of its sting, doesn't it? It implies that they don't expect all they've asked for. Now you have to be strong and continue the line that Giulia is not too bothered about Edoardo and that getting the dollars is difficult. What do you think you should offer?'

Guglielmo took the stage.

'It seems to me that we have to come up with an amount which will show that we are trying, though not necessarily desperately. It should be enough to be of sufficient interest to dissuade them from carrying out the threat. I would guess that somewhere in the region of $20,000 might be reasonable. What I do not know is when we should offer it.'

'Surely we offer it tonight. That way we can be sure they will not take a finger.' Enrico spoke positively.

I turned to Giulia interrogatively.

'I agree with the amount but, like Guglielmo, I am not sure when we should offer it. Tonight seems too early.

As Alberto was still missing, I carried on.

'Think of yourselves as a fruit machine, a one-armed bandit. You've paid out the guy who got the jackpot. He's quite pleased but as he walks away he gives you a nudge and surprise, surprise, some coins fall out. He gives you a kick and a few more fall out. He'll carry on kicking until the coins become so few that it's not worth his while continuing in case a passing policeman notices him.

'You offered to pay out a certain amount, $350,000. You were nudged a couple of times and now the offer is $541,500; a few more coins at each nudge. You've now been given the first kick. If too many coins fall out this time the temptation will be to give you a really hefty kick. If there's only a dribble, there may be just another gentle kick before the punter loses interest. $20,000, I think, is a little too much, a little too interesting. I'd suggest that somewhere in the region of $10–14,000 would be more effective. You have to live with the story that it's difficult to obtain. To make the offer tonight wouldn't support that. I'd say leave it until about the fifth day.'

There was no doubt that the package had thrown them but Guglielmo was a good chairman. He went through all my points again, sometimes breaking into rapid Italian. I took Charles outside again. I told him that it was often a good idea, once the advice had been given, to leave the team to their own devices for a while. It forced them to discuss things in their own way. You were not there to answer questions at the time and even though they knew you would be back, they often got things worked out for themselves.

'Why does Giulia look at you the way she does? Has something been going on there?'

No questions about the case, just about Giulia.

'No. We had a little misunderstanding earlier on but it's finished now. I think it's just a coincidence.' I should have said more!

The Soussis had decided to place the advert on the fifth day and make an increase of $13,000. This would bring the total on offer up to $544,500. This should be within the zone of acceptability. I personally thought that there would be another kick or so, another squeezing of the sponge. Their timing and the amount were about right.

That night I hosted a dinner for Guglielmo and Charles. I wanted Charles to do most of the talking, impress his personality on Guglielmo, gain his confidence. I was disappointed. He talked all right, but only about the case. His attitude was rigid. 'In such a case we'd do the following,' and so on. When he excused himself briefly, I put my question to Guglielmo.

'I want to go home for a few days. Are you happy if I leave Charles to advise you? I can be contacted on the telephone at any time of the day or night and fly back out within twenty-four hours if necessary.'

'I have no doubt that Charles is a very capable young man. I also have no doubt that by the end of the first team meeting he would have alienated both Enrico and Giulia. If we have got this right, events could begin to move quickly. If you left at this time, whatever your motives, and I am sure they are good, the Soussis would see it as a let-down.

'Charles is too rigid in his delivery of opinions. I am sure that he calculates the percentages absolutely correctly but personality is so important. You did not gain the Soussis' trust overnight, did you? What happens if the case reaches a critical point while you are away? We will be in the hands of a man we do not know. It may colour the decision-making. Do not go unless you have to, that is my advice and request.'

There was little point in ignoring that statement. There was also little point in keeping Charles in Rome. He might as well be back in London helping to take the workload off Maria. I sent him home, very disgruntled, the next day.

Three days later I got a call from the airport. It was Maria.

'Can you pick me up? I've taken a few days off.'

It was odd that she should come to Rome without telling me but I was delighted to see her. I picked her up myself. On the way back to the Byron she was strangely quiet, distant. I chatted away telling her about the case and that I thought another couple of weeks or so could see it finished with a bit of luck.

'Yes, Charles told me it seemed to be going well. Why did you really send him back?'

I told her about the dinner and Guglielmo's advice. She knew the form, surely, she knew how important the personal touch was, especially towards the end of a case. She asked me about the family and the team members. She kept referring to Giulia and the penny dropped. She was suspicious about her. It had to be something Cox had said. I should have told him everything. He had obviously misunderstood the situation and made one of his cryptic comments which had been misinterpreted by Maria.

I told her about the whole business. I had nothing to hide. I had to admit to a severe temptation, what man would not have been tempted? Nothing had happened. It might be a good thing if they met. I was not sure at the time whether I was believed or not. Maria went home a couple of days later and I was left with plenty of time to think about the problem. The separation had to end. It was causing suspicion, tensions we neither wanted nor needed. I knew it could become like a cancer, eating away at our relationship if some immediate action was not taken to excise it. For the time being, however, I had to concentrate on Edoardo Soussi.

Events moved quickly. The offer of $13,000 brought a tape and photograph plainly showing that Edoardo had suffered a beating. The Soussis held firm. They made a further offer of only $7,200. Angelo accepted and drop instructions were sent. Surprisingly, as a result of pressure from Guglielmo, the police were informed. Carrera had the drop car followed.

The drop was made on schedule but as the team drove away the police went into action but all but one of the ransom collectors got away. The other was shot; he died before he could give any information. There was now a danger that the gang would kill Edoardo.

Guilia became very depressed. Enrico, surprisingly, made valiant attempts to comfort her. Even Guglielmo was beginning to question the wisdom of telling the police in the first place. He had wanted to and now he was blaming himself for having been too persuasive. The police meanwhile mounted a massive search. They did not declare it but we all knew they were looking for the grave.

Four days later Edoardo was found. He was wandering, weak and battered from a savage beating, still manacled but very much alive, in a remote mountain village.

I did not stay to meet Edoardo. I never heard how he and Giulia resolved their differences, or if they ever did. Whatever happened I reckon he would have paid a high price for his infidelity! I had my own problems to resolve and it was these which occupied my mind on the journey back to London and Maria.

CHAPTER

9

Author's note

Central to success in negotiation is the ability to persuade the kidnapper that he had made a mistake regarding the wealth of the victim or his family. He has to be convinced that the money on offer is all he will get for a variety of reasons. Various techniques for achieving this have already been outlined in the preceding chapters, but what happens when the kidnapper has in his possession indisputable proof of the victim's riches? This must surely rob the negotiating team of any worthwhile strategy. Due to events which transpired during this case with the collusion of a remarkable policeman, both the client's identity and the location of the action have been hidden

THERE it was again. The soft, muted popping as a foot crushed a dry bracken seed pod. I kept very still, trying to control the shivering which wasn't entirely brought on by the pre-dawn cold. Beside me Giovanni broke into a sweat – I could smell it. Good, that meant he'd also heard the approach. Three feet in front of us, in four dirty sacks, was 700 million lire. Enough to kill for? Easily. There was a faint rustling, then the noises stopped. Whoever was coming had sat down, I guessed. He'd be waiting for those first pale streaks of dawn light to strengthen. He'd want to watch the money for a while, make sure there was no ambush.

Army training took over and I breathed lightly to reduce the motion of my chest and shoulders. Why is a sneeze always imminent at a time like this? There was a faint click from the same direction. To me it was unmistakable. I'd heard it too many times before. It was the sound of a safety catch being eased off – always the final little click to give it away. What sort of weapon was it? I wasn't worried about a pistol but if it was a shotgun or sub-machine gun we could be in real trouble lying so close together.

From the corner of my eye I could see Luigi's foot begin to twitch; lightly at first and then more violently. Damn it, I could hear it now. Bloody fool. No good blaming him, cramp can happen to anyone. Ever so slowly I began to reach out my hand. My cuff nagged on a branch and I lost a couple of precious seconds easing it free. 'Slowly, slowly,' I told myself. I got hold of Luigi's ankle and exerted a steady downward pressure. It worked, the shaking stopped. I brought my arm back just as carefully. Had the man seen me? I don't think so, he'd have fired or run.

It would be another thirty minutes or so before it was fully light. Would our crude camouflage be sufficient? We'd been unable to do more than pull a few handfuls of dead bracken over us when we'd settled in to wait over two hours ago. Christ! There he was! He seemed to be looking straight into my eyes. Bugger! It was a shotgun in his hands. No. He hadn't seen me. God, he must be blind. He was sitting cross-legged, back against a thick shrub to mask his outline; in front of him a fallen tree gave him a good cover. He was moving his head slowly as he looked around, listening intently for alien noises. He was a good woodsman. He sat very still, only the steady motion of his head betraying him. I could only hope his alertness would fade as his confidence grew. So, that was one of them, where were the others? There'd be at least two.

How long would they wait? I had the patience learned from many ambushes and uncomfortable surveillance tasks in Northern Ireland but I didn't know about my two companions. What I did know was that their pistols were holstered and that worried me. When they had to move they'd be stiff and cramped, giving our prey plenty of time to loose off both barrels with potentially devastating effect at that range.

Come on! Where were the rest of them? I couldn't hear anything apart from our own breathing. Was that one of them? Behind us! Had we been seen? Why had I let myself get talked into this one?

When Roberto Di Pierro was kidnapped he was very unfortunate indeed. He was snatched from the street in Naples as he left a meeting at his head office. At the time he was carrying a briefcase which the kidnappers took with them. The contents of the case were to give the gang a powerful edge in the negotiations.

Di Pierro was the president of one of Italy's most prestigious motor car dealerships. His empire was vast and he owned it jointly with his wife. It was day four of the case when I flew out to meet her.

Editta Di Pierro was a striking woman. In her early forties, her raven black hair had retained the colour and sheen of teenage years. Brown eyes and a straight, classic nose were features of a head held erect and proud. When she smiled her full sensuous lips parted to reveal brilliant, white, even teeth. Lovely without a doubt, but there was something slightly odd about her face. It took me a few minutes to realise that there was no curve to her abnormally long eyebrows. They lay horizontal, producing an odd effect, almost as if her head had a lid; if you gave the hair a gentle tug the whole face would separate.

She used her English competently and confidently. She told me I'd been recommended by Gianna Vencato. She knew my fees and my background; she wanted to use my services. She had told the police everything which had happened so far. The person she was dealing with was Captain Giovanni Colavolpe, head of the Naples kidnap squad. She liked and trusted him. She'd told him that she intended to use me and he'd welcomed the idea. He would be coming around later to meet me if I had no objections.

'Before I tell you what has happened, Signore, I want to explain our attitudes to kidnap, that is myself and Roberto. We have discussed it many times. We live with the threat like many others and we take as many precautions as we can but neither of us is prepared to live in a cocoon. We think the crime is disgusting, the worst form of blackmail. We both accepted long ago that if either of us were taken it would be a long affair. We will not simply hand over whatever the kidnappers ask for. We will fight to the last penny.

'We also decided that we would co-operate with the police. If no-one ever takes a stand against these thugs when will it ever end? That is our position. Whatever messages come from those who have taken him, I will know that Roberto wants me to stand firm just as I would want him to if I were captive. I know it will not be easy.'

Quite a speech! I reached for my case to start my brief. I was going to give it to her whether she wanted it or not. It would save questions later. I knew that from experience. She stopped me.

'We have a problem, Signore. I know that in these cases it is customary to bargain with the gang, to try to persuade them that getting cash is difficult. Try to get them to think they've made a mistake about the victim's wealth. I have spoken to others, not just the Vencatos. This is where we have the problem. Our company made profits of over thirty miliardi in the financial year which has

ust ended. Profits which have not yet been invested. The gang know
this. In my husband's briefcase which he was carrying at the time
was a copy of the newly audited company accounts.' She paused for
breath.

'This makes it difficult to plead poverty. The gang will also assume
that we have only shown on the account that which we want the
authorities to know about. They will assume we have more put away
somewhere. This is true of course, and must not be mentioned in
front of Giovanni.'

I ignored her statements for the moment and did my introductory
chat, background, business analogies and the like. I then asked her
what had happened so far.

'Are you not worried about the accounts?'

'Not unduly. We'll find a way around that in good time. First, I
need to know what's happened. Is the gang calling you here?'

'Not any more. They will call at a prearranged time to a telephone
in my friend's apartment. I will go alone in case they are watching
and I will record everything for you. Giovanni Colavolpe will be
able to listen in directly. They said they will call again in three days
time. That's tomorrow.'

'So they have actually called here?'

'Yes, twice, the day after the kidnap. They asked me to find what
they called a "clean" phone. I have not been able to tell them
anything yet; they just say what they have to say and the phone is
put down. So far they have not mentioned the accounts or a ransom.'

'It's unlikely but they may call here again unexpectedly. You must
be ready for this. If it happens before we have the chance to prepare
our tactics just keep insisting that you want proof that they are the
people who have your husband and that he is alive. Think of a
question only he could answer and put it to the gang. Tell them you
won't discuss money until you have the answer. I suggest we have
a little script.'

The 'script' isn't the detailed paper which the name implies. It's
just a short list of headings to help the person on the phone to get
the main points across. If the gang's negotiator is being abusive or
if tapes are being played, it's very easy for the speaker to lose his or
her way. Concentration on the notes helps. In Signora Di Pierro's
case it was very simple indeed:

Concern over Roberto	– No letter from him
	– Is he being well treated?

	– Is he alive?
	– You must prove this to me
	– Ask him (proof question)
Money	– Can't even think about money until I know he's alive
If pressed	– Far too much
	– We don't have that sort of cash
	– I will get what I can but prove he's alive

At this stage I couldn't advise on amounts to offer until the gang made a demand and she briefed me on the case. This was purely a holding script in the case of an unexpected call. She was happy with the notes and I asked her to give me the rest of the details.

She told me that the recordings were with Giovanni; he would be bringing them round later if I agreed to meet him, otherwise she would collect them. She was perfectly calm throughout the brief. She spoke in matter-of-fact tones which I found disconcerting. On the one hand it made a great change to deal with a person whose mind wasn't clouded by emotions but on the other it was so unnatural. Her husband had been kidnapped and she was discussing it as though it were an everyday occurrence. How often had I spent hours convincing families that it's just a business? Here was one who clearly understood that and I should have found it refreshing. But somehow I didn't.

When Roberto hadn't returned home by seven o'clock on the fateful day, she knew something had happened though she didn't immediately suspect a kidnap. She first thought of an accident; he was a ferociously fast driver. The one think she was certain about was that if he expected to be late he would have called. He always did, it was part of their self-devised security practice. She alerted the police who checked traffic accidents and hospitals in the Naples area with negative results. At this point she began to fear the worst.

'Keep calm,' Roberto had said. 'Read our plans and be ready when they call.' They'd spent a long time compiling an action plan in the event of kidnap and it was to this which Editta first turned. The first thing was to convey the suspicions to Giovanni, with whom they'd ad many a long discussion. Get the telephone tapped as a matter of urgency. They'd assessed a crude figure of what they may have to pay based on newspaper reports and Giovanni's advice. This was already accumulated in the cellar, a sum of 500 million lire.

They'd decided to make all decisions themselves. They wouldn't have friends or family as members of a negotiating team, it wasn't necessary. They would rely on the experience of the police for all advice on attempting to capture the gang and they would retain the services of a private consultant for the practical purpose of negotiation. They'd decided against insurance as they were worried about the motivation of the consultants. Were such men employed simply to reduce the underwriter's payout figures?

They'd arranged a system of telling each other by letter or tape how they were holding out. If they used their full Christian names to sign letters, all was well. If they dropped off the last letter, which can easily be done on a signature, then they were holding up but maybe getting tired; nonetheless, stay with the plan. If they used their pet names then they were in trouble of some sort. This meant take a chance and go for a quick conclusion, even if it's very expensive.

They'd thought about proof questions. They'd arranged these so that simple statements could be passed back and forth.

'What was the name of our German au pair when we first moved to Naples?' This meant that he or she wanted to tell the kidnappers about the heart problem and was the other in a position to act the part?

If the answer consisted of one name, Anne, then it meant go ahead. If both the au pair's names were used. Anne-Marie, it meant that for some reason the ploy wasn't to be used. All the questions they'd worked out had one or two word answers. If the reply was one word it meant agreement, two words, 'no'. It was simple and effective. Provided that the victim was mentally capable of recalling the answer to the question in the first place, the 'yes' or 'no' rule was easily remembered to either give consent or signify understanding of a situation.

They hadn't overdone it. They'd appreciated that too many questions could be difficult to remember as time in captivity took its toll of the mind. Just half a dozen was sufficient, they thought. They could refer to money using a question on America (dollar connotations for ease of remembering); a question about their watchdog observation) would tell the victim that the police would be on the scene at the drop; if one of Roberto's salesmen was referred to it would mean the police were going to attack the hide-out (Roberto called his salesmen the company's 'attack force'). A question about a missing diamond ring would ask the victim if he thought the kidnappers would really carry out their threats of mutilation or death.

They'd really thought it through, and even though it's the sort of advice I've given many clients it was quite eerie running through the list with this calm, collected woman. The question Editta had selected as the first was: 'What was the car you bought me as an engagement present?'

'An Alfa.' All was well; he'd not been seriously mistreated. 'An Alfa Romeo.' He'd been injured during the kidnap and was having a rough time.

I didn't like this one much at all. Even if Roberto told the gang that it was an Alfa, they might well inadvertently use the full title without thinking or vice-versa. I told her this. She thought about it but decided to take the chance anyway. It might be upsetting to Roberto's morale if he thought she'd forgotten all their plans at this early state. Privately I thought it might be upsetting to her morale if she thought Roberto was injured and she'd no way of assessing the extent of the damage.

The gang had called in the middle of the morning after the kidnap. The usual bald statement.

'Signora Pierro? We have him. If you want him back alive, do not tell the police. When I call back I want the number of a clean phone, a clean phone, do you understand?' She'd been unable to say anything except 'yes'. The call was terminated as soon as she'd indicated she understood. Ten seconds, that was all. She had arranged to use her friend's apartment which was quite close and the police tap was already installed. When the same man called a couple of hour later she'd passed him the number. All he'd said was 'Good. Be there at eight o'clock three days from now. It will be Franco who calls.' The voice was middle-class with a Naples accent. It was difficult to guess at the age but she thought about fortyish.

We went through my detailed questionnaire covering everything about events so far; details of her husband's character and her relationship with Giovanni Colavolpe. So far we didn't have a lot to work on and there was no need to change her script. I was pretty sure the next phone call would bring a demand, now the gang thought they had a clean line. Editta asked me if I were prepared to met Giovanni.

Well, why not. She'd said earlier on that he welcomed the idea (which may not have been what he was thinking underneath). His job would be to ensure her co-operation and I reckoned he'd say anything to keep her on side. I knew Colavolpe's reputation and it was good. He'd pulled off some good arrests but he'd also lost at least one victim who was accidentally shot in a raid. It wasn't clear from the press reports whether it was a police bullet or a kidnapper's. There's always a risk in these cases and that couldn't be held against him.

The police in different areas of Italy have varied opinions about my line of consultancy. Kidnap is a crime and so is the payment of a ransom but Italian law is flexible enough to turn a blind eye to trangressions if the motive is to save human life. Some members of the police and judiciary see us as jackals making easy money out of human misery. These are the ones who are blinded by the stark letter of the law. They've never sat through a case with the family, they've never witnessed at first hand the manner in which many tragedies have been averted by a proper understanding of the business. They've never appreciated the comfort which a family can derive from being correctly and gently educated about kidnap and ransom.

There are other policemen who do see that this is a service just as necessary as calling a consultant doctor to advise on an illness. They are aware that often lives are saved, incarcerations considerably shortened and very detailed logs are kept which have been very important to the acquisition of evidence in some past cases. I have very good relationships with the police and the judiciary in Rome, for instance. They know that the co-operation decision is left to my clients and they know that I give a balanced set of factors on which the client can base the decision. I'd have to wait and see what sort of man Giovanni Colavolpe was.

While Editta called Colavolpe I did a quick mental review. The initial contact had come very quickly. Families are often notified of the kidnap soon after it happens and then there is silence for a while. This is the softening-up process. The gang in this case looked as though they were going to make the actual demand quickly. The conduct of the negotiator on the telephone suggested an experienced man; the longest call had been about fifteen seconds. Total control of the conversation, confident and well-disciplined. Would Franco be as good?

On the part of Editta, there was a cool determination to be strong and businesslike. How long would this last? The gang had what appeared at first sight to be a trump card in the form of the company accounts. Well, let's wait and see what use they made of them. It was still an assumption that they'd kept the briefcase. The only fact I had was that Roberto had been kidnapped and he and his wife were prepared for it. Not much to be done until the contact the next day.

The apartment was impeccably neat. Everything in its place. Not even a newspaper lying around. The furniture was simple and comfortable but not luxurious, not what could be expected of a couple with their wealth. A long settee, two easy chairs and a small coffee table were the main items in the lounge. Two or three jardinières with green plants, a couple of simple inexpensive prints of mountain scenes on the walls, and that was it. This couldn't be their main residence, surely? No, she'd mentioned keeping ransom money in a cellar. This was a first floor apartment. One of her proof questions referred to the watchdog – no dog here.

She must have read my mind as she saw me looking around.

'This is a convenience apartment. We both work late at the business and occasionally stay over for the night. It is also the only listed telephone we have outside the business and so the answerphone is installed here. Why spend money on such a place? Our villa is in Torregaveta only fifty or sixty kilometres from here but often we're too tired to drive. I considered giving the villa telephone number to the kidnappers but it is too far away from the police station and also, if Roberto is not comfortable, why should I have luxury?'

I thought that this would most surely be luxury compared to Roberto's present situation but I refrained from saying it. On hearing the bell, she pressed the button to open the outer entrance to the building and peered through the spy-hole in the apartment door. It was Colavolpe.

'So, Signor March, we meet at last.' A warm, firm handshake and a friendly grin. We looked each other over warily, assessing, not fencing. He was a short, broad, powerful man. The big brown hands holding a soft fedora-style hat were nicotine-stained and capable. His face was battered in the manner of a boxer. The nose, set badly after a break, gave him the appearance of having a slight squint in his humorous brown eyes. Denis Healey eyebrows curled and twisted in all directions peppered with the same streaks of grey which were beginning to highlight his temples. Close-cropped hair accentuated a set of the biggest ears I've ever seen. They couldn't be ignored; they wiggled as he spoke.

I was looking down on him and I suppose that made him about five foot six or seven; from this angle I could see dandruff on the collar of the grubby, tan-coloured and unnecessary raincoat. If it wasn't for the eyes, he could have been a figure of fun. But full of laughter as they were, they held your gaze in a hypnotic fashion. I'd stake money on this fellow being a first-class interrogator. His shoulders were gently shaking with suppressed laughter.

'Not a pretty sight, eh? Blame my father, he was even worse. It's tragic, eh? But my mother was an angel, a truly beautiful woman, she could give me love but not looks. So, how do you like our Napoli, eh? You know Captain Carrera in Rome, eh? You are lucky to come in the summer, lots of pretty girls in Napoli in the summer. Did you fly direct to here, eh? What about this case, eh?' The last question thrown in sharply as his eyes flicked back to hold mine.

'I'd welcome your views, Captain. Signora Di Pierro has told me of the events to date. It seems fairly standard at the moment, though it looks as if we're to get a demand early. It'll be interesting to get the measure of Franco when he calls. I did wonder why they've decided to change negotiators. We may be in for a "Mutt and Jeff" tactic. I've suggested a short script for Signora Di Pierro to consider using which I'm sure she'll want to discuss with you. I'm impressed by the family's forethought in preparing the proof-questions as they did, though I've pointed out the dangers of the first one. I'm waiting for the next call in the hope that it will give us more to go on.' I used the 'we' and 'us' without stress but I was trying to get across in a subtle way that I was prepared to be part of a team. I don't think it was lost on him.

'We've compared the tapes with those from other cases and there's no match in any of our files. As you say, a fairly standard beginning. Now, Signor James March, I've agreed with Editta that if there is any method at all by which we can capture these bandits, we will do it, eh.' It was a challenge.

'It would give me the greatest pleasure to see them under lock and key. I dare say I've seen as many families as you suffering at the hands of kidnappers and it's never pleasant. I am retained by my clients to give the best advice I can offer on conducting the negotiations. The decision as to whether to co-operate with the police is not mine – it is for the family to decide. I often advise against it if I know the police track record to be miserable as it is in some areas of South America. True, I point out the dangers, just as a doctor would prepare his patient for a major operation. I never talk to the authorities if my client doesn't wish it, that would be a betrayal of essential trust. Likewise I will never discuss my client's financial matters. I'm sure Captain Carrera will substantiate this.'

'He already has.' Colavolpe's face was creased in smiles. Reassuring, but it didn't make him any prettier. 'So, we wait and see. If you are finished with Signora Di Pierro, why not come and have dinner with me? Have you a hotel, eh?'

I hadn't had time to check in anywhere yet and I was grateful for his offer of assistance. The city was packed with tourists at this time of year and it wasn't a place I knew well. Colavolpe knew a small family hotel which was very comfortable with excellent food and it was convenient for the apartment and police station. I'd no doubt that mine host would be keeping a weather eye open as well! There were precious few flies on this chap.

Colavolpe collected me from the hotel in the early evening. He said he was taking me for the finest pizza in Napoli; we were going, he said, to the west of the city, to Mergellina. I had a running commentary as he drove placidly among the chaos of evening city traffic, impervious to blaring horns and shouted abuse. He told me that Naples was the black sheep of Italy. Poverty, mismanagement, a dense population and organised crime have caused it to be described as a cross between Manhattan and Calcutta for squalor. But he told me the southerners could still teach the northerners how to relax and laugh and how to extend true Italian hospitality to their visitors.

We passed the Duomo and he took delight in repeating to me the grisly details of how the building contained the head of Saint Januarius, their patron saint. Two bottles of his blood were also there and twice a year on the same days there was a miraculous liquefaction of the blood. A wonderful event, I was told; apparently the day this stopped a great disaster would befall the city. Perhaps the 'old lady' up there (indicating Vesuvius) would spit forth death as she'd done on Pompei in 79 AD.

He was right about the pizza. We sat outside on chairs which threatened to break at each body movement only a couple of feet from the bustling traffic of the Piazza Sannazaro. Carbon monoxide fumes, interlaced with the smells of cooking fish, accompanied Neapolitan Pizza. Baked over a wood fire in a sort of clay oven, it was delicious; Colavolpe told me that it was only possible to get the pizza in the evenings because the old man who cooked them wasn't prepared to work during the day.

At one stage a shapeless bundle was lowered from a nearby window to a youth in a smart sports car. He emptied the contents onto the floor and put money into the rags before it was quickly hauled up again by an old woman. This, I was told, was probably a consignment of black market cigarettes or liquor. Whichever it was, my companion wasn't inclined to do anything about it; probably he preferred to protect his continued pizza supply.

Although Giovanni dominated the conversation with seemingly innocent remarks on Neapolitan life and legend, occasionally he slipped in a dart-like enquiry, trying to catch me off-balance perhaps. He asked about the SAS, other cases, some which I'd been involved with (though I didn't say so) and some noteworthy ones which we just used as an exchange of comments on the general business. He was deeply interested in the Northern Ireland situation and spent quite a while asking me various technicalities connected to ambushes and surveillance. He'd appeared relaxed all evening but even so I thought I sensed this as being the point where he decided that I was to be trusted.

'Tell me, James,' – we were past the stage of 'Captain' and 'Signore', fellow-conspirators almost – 'have you ever taken part in an actual drop of money, eh?'

'No. I wouldn't do that. As a consultant negotiator I break no laws. If I were to get involved in handing over a ransom I'd be acting illegally.'

'I believe you, but would you have admitted it anyway?' He was grinning ferociously again.

'Probably not.' As it happened I'd been telling the truth and for the same reasons that I'd stated. To be caught in such an act could easily have made me persona non grata in Italy. It had been a pleasant evening and we were both at ease with each other by the time he dropped me back at the hotel. We agreed to meet up at the apartment after the phone call had been taken the next evening.

Editta was excellent on the phone. When Giovanni joined us, we played her tape again.

'Hello, this is Franco. Is that the wife of Roberto?'

'Yes. Is he all right? I must know that. I have had no letter.'

'Yes. He's very well but we want some money you know....' She interrupted.

'How can you talk to me of money at a time like this? I want to know if my husband is alive. I want to hear from him....' Franco's turn.

'We have the bank books. We've seen thirty miliardi. We aren't greedy, we want only twelve. You don't have long.'

'I haven't got money. I can't think of money. How is my Roberto? Ask him what car he bought for my engagement. This way I will know if he is really with you. Maybe then we can talk about some money. Have you seen Roberto?'

'Yes I've seen him, of course I've seen him. What's this about a car? We want money. Soon. Do you understand?'

'Money, yes I understand but I want to know if Roberto is alive. Ask him the question, this will prove it.'

'What sort of car he bought?'

'Yes, for my engagement present. Go on, ask him. Is he with you now? Can I speak to him?'

'No. He's not here but I've seen him. I tell you he's OK. You have the figure we want, it is twelve miliardi.'

'But when will I know about Roberto?'

'Tomorrow. I'll ask him the question and tell you tomorrow and you'll tell me about the money. Don't tell the police or magistrates.'

'Wait. . . .'

'No. I'm going. Tomorrow at the same time. The money.' The phone was put down.

She'd been really good. Just the right hint of hysteria, the insistence to get her question across and the dismissal of the money was perfect. What a turn-up for the books Franco was. I looked across at Giovanni.

'How about that, James, how about our Franco, eh? Why should they choose him, I wonder?'

'I don't know. He's broken every rule in the book. He must have been talking for two minutes there. He let Editta lead him into conversation for far too long. What's a little worrying is that he's no professional, so what about the rest of the gang? Are they amateur? Did they hire someone to make the initial contact and get it set up? It's been done before, I understand. I didn't recognise the accent. It was very harsh, harsher than even a Calabrian. Do you know it?'

'He's probably a Sicilian. Does anything else occur to you, eh?'

'Two things actually. One which will obviously have struck you as well,' I grinned at him. 'If he continues to act this way, there is every chance that Editta will be able to get close to him over a period of time. Perhaps if the conversations were to increase in length each time, not too obviously, do it stage by stage, we may get him on the phone long enough for you to trace him. How long does that take you nowadays?' I knew the answer roughly but some forces are better equipped than others.

'We could possibly do it in ten or twelve minutes if all went well. Twenty minutes would be perfect and certain. Anything else, eh?'

'I'm assuming the "bank book" is the company account. It suggests that Franco at least is no accountant. I'm inclined to advise that we get a good trusted accountant in and we start to think of ways of disproving the figures. Franco isn't alone, that's for sure; there may be someone in the gang who does understand accounts which is why we need an expert in my opinion.'

'What did you think of the demand. Very high, eh?'

'Under the circumstances it's understandable. In Rome it's not unknown to get first demands of twenty miliardi and ten is very common. What we need to find out is what their level of expectancy really is. Has the account book made them throw the going rate out of the window? We'll see how they react to our offer.'

'What do I say tomorrow?' She'd been listening calmly. This was the first question.

'Let's talk about it. The big unknown is that we still don't know whether we're dealing with amateurs or pros. The first guy was disciplined, no doubt about that. Franco on the other hand doesn't appear to be too bright. That could be an act. He may be trying to get close to you, to build up a rapport for a variety of reasons. There may for instance be a sudden switch back to cold hard professionalism if Franco doesn't seem to be making progress with you. This is debatable; he took a risk with the length of time he spent on the phone. If you are able to get him talking as time goes on I'd be inclined to think that he's just not too bright. For the time being we don't know which category they're in so I would treat them as professionals.

'This means that whatever offer we put in should be realistic. It should be enough to let them see that the going rate at least is achievable and it should be consistent with what you could reasonably be expected to raise quickly. We have to try to get them to discount the "bank book" if we can. An initial method might be to say that it's not possible for anyone to take money out of the company without your husband's signature. It's worth a try. How do you feel about getting an accountant in?'

'That's not a problem. I'd trust the company accountant. He's a good friend and he'll keep quiet.' She raised one of her strangely level eyebrows at Giovanni. It gave a sort of Picasso cast to her face in the evening shadows.

'This all sounds very sensible to me. You'll have to be very careful with Franco. He may not realise what is happening but if we are dealing with an experienced gang and he reports that you're trying to keep him talking they'll be on to you very quickly and Roberto may suffer, eh? Accept that it may take some weeks.

'Both Roberto and I know that some cases have lasted over a year. That's one reason why I'm an equal partner in the company. I have the power to keep it running during his absence.' She was as controlled as we were.

My God, they certainly had planned this thing down to the last detail. What a remarkable couple. I hoped I'd have the chance to meet Roberto. We got together to formulate her next script with Giovanni listening and taking notes.

Editta didn't require much in the way of prompting. She'd shown herself to be a natural, but no-one knew what the effect of a tape of Roberto's voice would do to her and on balance I persuaded her to accept having a script. It was another simple one.

Proof	– Have you an answer to my question?
	– Is he well?
Demand	– It's impossible
	– Only Roberto can sign
	– I only have my own money
Offer	– I have to be careful of the police and tax men
	– I can only offer you 300 millions
Conversational	– Can he write to me?
	– Can I speak to him?
	– Are you married – can you imagine how I am feeling?

Beyond this she was well able to improvise. It was agreed that the accountant would be briefed and put to work to come up with convincing explanations as to why the thirty miliardi was not realisable cash.

So began the long process of getting close to Franco. Editta was fantastic. The first call after her proof question gave her to understand that Roberto was well enough: 'Alfa.' A superb actress, she could summon up hysteria and concern instantly. Franco never

spected her and certainly wasn't reporting his conversations back
the gang. The accountant came up with every plausible excuse he
uld find from unpaid taxes and threats of business closure to an
entual confession that the books had been cooked in order to
tisfy investors. In the end it was the statement that no-one but
oberto could sign company cheques that convinced the gang.

We were dealing with amateurs. We became more sure as the case
ogressed, but there was no explaining Franco's equanimity. He
ever lost his temper once. At every call Editta would ask about
oberto and whether his heart was standing up to the stresses of
ing a prisoner. She managed to extend the phone calls up to fifteen
inutes or so quite regularly but Giovanni never seemed to be able
pick up a trace. It was very disappointing to all of us.

Editta was masterly in her offer proposals. Every week she'd ask
coded question and the answers were always correctly given. We'd
owly reduced the gang's demands down to one miliardi while we
ad painfully crept up to 670 millions. She fought every inch of the
ay. As far as the gang were concerned she borrowed little scraps
om friends; she imposed on her mother; she sold the car and pieces
jewellery and now she told Franco she had exhausted all her
sources. By now she felt as though she knew Franco well. Over
e last three months he'd let slip his wife's name and the difficulties
had feeding his large family of four boys and three girls. He
anted to go north where there was work but his wife wouldn't leave
alabria. None of this information seemed to help Giovanni in the
ightest. He was as amiable as ever though his impatience showed
ery time his staff failed to make the trace.

We'd decided that the sale of a small, almost forgotten piece of
nd outside the city was sufficient to enable Editta to raise her offer
700 million lire. In the longest conversation yet she put this across
Franco. That was it, she told him. There was no more. All her
iends thought she was gambling the money away and wanted
othing more to do with her. Her life was a total misery and she
dn't know where to turn. 'Was Roberto still well? Would Franco
ease ask him the name of the German au pair they had when they
st moved to Naples?' 'Yes he'd ask. He'd tell her in two days.'

At the next call, Franco capitulated:

'Hello, this is Franco.'

'Hello, Franco, how is my husband? Did he answer my question?'

'Yes. He says Anne. He's not so well, Signora. He complains of
est pains. We're going to let you have him back. If you go to the
tle restaurant by the station at nine o'clock tonight you will find a

Coca-Cola can on the top of the litter bin to the right of the fro[n]
door. There is a....' There was a strangled grunt and a calm voi[ce]
was heard.

'It's all right, Editta. I've got him.' Giovanni!

Late that night Giovanni joined us at Editta's apartment. A co[n]
tented, somewhat smug Giovanni.

'Don't worry. Everything is under control. Franco is tucked aw[ay]
nicely. The gang do not suspect. He had the drop instructions wi[th]
him. I have them here, eh. He would have put them in the bin aft[er]
making the call.'

Something occurred to me.

How long have you known where he was calling from?'

'For about a month, eh? What was the point of picking him u[p]
too soon? If Roberto's being held in Calabria it's a real jungle dow[n]
there. There was no guarantee that Franco knew the whereabou[ts]
of the hideout because he made his calls from the Castrovillari [on]
the Calabrian–Basilicata boundary. His accent put him furth[er]
south, there was never more than two days between the calls and w[e]
decided on balance that the chances would be better if we waite[d]
until they accepted the money. You're not the only one who ca[n]
keep secrets, eh?'

The ugly, mickey-taking, cunning rogue! I'd believed his stori[es]
about the inefficiency of his staff when I should have suspected th[at]
a man like him wouldn't have tolerated such people. I asked why [he]
was so sure the gang didn't suspect.

'Franco's instructions were to place the Coca Cola can and the[n]
move down south to a rendezvous point. It is to Franco that t[he]
money is being delivered. He is to deposit it in the hills. He had on[ly]
to call the gang to say that the instructions had been picked up befo[re]
moving out of town.' A pause more for dramatic effect than anythi[ng]
else, I believe.

'He had the simple choice. Make the call with no funny busines[s]
in which case he thinks he goes free after we've picked them up, [or]
say nothing and I throw away the key. This is Naples – he believe[s]
me, eh. When he called the gang he said you'd asked anoth[er]
question, something about the name of a salesman your husba[nd]
sacked last year. Franco wouldn't have called you again anyway b[ut]
it's just possible that they'll mention it to Roberto, eh.'

That was a good try. If it was mentioned to Roberto he would [be]
aware that some sort of police action was going to take place. At lea[st]
he'd keep his head down. Giovanni produced the drop instructio[ns]
They were relatively simple as these things go. First, Editta had

...d a trusted man volunteer to drive. He could have one companion, ...t Editta, to help with the money and the driving. She must hire a ...ite Fiat. It must not have any form of radio aerial; no roof ...ck, nothing which may be used for communications or tracking ...tennae.

The drop team was to leave Naples on the southbound autostrada ...8, drive down to Nicastro and there join the northbound E1. From ...at point they were to observe the road signs carefully and take the ...st turn-off west to Serrastretta. In the middle of the village there ...as a public telephone. They were to park close to it and put on ...nerican-style baseball hats. The drop team was to be there at ...actly three-thirty 'two days from now'. I looked at Giovanni's ...ap. It was a long way, about 650 kilometres.

At three-thirty the phone would ring and the passenger was to get ...at of the car and answer it. He would be given instructions. If he ...derstood, he was to keep his hat on as he got back into the car. If ...ything was not clear he was to remove his hat. If that happened, ...e phone would ring again five minutes later.

Giovanni explained that Franco was under instructions to make ...e team go through three more telephone check points where he ...uld observe them. He, Giovanni, had noted all those points. The ...am would then be given details of where to leave the money. ...anco was to collect the sacks, take them to his drop-off point ...d then retrace his footsteps to observe the route in until he was ...mmoned back. He didn't know exactly where the hide-out was, ...ly that it was the area of the drop-off point. He had passed his ...rections on to Giovanni.

'How many of them are there?'

Giovanni continued to look at the map as he answered.

'Four. Three now that we have Franco. All Calabrians; Franco is ...om Sicily originally by the way. Those men will be good in the ...lls and woods. They're a tough uncompromising lot down there, ...e shall have to be very careful. Something's worrying you, eh?'

'Not really, it's your ball game but I can't help thinking that the ...de-out must be pretty close to where Franco is supposed to leave ...e money. 700 million lire is a hell of a load for one man. Whether ...s one slow journey with all the money or two fast ones with half ...it, it still limits the distance.'

'He goes by car to a clearing. From there it's only about a hundred ...rds to the hiding place. He then moves his car about a mile back ...wn the track and returns to his vantage point. We can lighten his ...ad; it only has to look like money after all. But you're right, it looks as though the hide-out is close, which could give me problem moving men in to seal the area. Out of all those policemen there bound to be someone who falls over and makes a noise, eh?'

'Can't you use just a few men? A couple of very good one Men who know how to move in the woods. Rely on stealth ar surprise.'

'The SAS factor, eh? So what would you do, my friend?'

'I assume you've selected a "Franco"?'

'Yes. You see him before you.' Very cool he certainly led from tl front.

'You've selected a drop team?'

'Uh-huh.' That told me a lot.

'What's the cover like in that part of the country? I've never beer

'As thick and tightly packed as American sailors round a Neap litan brothel, eh'. It was Editta's little gasp which reminded us th we were in female company. Giovanni made a mute gesture apology. She waved it aside and stood up.

'No matter. It's man's talk. I would like to know the final pl though. I'll make some coffee.'

For the first time in three months there was weariness in her voic Over the last few hours her face had started to sag with fatigue. wondered how many sleepless nights she'd had. That's when tl secret fears would have come, at night; alone, it's the worst time all. I was relieved to see the pressure signs, though, it meant she w human after all. The next few days were going to be hell for her. knew the agonies of the final wait and on top of this a difficult poli action to think of as well. I knew she trusted Giovanni but she w very capable of working out the hundred and one things that cou go wrong no matter how well he laid his plan.

'Hmm. It's risky but if the ground cover's that thick you mig get away with just three or four good men. It's worth a though Look, you know Franco's drop-off point already. How about gettir men in there the night before, you'd just have time.'

'No. I couldn't guarantee any of my men being able to stay und cover that long. It's too risky for Roberto.'

'What time is Franco to make the drop?'

'One hour before dawn, say four a.m., eh.'

'Another possibility is to make the drop early. The two men wl take the money to Franco follow you up by car insofar as that's sa continue on foot through your observation post, picking you up the same time then moving into an area where they can ambush t money. A fourth man can do a dummy run with Franco's car at t

222

rrect time and behave as he would have done, or should I say as
ou'd have done.'

'It's possible, it's also risky, eh?'

'Let's look at the risks. They may have staked out the area early.
hat's unlikely if they've believed Franco. One of them may go to
in Franco at his observation point. That's highly likely, though it
epends on the ground and how much they feel they have to cover.
hey may accidentally stumble on the hidden men. An obvious risk
ut an acceptable one, I'd have thought. You don't know how
ctically well you'll be able to position your men but that's always
problem on uncharted ground. Those are the main risks to your
fety.

'The risks to Roberto are considerable depending on the nature
the gang. We can't rely on them all being as mild as Franco. It's
obably safe to assume they'll leave at least one of their number
ith him while they go to collect the money. I'd have thought the
eer bulk would require at least two of them. This means all three
uld go to the drop-off or two could go and they'd recall Franco to
sist once they're satisfied.

'If you don't get them all, and quietly, then everything hangs on
hat orders have been given to Roberto's guard. If only one or two
me forward and if you can take them without any fuss there's a
ry good chance that you can persuade them to lead you into the
de-out. The whole plan would need some firming up, of course.
he siting of your support group which probably won't be able to
t very close. Communications, timings and that sort of thing but
reckon it could work.'

'So do I. Some tightening up as you say but the odds are reasonable
ough for me. Editta, I know you're not happy, how could you be?
a my professional opinion, I believe there is a very good chance of
pulling it off. What do you say, eh?'

'I will stand by Roberto. I will not try and change your minds. I
ant to insist on one thing, though, and that is that you do take the
ctual money. If anything does go wrong then maybe there would
ill be a chance for Roberto.'

She was right, of course. It did add an extra if somewhat uncertain
ercentage to Roberto's overall survival possibilities.

'I bet you wish you were coming along, James, eh?'

'Of course, but the law is the law, Giovanni. I'll be with you in
pirit, count on that.' What a sucker! I should have seen it coming.

'I'm the only law who needs to know, eh. There's a risk as you
now and I couldn't arm you but I'd welcome some on-the-ground

support especially if we have to make last-minute changes. Or hav
you forgotten how to move in the woods, eh?

By the time Editta had added her exhortations I was well an
truly in it. In truth I wanted to go; it would be immensely satisfyin
to see a case right through by taking part in the drop even if it wa
to be 'manufactured'. It would be an insight into the business whic
I'd never thought to get. Why not? He sensed he'd won and clappe
his hand on my shoulder.

'Well done, James. Magnifico. Come. To the hotel. I think you'
better drive the car tomorrow. You're too damned tall to get in an
out answering the telephone, you'd attract too much attention. W
have to go through the motions of the drop to Franco right from th
start just in case the watcher is being watched, eh? I have to find
way to hide these damned ears and hope that Franco's clothes an
hat will be sufficient disguise at long range. Come. We'll talk in th
car and get an early start to briefing tomorrow. May we use th
apartment, Editta, eh?'

She was desperately tired now that the need for acting was over
I don't know what had given her the strength to carry on; she'
hidden it from us too, not just the kidnappers. In between time
she'd continued at the office. That would have helped, of course
but still she'd have those long, haunting, wondering nights alone i
that spartan apartment. I suggested she took a sleeping pill tha
night but her only response was a weak smile and the words: 'Whe
Roberto's back, when he's back.'

The little Fiat wasn't suited for a man my size and I was gettin
very cramped. We'd faithfully followed the drop plan according t
Franco's instructions and we were now grinding our way up int
the Sila Piccola mountains. It was a narrow badly surfaced road an
the rented car was beginning to rattle; it sounded as though we'
shed an exhaust bracket. Not much further, about two kilometre
according to Luigi. He seemed a capable man; he was himself
Calabrian, he'd been brought up twenty or thirty kilometres to th
south of us. Simbario, I think he'd said, right up in the mountains
The road now degenerated into a grass track.

Calabria was in complete contrast to the Italy I knew so well. We'
wound our way up mountain-sides through unkempt, moulderin
ruins. Vineyards everywhere in haphazard terraces and countles
acres of olive trees decorated the flanks of the foothills. As we'
progressed upwards the forestation had become more dense an
dark, with low ominous trees, and it wasn't dificult to imagine the fea
in the hearts of travellers not so very long ago when the mountains c

...labria were famous for the bands of fierce brigands who ruled the ...ods. At one point as we crossed the range. I was sure I could see ...th the Tyrrhenian and the Ionian sea.

Luigi had been as taciturn as befits the Calabrian of folk-lore. ...e'd given me the directions carefully and precisely; if he was in ...y way nervous it didn't show. Almost as broad as Giovanni was ...ll, his shoulder constantly pushed against mine in the narrow ...nfines of the Fiat. I'd watched him when he got out of the car; he ...oved like a cat, smoothly and effortlessly sliding his bulk in and ...t of the small door. They made a formidable partnership. In the ...ck of the car was Paolo. For most of the day the poor devil had ...en lying, covered by a blanket, half-on, half-off the narrow back ...at. Giovanni had insisted he travelled with us. He was taking no ...ances of anyone getting lost. Paolo was the one who'd do the ...mmy run with the car just before dawn.

'Here,' growled Luigi, 'on the right.'

We pulled into the small clearing carefully. We'd only been using ...r sidelights for the last few kilometres. The clearing was on a bend ...d Paolo could easily roll the car back silently down the road. We ...l got out and stretched the kinks away. Paolo seemed unperturbed ...r his ordeal. We were to go the rest of the way on foot to join ...iovanni who should have looked over the drop point and selected ...r cover by now. We had about two kilometres to travel, first on ...e rough track and then cutting off east into the trees to locate ...iovanni.

Luigi invited me to lead off. Moonlight highlighted the centre and ...ft hand side of the track and so we travelled in the shadow on the ...ght. There was probably no real need for caution at this time but ...kept the pace slow and moved as silently as I could. All the old ...rills, left behind so long ago in Ulster, were coming back; I was ...joying it. Luigi moved very well, quietly and with the constantly ...eeping eyes of the woodsman. Paolo was bloody awful, blundering ...d crashing about like a beached turtle. He'd be impossible when ...e got in among the trees and bracken. A slight hiss from Luigi ...opped me dead. What had he seen?

He gave me a thumbs up. OK, so it wasn't the enemy; what was ...then? He had Paolo by the throat and from the expression on the ...tle man's face whatever Luigi was saying was being listened to ...ith the greatest attention. Luigi turned back to me and with a wink ...hich was hidden from Paolo indicated that he was finished. Paolo ...asn't silent but it was an immense improvement. I saw the bent ...acken which Giovanni had used as his indicator and made sure

that Paolo had seen it. Just to be sure he wouldn't miss it the secon[d]
time round, I placed a dead branch over it as well.

I moved off very, very slowly through the noisy bracken. Ever[y]
twenty metres I stopped and made Paolo look back so that he coul[d]
fix the silhouettes in his mind and remember his route back to th[e]
car. We didn't want him getting lost. Giovanni was sitting on th[e]
ground, masked by a thick clump of bracken so he had the advantag[e]
and saw us first.

'I'm pretty sure there's no-one about,' he whispered gently to u[s]
'There's only one bloody place where we can hide and be sure to se[e]
the money and it's nearer than we wanted. It's a tiny hollow an[d]
we'll have to stay close together.'

'Hobson's choice,' I breathed. 'It so often is.'

Giovanni had Paolo in a tight grip, their faces only half an inc[h]
apart.

'You go back to the car now. Coast it down the hill. No lights, n[o]
even brake lights, hand brake only. Back as far as the cross road[s]
You don't set out to return until exactly two-thirty, eh. That shoul[d]
get you to the clearing just after three, about an hour earlier tha[n]
Franco was instructed. Drive straight up to the clearing. You can'[t]
miss it, it's on the left about four hundred metres up the track. Tur[n]
out your lights, get out of the car and thrash around a bit as you pu[t]
the money down. Do that twice then get back in and return to wher[e]
the car is now. Take the bulb out of the courtesy light. I don't wan[t]
your face lit up, eh.' He grinned as I held up the bulb. 'Take Franco'[s]
hat, pull it well down over your face. After you park the car yo[u]
return here. Quietly. You sit exactly where I've been sitting and yo[u]
stay away. From here you can see in all directions. If anyone doe[s]
approach you for God's sake take him out silently, hit him with [a]
stick. No guns. Do you understand, eh?' He'd been through [it]
countless times with Luigi in the car so he damned well ought to b[e]
now.

He nodded violently.

'If you fuck this up, it'll be your last fuck of any description, e[h]
Go. Quietly.'

He went. Quietly.

Giovanni asked me to have a scout around. Two sets of eyes ar[e]
better than one. It took me an hour and a half to circumnavigate th[e]
drop area. At one point, coming in from the east, was a faintl[y]
discernible track. It stopped short of the small clearing where th[e]
bags of money would lie covered by leaves. I guessed it had bee[n]
used for a reconnaissance of the site. It wasn't old, not establishe[d]

st the trace of the passage of maybe two men through the bracken. he only other aproach route seemed to be the main track but as it ided at the drop site I guessed they'd probably leave that under franco's' watch. My findings did at least give us a hint of the danger ea.

I reported this to Giovanni; he grunted approvingly. He reached to his pocket for the hip flask. I put my hand on his arm.

'I wouldn't do that. The smell of scotch will hang around for ages this undergrowth. Save it for the celebration.'

We were in place by one-thirty. We'd confirmed that the hollow as the only tenable position. It was a narrow L-shaped depression out eighteen inches deep at the lowest point. Luigi was lying along e short length of the 'L', watching the main track. Giovanni and were side by side watching to the east, where I'd picked up the oor.

Paolo had made his run right on time; he did exactly as he'd been ld. The threat to his sex life had been effective all right. We picked p the squeal of his brakes as he parked in the cutting. We heard no und as he, presumably, moved up to Franco's position.

It was about four-fifteen as far as I could judge when I first became vare of the movement. It was coming from the east.

he one with the shotgun lifted his head as he heard the same noise om behind our position. He didn't look alarmed. Was he expecting omeone then? No. He eased the shotgun up slightly, into a better ring position. No, he was just very confident that he couldn't be en. It was now light enough for me to see the black muzzle; it oked enormous to an unarmed man. The noise behind had stopped.

Whatever it was Luigi hadn't seen anything. I'd suggested the ly viable form of communication for us in that hollow. We each d a strong piece of thread fastened wrist to wrist to the next man. eing in the middle, I was connected to each of them. This was fine, had no gun to think about. Two or three sharp tugs – enemy to y front, stand by. One sharp tug after that – sorry, my mistake, lse alarm. Two steady tugs – get ready to move. The thread would eak at a violent pull as we got up; it wouldn't hinder anything but was strong enough for our signalling purposes.

I heard a muffled shout from Paolo's direction. The man heard it o. He was on his feet moving fast towards the money. The blur I w from the corner of my eye was Luigi. He was up and on him fore he knew what was happening. Giovanni was a bit more isurely. When he jumped up, his pistol was in his hands, covering

the Calabrian sitting stunned on the ground. Luigi had taken off lik
a bat out of hell in the direction of Paolo.

'I told you I had a couple of good men didn't I, eh?'

He had handcuffs on the Calabrian. Luigi came back virtuall
dragging the hapless Paolo.

'The bastard got away; this little shitpot was asleep.'

'I wasn't. He was just too damned big for me. He's a soddin
gorilla, not a man.' Luigi flung him aside.

'Can you track him?' he directed it at me.

'In the early morning dew? Easily, but not fast enough to sto
him getting to the hide-out.'

'Wait,' Giovanni said. 'James, go take a pee. Down by the car, eh
In fact I'll come with you.' Luigi was grinning widely.

We escorted the unhappy Paolo down to the car where a suddenl
soft-hearted Giovanni gave him a healthy shot of whisky.

'Don't worry, Paolo, we can't all be like Luigi. Was he truly a
enormous as a gorilla, eh?'

Paolo wasn't in the mood to answer.

'I know we could follow him into the hide-out, James, but we'
be sitting ducks on the way in. It'll take the others a good forty-fiv
minutes to get here. Let's see if Luigi can talk some sense into hi
fellow Calabrian, eh.'

When Luigi finally summoned us with a low whistle we went bac
to be met by a strange sight. The bandit was on his knees. He ha
two small rocks in his hands and he was tapping them togethe
rhythmically. Two close together, pause, two well spaced taps, paus
and a repeat. After each sequence he listened carefully. Six or seve
times he repeated this pattern and at last we heard the faint reply
Question and answer echoed between the two stone-tappers. Ther
was a pattern but I couldn't pick it up, certainly nothing resemblin
morse code. Eventually he put the stones down, looked at Luigi wit
a gesture of defeat and whispered: 'I don't know.'

'What the hell doesn't he know, eh?'

'It's an old form of communication in this part of the country. I
was used by the old brigands and now the shepherds. I never learne
it myself. But when this pig's offal told me it was the only way t
talk to his partners I told him to tell them to release the prisone
and bugger off before the rest of the lads get here.' He kicked th
bandit, not too hard I noticed. 'He's told them but he doesn't kno
if they're going to do it. Try again.' Another kick.

For maybe twenty minutes the man tapped away with his stone
but there was no reply. The support vehicles still hadn't arrive

espite Giovanni's summons on the radio we'd left in the car.

'What do you think, James? Put this fellow in front and go to the
ide-out?'

'If they've got any sense, they'll be long gone. We've no way of
nowing what this character said with his stones but he'd certainly
ot want them to kill Di Pierro with him kneeling there in handcuffs.
's my guess they'll be away.'

There was no need to track the escapee. The Calabrian was
een enough to show us the way. The hideout was a well-hidden
ave. Good fields of view and good defences; I was glad we weren't
alking into a firefight. Inside it was easy to see where Roberto
ad been kept. There was a chain anchored by a hefty piton to
e cave wall. It ended in a manacle, now swinging free. Filthy
lankets on the floor and a bucket of faeces told their own grim
ale.

'They can't have taken him with them, eh?'

'No way he'd have been able to keep up with them after a few
onths chained to that bloody wall.'

I could guess what had happened. He'd been released and he'd
ed as well as he was able; he'd be head down in the thick bracken
mewhere. He'd have no way of knowing we weren't members of
e gang. He'd be suspicious of everything.

'Call him, Giovanni,' I suggested.

Giovanni walked up and down shouting at the top of his voice:
Roberto Di Pierro. It is me, Giovanni Colavolpe of the Naples
olice. Stand up if you can or shout so we can find you.'

I started casting up and down looking for his trail when a thought
ruck me.

'Mention the watchdog and the salesman. It's worth a try. He'll
e very nervous after all this time but if he's as disciplined as his
ife he'll have all those questions fixed in his brain.'

'Roberto Di Pierro, the name of your watchdog is Giovanni Col-
volpe. I'm the best salesman in your company.'

'I'm over here in the rocks by the stump of the tree burned by
ghtning. Just one man comes forward. I have the shotgun.' He'd
ade quite a good distance considering it was uphill. We could see
e tree about two hundred feet up the slope.

'I'll go, he knows me. Shit.' He clapped his hands to his forehead.
We've forgotten the money. For Christ's sake, Luigi, get back there
efore some robbing Calabrian bandit comes along and swipes it,
.'

'Eh. Luigi, get on the radio. Tell those lazy buggers in support to go home, eh. Tell them to call Signora Di Pierro. Roberto's coming home, eh.'

I had also decided during that long, cold wait that I too was going home.

CHAPTER
10

EVERY kidnap case is different. Each one brings its own set of problems; the make-up of individual characters comprising the negotiating team, new tactical developments for either kidnapper or negotiator to analyse and exploit, or it may be a new country with different laws and law enforcement agencies to consider.

There is one common facet in resolving these problems, I consider it to be the most important aspect of the whole business. It is essential that the negotiator be accepted by the client as an equal from the earliest possible moment.

Most companies operating in the kidnap and ransom business arena describe themselves as being in the loss assessment, risk analysis, crisis management or security survey fields. This is perfectly logical; no one openly advertises the handling of kidnap and ransom negotiations and most such companies need other security related business in order to remain profitable. This being the case, the client's first thoughts on the consultant he is to meet can be centred on 'security consultant' and all that term can imply. A common mental image of a security consultant is of a seedy, mackintoshed figure with a furtive manner and a briefcase full of nefarious devices.

There are no qualifications necessary for a man to adopt the title of security consultant; the overall security field has more than its fair share of cowboys and this is the state of affairs in virtually every civilised country in the world. Of course there are responsible associations and institutions which turn out individuals trained in a variety of disciplines but there is no legal requirement to attend their courses: The resultant diplomas do not signify a degree of excellence awarded by an officially sponsored, competent body. There is no discernible legislation which requests or requires a man setting up as a security consultant to prove his knowledge and integrity.

A perusal of the names on the boards of directors of many companies in all areas of business will sometimes show well-known personalities from military, police or diplomatic circles but it is not these men who are going to attend to the client's needs. They are generally there to attract business through personal contacts or reputation and lend credibility in an area that can be viewed by the uninitiated as being shadowy if not shady. Sometimes they are so senior that they have lost touch with the reality of ground situations simply because they have been absent from the day-to-day field problems for so long.

A number of security companies have had media exposure in the past which has raised questions of an ethical or methodology nature. The public invariably examines those newsworthy questions without necessarily analysing the answers in defence which may appear days or weeks later. In short the client often has an inaccurate, preconceived image of the consultant negotiator to whom he turns for assistance.

This barrier has to be broken down as quickly as possible. This can only be achieved as the result of a demonstration of competence and confidence. Any consultant drawing fees from a client has to justify the right to those fees. Granted, the negotiating team is the decision-making body in any kidnap case, but there will be times when the stark presentation of options is insufficient and the members ask for a positive recommendation. It is not morally possible, in my view, for the consultant to stand on his dignity (or lack of confidence) and say: 'I'm sorry, that has to be your decision. I have given you the options.'

It follows that in order to warrant the request for a firm recommendation, the consultant has to be viewed as an equal or at least with respect by the client and therefore he must consciously work towards achieving this status.

It is as though the team are passengers in a small boat heading out of the storm riven seas towards the haven of an island lagoon; to get into the safety of calm waters, the boat has to pass through the whirlpools, fierce currents and savagely sharp sub-surface rocks of a coral reef. The captain of the boat has the helm but such are the dangers of the unknown waters he appoints a look-out to stand in the bows. The look-out calls out his commands: 'Port now. Starboard. Lay off.' The captain does not question this advice even though he retains command of the vessel.

The passengers can hear the waves pounding against the hull, they can sense the scraping, threatening rocks as the boat pitches and tosses through the maelstrom. It is teamwork at its finest, calling for trust between the look-out, the captain and the passengers. As the boat progresses, avoiding disaster after disaster, that trust grows stronger, developing into exactly the sort of relationship I try to engineer as a consultant negotiator.

I am lucky in that I am a very aware traveller and I have varied interests. I enjoy reading about the countries I visit, I enjoy the arts, the philosophies of the east and I have a sense of history. Within these interests there is usually some knowledge which allows me to directly relate to my clients. For example on one of my Roman cases I shared a great interest with my client in water colour paintings. He had a fine collection and I immediately recognised and commented on some of the painters. This established an immediate rapport – straight away I became an equal in his eyes.

Italians in particular have a great love of the soil, the family roots; they are constantly drawn back to them. In a large number of cases this manifests itself in families escaping at the weekends to country retreats. These would sometimes centre on vineyards they owned. I enjoy the study (and consumption) of world class wines; by necessity this requires a recognition of national and lesser class wines with some knowledge of how they are created. On occasions this has given me a point of identity with Italian clients.

These wide interests have also helped me in other ways. One of the hardest things to cope with as a negotiator is the loneliness. The long, late night hours alone in a hotel room poring over notes from the case. Analysing and re-analysing every sentence, phrase and word; looking for the message which is always there. All communications from the kidnappers contain a message. It is rarely just the obvious statement of fact. There will be cryptic connotations, not always deliberate – the kidnappers after all are also subject to psychological and physical pressures – these hidden messages have to be extracted in order for the 'look-out' to steer a safe course through the troubled waters.

If the negotiator is not aware of the effects of the loneliness factor, not able to recognise the symptoms of lethargy and the inability to concentrate, he will fall down on the job. I have recognised them in myself and it is then that my far-ranging interests have enabled me to take advantage of my surroundings and enjoy the sheer beauty, culture and history of cities like Rome, Milan, Naples, Bogotá, Lima and a host of others. Time and time again this ability to take in, study and enjoy those local facilities has helped to restore the balance of perspective.

It is the practice in some companies to resolve this potential problem by frequently changing consultants. This may have a small advantage in bringing another brain to bear on the case but it is very much out of balance when it is compared with the benefits of maintaining a constant presence with the negotiating team. How long does it take the passengers in the boat to develop the same degree of trust in another look-out after having been safely guided by the first? At which point during the unpredictable passage do you switch men?

Successful negotiation is dependent on so many factors: the trust of the team; gaining an intimate knowledge of the kidnappers; a knowledge of tactics and counter-tactics; an ability to spot and exploit a weakness; a physical demonstration of personal ability and integrity; and a constancy of strategy. Even though strategies may change, they must be changed precisely and accurately, which requires fine judgment.

The factor of loneliness can strike the unwary in a number of ways. I have seen consultants, my own and others, succumb to alcohol. I have seen it develop into the need to talk to someone outside the case, often with a desire to impress, which can be disastrous to security. I have seen marriages fail and characters change under this and other stresses of negotiation. It is no small thing to strive for the essential recognition by the team with the natural follow-on result that you take on executive status; thereafter accepting responsibility for the life or death of the victim. This is not the fast-moving battlefield of the military officer. It is remote, full of the imagined, the unseen; the objective may be similar but the progress towards it is slow, painstaking and meticulous with little margin for error. The minefields have to be negotiated sensitively and accurately in order to avoid the potentially terminal explosion.

The SAS holds to a tactical tenet which I believe is applicable to kidnap negotiations: 'the man on the ground is always right.' The man on the ground is the only one who can see what is happening. He is the only person who can accurately assess his supporting forces. He is the only person who has ground 'feel'. I can remember bumping into a novice negotiator in a hotel some years ago. I knew him from my army days. He was employed by a security company to handle a fairly fraught case concerning an amateur gang. He had an instinct to advise on a particular scale of offers but he had been

old by his controller (in a remote office in another country) to adhere
o their instructions.

Their plan appeared to be based on computer predictions. Computers can only analyse statistics, they have no ground 'feel'. Unless
extreme care is exercised they can lead the user into adopting a
trench warfare attitude. In this case for instance they could not
differentiate between the wealth levels of Italian families. Put crudely
here are the super-rich, the very rich and the average-rich. In this
case the young man was advising a super-rich family. The gang
knew the true value of the victim and their level of expectancy led
them into setting their demands accordingly.

In a case like this it is no good asking the computer to review past
cases and predict how the scale of offers should be calculated. The
consultant was torn between his instructions, his own instincts and
what I had outlined to him about the safest procedure in those
circumstances. Discipline or fear of retribution won out in the end.
He ignored his own leanings and my warnings and advised an offer
which was far too low. This may have been correct in the case of an
average-rich family, of course. The result in this instance was that
t upset the gang to such a degree that a mutilation which could
probably have been avoided took place.

It would not be proper to mention the scale of fees charged in
the business. Different business overheads, different parameters of
service and a host of other considerations enter into the calculation.
In my opinion the fees are commensurate with the risk and responsibility. I have personally operated free of charge on a number of
occasions. This may have been because a parallel case came up while
I was already retained (in which case the first client's permission
must always be sought), or because the family in question was in
poor financial circumstances (kidnappers do make mistakes). On one
occasion it was a very lengthy case which I was able to advise on by
telephone from my London office. It is very interesting to note that
when the services have been provided at no charge to the client, that
client has usually expected far more than the ones who paid. It is
almost as though there is a suspicion about the quality of something
which comes for nothing.

There are other stresses on the consultant negotiator. The threat
of imprisonment, not necessarily legally, is ever-present in some
countries. It is not an extreme statement to say that there can, on
occasions, be a threat to life itself. Victor Sasson was a well-known
negotiator in South American circles; rumour was rife that he had
been known to deal with both sides. He came to a very untimely and

unpleasant end when he was reported murdered some years ago. I is unlikely that this would happen to a person who plays the game straight. But it is a business where emotions run high and personal physical security can never be too far from the negotiator's mind.

The crime of kidnapping is decreasing at the moment. It seems to me that the prime causes are firstly, the growing international co-operation between governments and law enforcement agencies coupled to ever-hardening attitudes towards criminals and terrorists and secondly, the relative ease with which criminals can make money from international drug trafficking. The rewards are higher, the risk lower; access to the commodity is easier and a market is readily available.

The aware family or corporation should not take too much comfort from this statement. That same increasing co-operation within the international legal and political processions will inevitably affect the drugs trade in much the same fashion and it is quite possible that criminal kidnapping, particularly in the 'traditional' areas, could flourish once again.

Appendix

1

THESE appendices serve to demonstrate the scale of kidnapping in just one of the high threat areas when the crime was at its peak. Appendix 1 deals with those cases in Rome during the period 1969–1981. All details are from publicly available sources.

Name	Detained	Ransom (Lire)
1969		
Egidio Bonanni	2 days	Not known
1973		
Paul Getty	159 days	1,300,000,000
1975		
Gianni Bulgari	30 days	1,300,000,000
Giuseppe Di Gennaro	4 days	No demand
Claudio Chiacchierini	17 days	800,000,000
Amadeo Ortolani	10 days	900,000,000
Giuseppe D'Amico	43 days	1,000,000,000
Fabrizio Andreuzzi	10 days	400,000,000
Claudio Francisci	8 days	300,000,000
Alfredo Danesi	14 days	700,000,000
Angelina Ziaco	18 days	200,000,000
Ezio Matacchioni	10 days	None paid
1976		
Marina D'Alessio	29 days	550,000,000
Maleno Malenotti	2 May (Probably deceased)	

Renato Filippini	40 days	200,000,00
Annamaria Montani	44 days	300,000,00
Alessandro Lamburghini	23 days	500,000,00
Giuseppe D'Ambrosio	1 day	Police free
Renato Penteriani	66 days	Not know.
Mario Bregni	53 days	300,000,00
Michaela Zarak	8 hours	Police free
Savio Costantini	44 days	250,000,00

1977

Stefano Scarazza	53 days	300,000,00
Lucilla Conversi	85 days	Police free
Massimo Baldesi	79 days	Not known
Patrizia Spallone	2 days	Police free
Nazareno Fedeli	26 April (Probably deceased)	
Rosario Nicolo	37 days	1,000,000,00
Roberto Giansanti	52 days	350,000,00
Leone Concato	28 May (Probably deceased)	
Alberto Fiore	47 days	351,000,00
Ambretta Mazazantini	85 days	200,000,00
Massimiliano Grazioli	7 Nov (Probably deceased)	
Otello Mozzetti	34 days	350,000,00

1978

Sergio Sonnino	63 days	250,000,00
Giovanna Amati	43 days	800,000,00
Michela Marconi	40 days	Freed
Angelo Appolloni	28 days	Police freed

1979

Ettore Bernardi	5 days	Freed
Francesco Falco	2 days	Police freed
Angelo Jacorossi	98 days	800,000,00
Ercole Bianchi	495 days	Not known

1980

Barbara Piatelli	342 days	1,000,000,000
Carlo Teichner	67 days	600,000,000
Renato Armellini	262 days	2,000,000,000
Tommaso Ossi	93 days	1,000,000,000
Heinrich Oetiker	129 days	800,000,000
Antonelia Montefoschi	15 July (Died on 19 July)	
Valerio Ciocchetti	3 Dec (Found dead on 27 February 1981)	450,000,000

1981

Silvia & Micol Incardone	59 days	500,000,000
Giovanni Palombini	(Not known at time of writing)	
Marcello Molinari	73 days	Freed
Cesare Menasci	86 days	800,000,000
Mirta Corsetti	17 July (Still in hands of captors at time of writing)	

Appendix

2

Appendix 1 showed the figures for the city of Rome. This appendix takes the whole of Italy for the period of 1979 only.

Name	Town	Kidnapped
Teobaldo Ambrogio	Cosenza	1.1.79
Dino Armani	Milan	8.1.79
Giovanni Morandotti	Novara	12.1.79
Giovanni Apriliano	Not known	17.1.79
Luigi Balzarotti	Milan	17.1.79
Marco Gatta	Turin	19.1.79
Giuseppe Porcheddu	Ittiri	21.1.79
Enrico Gnutti	Brescia	22.1.79
Francesco Morgante	Reggio Calabria	22.1.79
Silvio Lami	Near Pisa	30.1.79
Pietrino Rujo Cicalo	Nuoro (Sardinia)	31.1.79
Armando Montanari	Guastalla	31.1.79
Dino Toniutti	Malcomer (Sardinia)	31.1.79
Lino Fava	Cento	4.2.79
Evelina Cattaneo	Milan	5.2.79
Carlo Alberto Pini	Lunezzare	7.2.79
Giovanna Barresi	Reggio Calabria	9.2.79
Dino Ursa	Agrigento (Sicily)	12.2.79
Mimo Perez	Brindisi	14.2.79
Unknown Girl	No Information	
Prof. Giovanni Ruggiero	Bologna	19.2.79
Ludovico Gnech	No Information	24.2.79
Ambrogio Silva	Desio	27.2.79
Ettore Bernadi	Cisterna	27.2.79

Enrica Lambiasi	Latina	5.3.79
Francesco Falco	Rome	8.3.79
Antonio Ferrara	Palermo	1.4.79
Salvatore Scilio	Catania (Sicily)	6.4.79
Pasquare Venture	Brianza	12.4.79
Baroness Anna Franchetti	Sassari (Sardinia)	13.4.79
Giuseppe Omini	Milan	14.4.79
Claudio Gigante	Sesto San Giovanni	19.4.79
Saverio Balsamo	Milan	23.4.79
Gaetano Casillo	San Giuseppe Vesuviano	8.5.79
Pasquire Stramaglia	Bari	17.5.79
Francesco Doneda	Bergamo	21.5.79
Pierangela Perego	Lecco	29.5.79
Mario Stangoni	Sardinia	12.6.79
Lucio Vaccari	Piacenza	15.6.79
Adriana Daini	Pistoia, Ponte Petri	15.6.79
Luigi Amoruso	Torre del Greco	15.6.79
Giuseppe Aloi	Reggio Calabria	27.6.79
Luisa Scacabarozzi Cinque	Olbia (Sardinia)	7.7.79
Cristina Scacabarozzi Cinque		
Roberto & Ornella Pancrioli	Porto Taverna	12.7.79
Santo Arrigoni	Paladina (Faked own kidnap)	
Fabio Sculli	Ferruzzano	29.7.79
Silvio Olivetti	Olbia (Sardinia)	17.8.79
Nevio di Lorenzo	Modena	17.8.79
Guido Freddi	Frecco	20.8.79
Annarita Matarazzi	Siderno	21.8.79
Rolf, Daphne & Annabelle Schild	Sardinia	21.8.79
Marina & Giorgio Casana	Sardinia	22.8.79
Fabrizio de Andre & Dora Ghezzi	Tempio Pausania	27.8.79
Lorenzo Barberini	Pescara	8.9.79
Angelo Jacorossi	Rome	11.9.79
Benigno Brai	Cagliari	19.9.79
Francesco Trogu	Sardinia	2.10.79
Tito Sachi	Sardinia	12.10.79
Riccardo Aldighieri	Cremona	26.10.79
Emilia Mosca	Besana Brianza	27.19.79
Alfredo Battaglia	Not known	30.10.79
Sandro Ghirardelli	Ferrara	5.11.79

Mario Montalbetti	Varese	5.11.79
Michele Cucchiara	Agrigento	8.11.79
Marco Forgione	Cosenza	10.11.79
Giovanni Oppo	Ghilarza	10.11.79
Cesare Pedesini	Milan	14.11.79
Angelo Fumagalli	Oggiono	15.11.79
Antonio Orru	Cagliari	17.11.79
Diego Rossi	Stra, Venice	23.11.79
Marcello Talladira	Turin	28.11.79
Guiseppe Parodi Spinola	Milan	3.12.79
Francesco Massoni	Stradella	4.12.79
Eugenio de Paolini del Vecchio	Casoretto	11.12.79
Paolo de Stafani		
Ercole Bianchi	Rome	12.12.79
Pierino Pighi	Milan	12.12.79
Leonardo Rossi	Milan	16.12.79
Damiano Gnutti	Brescia	22.12.79

Appendix

3

In a peak year the kidnap and ransom premiums paid reach very high figures. The table below gives 1981 as such a year.

Area & Country	Total Premiums (in millions)
1. **United States**	US$30.0
2. **Europe**	
2.1. Holland	US$ 2.0
2.2. Germany	US$ 4.0
2.3. Switzerland	US$ 3.5
2.4. Sweden	US$ 2.0
2.5. Italy	US$12.0
2.6. France	US$ 2.5
2.7. Spain	US$ .5
2.8. Remainder	US$ .5
	US$27.0
3. **Central America**	
3.1. Guatemala	US$ 6.0
3.2. Salvador	US$ 2.5
3.3. Honduras	US$ 1.0
3.4. Mexico	US$ 3.0
3.5. Remainder	US$ 1.0
	US$13.5

4. South America

4.1.	Colombia	US$ 1.5
4.2	Uruguay	US$ 1.0
4.3.	Argentina	US$ 1.5
4.4.	Brazil	US$ 2.0
4.5.	Remainder	US$ 2.0
		US$ 8.0

5. Far East

5.1.	Japan	US$ 1.5
5.2.	Remainder	US$ 1.0
		US$ 2.5

6. Rest of the World   US$ 2.0

7. Total World Market   US$83.0

Robert Hughes
The Fatal Shore £5.99

The epic international bestseller

'The very day we landed upon the Fatal Shore,
The planters stood around us, full twenty score or more;
They ranked us up like horses and sold us out of hand,
They chained us up to pull the plough, upon Van Diemen's Land'

'Robert Hughes' magnificent epic book traces the fate of the
160,000 men, women and children transported between the
despatch of the first fleet in May 1787 to Botany Bay, and the arrival
of the last convict ship in January 1868 in Western Australia. This
gory, grim but always compelling panorama evokes the almost
unimaginable horrors and atrocities, both of the passage itself and
the disciplinary apparatus of what amounted to a police state . . .
a hell-hole of chain gangs ruled by the cat o'nine tails' LISTENER

'With its mood and stature . . . becoming the standing opus on the
convict years' AUSTRALIAN SUNDAY TELEGRAPH

'A unique phantasmagoria of crime and punishment, which
combines the shadowy terrors of Goya with the tumescent life of
Dickens' THE TIMES

'Popular history in the best sense . . . its attention to human detail
and its commanding prose call to mind the best work of Barbara
Tuchman' WASHINGTON POST

'An impressive book, written with power and passion, lit by flashes
of wit and imagination' SUNDAY TIMES

'One of the most carefully and brilliantly researched books I have
ever read . . . compelling, hard-driving narrative'
JOHN HOOKER, THE AGE

'Full-blooded and monumental' NEW YORK TIMES

John Costello
Mask of Treachery £6.99

'In 1979 I cornered and flushed out the then Sir Anthony Blunt, a smooth, tough and seasoned spy if ever there was one. Now, *Mask of Treachery* causes my heart to miss a beat or two . . .' ANDREW BOYLE in THE DAILY TELEGRAPH

'New and explosive material about the activities of Anthony Blunt. Costello shows how the old spy became a homosexual mole for Stalin inside Buckingham Palace, when he carried out a secret mission in the American occupation zone of Germany on behalf of King George VI. Blunt recovered royal family papers and among the documents was hard evidence about the dangerous political flirtation between the Duke of Windsor and Hitler. As a reward Blunt became Keeper of the King's Pictures and allegedly used his position to provide Stalin with information from the pinnacle of the British establishment.

'This fascinating book asserts that Blunt's knowledge provided him with a gold-plated insurance policy. For years his threat to reveal the royal secret saved him from exposure' THE DAILY MAIL

'Costello's assertions about Blunt and Britain's band of upper-class traitors . . . raise questions about the incompetence, self-protectionism and curious sexual habits that were rife among the British ruling elite' INTERNATIONAL HERALD TRIBUNE

Researched from British Intelligence files available in America but classified in Britain, *Mask of Treachery* could not have been written under the Government's new Official Secrets Act.

John Pilger
Heroes £5.99

'A tough, responsible book ... Pilger's strength is his gift for finding the image, the instant, that reveals all: he is a photographer using words instead of a camera' SALMAN RUSHDIE, OBSERVER

'Pilger's *magnum opus*: a passionate and utterly absorbing collection of reports from the firing lines, both abroad (Vietnam, Cambodia, South Africa) and home (the East End, the miners' strike, Fleet Street) by one of the dwindling bunch of journalists in this country with heart as well as a hard nose' TIME OUT

'Pilger is the closest we now have to the great correspondents of the 1930s ... The truth in his hands is a weapon, to be picked up and brandished – and used in the struggle against evil and injustice' GUARDIAN

'Some remarkable reporting is reprinted here ... It contains some memorable snapshots of a harsh world' TIMES LITERARY SUPPLEMENT

'He is a true model for his peers and followers. Let them study for instance the awesome opening pages of the long chapter, "Year Zero", which unforgettably describes the hideous and desolate remains of murdered Phnom Penh ... mark, shudder, reflect and profit. There are other passages just as fine' SPECTATOR

'If I were a modern history teacher, I'd start the year's course by slinging copies of it across the desk and telling them to get on with it' DUNCAN CAMPBELL, CITY LIMITS

'What makes Pilger such a compelling writer is his sharp use of irony – his sense of the ridiculous makes the tragedies of his heroes seem all the more vivid' TODAY

'A number of these pieces are humdingers' CLANCY SIGAL, NEW SOCIETY

'Powerful ... scathing ... impressive' CHRISTOPHER HUDSON, LONDON STANDARD

All Pan books are available at your local bookshop or newsagent, or can be ordered direct from the publisher. Indicate the number of copies required and fill in the form below.

Send to: **CS Department, Pan Books Ltd., P.O. Box 40, Basingstoke, Hants. RG21 2YT.**

or phone: 0256 469551 (Ansaphone), quoting title, author and Credit Card number.

Please enclose a remittance* to the value of the cover price plus: 60p for the first book plus 30p per copy for each additional book ordered to a maximum charge of £2.40 to cover postage and packing.

*Payment may be made in sterling by UK personal cheque, postal order, sterling draft or international money order, made payable to Pan Books Ltd.

Alternatively by Barclaycard/Access:

Card No.

Signature:

Applicable only in the UK and Republic of Ireland.

While every effort is made to keep prices low, it is sometimes necessary to increase prices at short notice. Pan Books reserve the right to show on covers and charge new retail prices which may differ from those advertised in the text or elsewhere.

NAME AND ADDRESS IN BLOCK LETTERS PLEASE:

Name

Address

3/87